COLOGIC–ECONOMIC ANALYSIS FOR REGIONAL DEVELOPMENT

Walter Isard

CHARLES L. CHOGUILL / JOHN KISSIN

RICHARD H. SEYFARTH / RICHARD TATLOCK

WITH THE ASSISTANCE OF

KENNETH E. BASSETT / JOHN G. FURTADO

RONALD M. IZUMITA

ECOLOGIC–ECONOMIC ANALYSIS FOR REGIONAL DEVELOPMENT

SOME INITIAL EXPLORATIONS WITH PARTICULAR REFERENCE TO RECREATIONAL RESOURCE USE AND ENVIRONMENTAL PLANNING / REGIONAL SCIENCE AND LANDSCAPE ANALYSIS PROJECT, DEPARTMENT OF LANDSCAPE ARCHITECTURE RESEARCH OFFICE, GRADUATE SCHOOL OF DESIGN, HARVARD UNIVERSITY

Fp ***The Free Press, New York***

COLLIER-MACMILLAN LIMITED, LONDON

Printed in the United States of America

The Free Press
A Division of The Macmillan Company
866 Third Avenue, New York, New York 10022

Collier-Macmillan Canada, Ltd., Toronto, Ontario

Library of Congress Catalog Card Number: 75–134313

Printing number
1 2 3 4 5 6 7 8 9 10

Contents

List of Tables

List of Charts

Preface

The combination of the two words *Ecologic* and *Economic* in the title of this book, is an unusual one. It is set forth, nevertheless, as a true combination, in the sense of a synthesis of analyses of two systems within the world of actuality. Throughout this book, we stress the need for this synthesis. We constantly assert that no longer can regional development and regional planning be treated in their traditionally narrow contexts. Emphasis on the strict economics of such development and planning, with only passing consideration of physical environment and design, let alone of social, political, and other cultural factors, can no longer be tolerated. Whether we look at the problems of planning and development within the New England states, or metropolitan Budapest, or the environs of Lake Baikal, or in innumerable other regions of the world, we are confronted with the reality that (1) control of ecological and physical disturbances and (2) design of the environment are key elements of economic development and planning work. Even conscious redesign of the environment may be required.

The above view represents a new dimension which must be brought into our current-day analysis. When the research for this book was begun, on the wise use of Continental Shelf resources, the need for this new dimension was not clearly perceived. In many ways the authors stumbled into a full and sharp awareness of this need. This stumbling is reflected in the structure of the book. We cannot say that this book systematically attacks and studies the resource development potentials of a case area, against the background of this broader conception of regional development and planning. Nonetheless, in our attempt to help evaluate the Continental Shelf resources of the United States, with particular reference to a New England site (as was required by the contract which provided the basic support of our research) we have been able to probe somewhat systematically into some of the basic interrelations of this broader conception.

This book is not a traditional work; it contrasts sharply with books the senior author formerly has written or contributed to. It combines many objectives in a way which is not highly structured. A first objective is to make regional planners and other social and environmental analysts at or close to the decision-making level aware of the intricate interrelationships between the economy and the ecosystem, and between economic development and environmental management. For such individuals, it was necessary to present in a broad non-technical fashion some of the conceptual framework and methodology.

A second objective is to demonstrate how existing methodology can be put to work on current problems. Here again, it was desirable to present such methodology briefly and in broad, text-book fashion (and to refer the reader elsewhere for full, technical discussion) while illustrating the use of one or more elements of this methodology in a particular case study.

A third objective is to achieve some scientific advance. Here the authors were motivated not only to develop a conceptual framework more adequate to the task of interrelating the economic and ecological subsystems but also to demonstrate how the requisite empirical materials can be obtained in order to make such a framework operational.

A last objective is to conduct a case study for the development of an area wherein the interdependence of the economic and ecologic subsystems is explicitly involved. Not only does this require the collection of a meaningful set of highly detailed data and their proper processing, but also forces a formulation, against the background of our extended conceptual framework, of at least a somewhat more adequate methodology than has hitherto been employed.

Because of these several objectives, this book will undoubtedly provoke much criticism. There will be those economists and regional scientists who find the presentation of techniques in Chapter 2 too superficial and not sufficiently refined—but our aim is not to discuss in full these techniques and all the evaluations that have been made of them elsewhere, but rather to acquaint planning analysts and natural scientists with them. There will be those natural scientists who will undoubtedly find Chapter 3 much too oversimplified and insufficiently documented; but again much of these materials are presented merely to acquaint planners and social scientists with the ecologic system. There will be scholars who undoubtedly will claim that a broad conceptual framework such as depicted in Table 4.3 should not be seriously set forth until many, many more of the cells have been filled in with real data and until some formal statistical testing of stability of the production process within the ecosystem is conducted. To meet this criticism would require several decades of research. Such would preclude the opportunity of our having a full reaction from the academic community that might suggest changes in emphasis and approach before committing additional heavy investments in this area of research. Hence we believe that a forceful presentation of our initial exploratory efforts, however tentative, is consistent with wise research policy. Furthermore, we would be pleased if our inadequate materials motivate natural scientists to put together their data and findings in a more consistent, comprehensive framework. Most natural scientists pursuing research in their own specialized domains have failed to effect a systematic, coordinated presentation of their diverse findings within the highly interrelated ecosystem.

Finally, there will be those who find our case studies—e.g., those on ilmenite recovery and on the recreational complex for the Nook site of Plymouth Bay—as insufficiently developed. Admittedly we could have pursued the research for these case studies at greater depth and length; but our purpose is not to present complete, fully documented case studies, each of which could well require a full book-length manuscript. Rather, our purpose is to indicate how case studies can be deepened and made more relevant against the background of our extended conceptual framework and hopefully more adequate methodology.

Hence, while we recognize the validity of many criticisms that the "unfinished" character of this book may generate, we reiterate that our research represents only an initial effort. It is only an initial scientific exploration of the linkages between the economic and ecologic systems. It is only an initial attempt to acquaint analysts at the decision-making levels with such linkages and some of the methodology available for examining the implications of diverse policy alternatives. It is only an initial probe into the application of some of this methodology.

The authors wish to acknowledge the valuable assistance received from Professor Peter L. Hornbeck, Eliahu Romanoff, and Douglas M. Amadeo. They are particularly indebted to Professor Charles W. Harris who, in the initial stages, served as co-director of the Regional Science and Landscape Analysis Project within the Research Office, Department of Landscape Architecture, Graduate School of Design, Harvard University. As director of the research office, Professor Harris created conditions under which productive research could be pursued.

The senior author assumes full responsibility for the book. At many places he overruled his associates, especially John Kissin, when they urged that more time be spent on improving, refining, and restating more rigorously parts with which they were dissatisfied, or where they differed from him in matters of analytical judgment.

Much of the basic research was conducted under contract #CWB11422 with the Environmental Science Services Administration, United States Department of Commerce, partly with funds provided by the Economic Development Administration, U.S. Department of Commerce. The authors gained much from the wise counsel of Doctors John H. Cumberland, James R. Hibbs, Milton G. Johnson, and Charles B. Crittenden, associated with these governmental units. We also wish to acknowledge support, particularly for the development of the conceptual framework, from the National Science Foundation and Resources for the Future, Inc.

Cambridge, Massachusetts
July 1969

Introduction

As stated in the Preface, this book attempts a synthesis of analysis of both the ecologic and economic subsystems of the real world. We maintain that such synthesis is essential for effective regional planning in today's world, whose internal interrelationships continue to grow more complex and intricate. We insist that effective attacks on the range of new problems which we now confront—air, water, and sonic pollution; solid waste disposal, open-space preservation, to name only a few—must be framed in such an enlarged dimension. We therefore are motivated to seek both new conceptual frameworks and more adequate methodology, basing these upon new developments and extensions of existing conceptual frameworks and methodology.

To achieve its objectives the book presents its basic materials in the next four chapters, and certain recommendations and concluding remarks in a brief, final chapter.

In Chapter 2 we discuss in summary fashion several traditional economic and regional science techniques for regional analysis. We do so to give the reader some notion of how standard techniques may be employed, particularly as they apply to Continental Shelf resource evaluation. Thus, using comparative cost analysis, we examine several mineral resources of the Continental Shelf. We then illustrate how the direct and indirect implications of any development may be studied using an input-output approach. The use of the gravity model is next examined, particularly with reference to its capability for estimating demand for recreational activities. Finally, we explore the use of the industrial complex, or more simply, the "complex" approach, to investigate the feasibility of possible recreational complexes.

As already indicated, analysis must go beyond the economic. Accordingly, in Chapter 3 we look at natural resources from an extra-economic standpoint. We briefly discuss resource classification and several critical ecologic principles. We proceed to illustrate how these principles and their associated subsystems—the food chain, photosynthesis, and the phosphorus cycle—can be put into an input-output, programming format paralleling procedures in economics and regional science.

In Chapter 4 we take the first step toward achieving a synthesis of economic and ecologic analysis. We develop a huge interrelations table to record flows among activities. We illustrate in detail how the ecologic and economic systems are interrelated via these flows. Although we do not present a table complete with all the flow data, or even approach such a state, we do illustrate some of the key interdependencies which such a table can reflect. Thereby we demonstrate how economic and ecologic analysis can be, in actuality, fused to an important extent.

In Chapter 5 we proceed to a case study. We consider the general Plymouth-Kingston-Duxbury Bay area. Since no mineral deposits of any significance occur in the shelf of this area, and since it lacks potential for fishing and industrial development, only its recreational possibilities are examined at some depth. Several sites for recreational development are identified. Through a comparative cost analysis of the several sites, covering both ecologic and economic costs, an optimal site is determined. For this site a recreational complex is developed. We use the gravity model to estimate demand, an input-output model to check for consistency of total input requirements and to estimate total capital investment, and standard cost and revenue procedures to calculate profitability. "Complex" and comparative cost analyses are then employed to determine the relative profitabilities of complexes of different sizes at the several sites. This last step once again requires consideration of ecologic cost.

Finally, in the concluding chapter we briefly spell out the potentials of our study for the further development of a methodology for the synthesis of economic and ecologic analyses. We also say a few words on the interrelations among resource development, economic growth, and comprehensive coastal zoning.

Economic Models for Regional Analysis

2.1 *Introduction*

In the description and analysis of the operation of a regional economy, regional scientists, economists, planners, and economic geographers have developed a number of useful tools and techniques. It is beyond the scope of this book to consider and evaluate each of these tools and techniques. Rather, we limit ourselves to a cursory description and illustrative use of several of these techniques which have been found to be generally useful and which have a high degree of validity for the problem being examined. These techniques are: comparative cost analysis, the input-output technique, the gravity model (spatial interaction analysis), and activity complex analysis. They are examined in turn in the four sections which follow. Later in the book they are employed in the fused economic-ecologic analysis. The interested reader is referred elsewhere for a full discussion of these techniques and others (especially linear programming) which we do not cover here.[1] Also, the fully informed regional and other social scientist may wish to proceed directly to Chapter 3 after having perused Section 2.3 of this chapter.

2.2 *Comparative Cost Analysis*

2.2.1 Introduction

Comparative cost analysis provides a useful tool for the regional planner in evaluating the opportunities and potentials of his region, relative to other areas, as a location for potential economic development. An industry may be interested in locating a new plant in the region. Investors may be considering the exploitation of an untapped mineral resource. A state agency may be considering the investment of funds in a new recreational facility. In all these cases, a number of factors must be examined and evaluated. There must be a market, or access to a market, for whatever is produced, whether it be a manufactured commodity, a mineral, or a recreational service. Necessary inputs must be available for the activity. These inputs must be available at a cost which does not exceed the revenues from the potential operation. And so forth.

Consider the establishment of a new manufacturing facility. Assume that the firm, or some regional planner, has identified an adequate demand for the new commodity—that is to say, a potential market exists. The firm must then determine the best location for the facility—i.e., where it should be placed. Although in theory the firm may have the entire world from which to choose, in practice there will probably be only a few feasible sites from which to serve the potential market.

The location problem facing the firm then, is: How to determine which of these sites is best? In general, the site chosen should be the one which is most profitable—

[1] Isard *et al.* [9]. Also see various issues and volumes of *The Journal of Regional Science*; *Papers*, Regional Science Association; and *Journal of American Institute of Planners*.

i.e., the one which yields the greatest difference between the benefits resulting from location of the facility at the site and the costs incurred by the facility's operation. If the analysis is made exclusively in terms of monetary considerations, there will be differences among sites with respect to costs. Both capital and operating costs may vary among alternative sites because of differences in the cost of transporting raw materials or outputs, differences in the physical conditions which can affect construction costs, or differences in wage or tax rates. If we then assume that the firm's decision is to be made on the basis of an established or anticipated pattern of markets and a given geographical distribution of raw materials and other productive factors used in the industry, the objective of a comparative cost study is then to determine in what region or regions the industry could achieve the lowest total cost of producing the required output and delivering it to the market. Such studies frequently reveal that certain component costs do not vary among sites. For instance, labor costs may be fixed by union contracts, in which case such costs can be ignored. Accordingly, comparative cost studies need compare only those costs which are known, or believed, to be affected by the choice of location.

With the comparative cost technique, it is possible to include more than strictly monetary economic costs. Associated with different locations may be different amounts of damage or benefit by pollution. Even if the amount of pollutants generated by a facility would be the same at the alternative sites at which it might be located, the populations or natural resources may vary among these sites, and so might the resulting ecological damage (costs) or benefits from the construction and operation of a facility.

The comparative cost studies presented in this book illustrate the application of the technique. The first study presented in section 2.2.2 is on the iron and steel industry. Costs which vary from location to location are first isolated and then assessed. The objective is to find the least cost location of an integrated iron and steel works to serve a potential market. Cost calculations are made relative to that market. After the technique is demonstrated, it is then modified in such a manner as to make it more directly applicable to the evaluation of Continental Shelf mineral resources. Variants of the technique are considered.

In section 2.2.3, the potential for developing offshore ilmenite is evaluated. Here the comparative cost problem involves determining the cost of dredging ilmenite, a titanium ore, and delivering it to the milling process. Dredging costs are computed both for ore found offshore, in the Continental Shelf region, and for inland sources. It is unnecessary to go beyond the milling process because at the present time, regardless of whether the ore comes from offshore or from some inland location, the costs of the milling process and the delivery of the mill output to the consumer are basically the same.

Thus the comparative cost variant used here represents one of the simplest. The investigator need only compare the cost of operation for the offshore technique of dredging with the costs of operation for the onshore operation. Scale economies do enter the picture and indicate that with conventional equipment offshore operations at usual scales cannot meet the competition. To meet this competition, the offshore operation must have a scale at least as large as the onshore operation. In fact, a "super equipment" technology is assumed so as to evaluate the potential fully. Thus, this variant of comparative cost emphasizes the critical need to consider new technology for exploiting Continental Shelf resources, particularly with respect to scale economies that such technology might promise.

From unpublished manuscripts,[2] three additional studies of Continental Shelf mineral resources are summarized in Appendix A. These studies concern phosphorite, refractory magnesia, and sulfur. The study of phosphorite involves a comparative cost variant which points up another relationship often found basic. Here we have a situation of a resource deposit much closer to certain ultimate consumers than

[2] See Isard, Bassett, Choguill *et al.* [10], Appendix A.

current deposits. Therefore, the investigator must fully explore the transport cost advantages that are possible, and in fact, develop production situations or structures which maximize the exploitation of these advantages. In the case of phosphorite, an old established location, Florida, ships to Western markets by sea to West Coast ports. The Continental Shelf phosphorite deposits are located off these West Coast ports. The problem, then, is to determine whether these phosphorite deposits can be exploited and made available to West Coast ports at a price competitive with the delivered cost from Florida.

Another critical element, though less important but frequently strategic in other studies, centers around the quality of the resource. In the case of the offshore phosphorite, this quality is somewhat inferior.[3]

A third mineral study compares the recovery of refractory magnesia from seawater with similar recovery from land sources. Here is a resource which is essentially a saltwater resource, and not necessarily unique to the Continental Shelf. But given current technology, it is obviously much more economical to locate such a plant using saltwater at the shore's edge and thus utilize the water lying above the Continental Shelf, than to locate in mid-ocean.

In this third mineral study (in which quality differences also are significant), two fairly different technologies must be explicitly costed: one, using extraction from seawater, and the other, a landward mining operation. As a result, there are major differences in labor, fuel and power costs, and annual depreciation; major differences in annual depreciation reflect major differences in investment costs for any given capacity. But here too different transport costs to markets are also significant. Thus the comparative cost analysis requires comparison among (1) total production outlays on the one hand, and (2) transport outlays on delivering final product on the other.

In the sulfur study, differences in transport costs are not a major factor. The critical factors developed in this study are major differences in quality of resource deposits and major engineering and technological differences due to the difficulties in getting at the ore (resulting in major differences in capital and labor costs, etc.). This last case also points up a basic factor which the investigator and regional planner must always bear in mind. When the supplies of a mineral resource are being depleted, then comparison of the cost of using offshore deposits must be made not with the cost of existing operations, but with the estimated cost of operations using existing onshore deposits twenty or thirty years from now.

From the studies which were pursued, it can be seen that the comparative cost technique is extremely flexible, and thus is valuable for planning resource development. The variants included in these studies demonstrate this flexibility. In examining other industries and mineral resources, still other variants might be optimal, depending on the particular characteristics of each activity. It is hoped that these studies demonstrate how one goes about developing that variant which is best for any specified activity.

2.2.2 The Iron and Steel Industry

The comparative cost technique is particularly adaptable to the study of heavy industrial location. Suppose that the planner is interested in determining whether his region holds an advantage as a potential site for iron and steel production. Suppose he is involved in planning within the New England region, and is interested in a study of New England as a possible site for an integrated iron and steel works. He may then wish to conduct a study similar to one already completed.[4] Although

[3] The interested reader is referred to Appendix A for a detailed statement of the conclusions of this study and those on refractory magnesia and sulfur, to be noted.

[4] Isard and Cumberland [11].

the cost data need to be updated, the study clearly indicates the method of analysis. The treatment of the iron and steel industry is further advantageous as the technology of the industry is relatively well established and known. In the mineral studies, the production process is much more under flux.

Historically, the iron and steel industry has proved to be transportation-oriented. Although the costs of ore at the mine, coal at the mine, labor, and capital are significant, differences in these costs at different sites are much less critical than the differences in the cost of transporting coal, ore, and the finished product. Hence, this study focused upon transport cost differences.

A number of alternative sites for a new integrated iron and steel works in the New England area were examined. These included Fall River, Massachusetts, and New London, Connecticut. In addition to these potential sites, a number of established steel centers were included in the analysis. This addition was necessary because new New England production would be competing with the established centers for the diverse markets. The older centers included in the analysis were Pittsburgh, Cleveland, Sparrows Point (Baltimore), Buffalo, and Bethlehem, Pennsylvania. Furthermore, a new competitive site in another region—Trenton, New Jersey—was considered.

At the outset, it was possible to eliminate certain elements of cost that would be the same at nearly any production point in the northeast United States. Labor requirements per ton of output are the same. Furthermore, since union wage contracts are negotiated on a national basis, labor costs at all the sites considered would be about equal. Capital and site costs were also judged to be equal. Although taxes were judged to be an important element of cost, the regional variation was again felt to be minor. Scrap prices in 1950 were found to be significantly lower in the Boston area than in the older established steel production centers.[5] However, this low price of scrap was felt to reflect the lack of local demand for scrap. If an iron and steel production unit were placed in New England, this would lead to greater demand for scrap and would probably tend to eliminate most of the Boston area's advantage in scrap.

Hence after careful consideration of all factors, the key variables for the analysis were judged to be the cost of assembling coal and iron ore at the production site and the cost of transporting the finished product to the market. So after adjustments were made to reflect differences in quality and price of ore at the major iron ore sources, the analysis centered upon identifying the differentials in transport costs on coal, iron ore, and the finished product.

Consider New York City as a major market for New England produced iron and steel products. For each production location the transportation costs on the three key elements can be readily calculated and compared. These costs are presented in Table 2.2a.

Notice in Table 2.2a that two alternative sources of ore were considered for the possible New England production centers. In each case, it was demonstrated that it was less expensive to use Venezuelan ore than ore from Labrador. Due to the differences in the composition of the ores, different amounts of coal were required per ton of finished product.[6] In each case, the coal was assumed to originate in West Virginia and Eastern Kentucky.

On the basis of this analysis, it is obvious that the Trenton location has a cost advantage in serving the New York market. The lowest-cost New England location is New London, when Venezuelan ore is used. Its main disadvantage relative to Trenton is in delivering finished product. The transport cost of a delivered ton of finished steel from New London to New York City would be $17.90, compared to $13.13 from Trenton. In addition to Trenton, Bethlehem and Sparrows Point can serve the New York market at a lower cost per ton than New London. After competitive position in a number of other major markets was examined, and after

[5] *Ibid.*, p. 253. [6] *Ibid.*, p. 254.

Table 2.2a Transportation Costs on Ore and Coal Required per Net Ton of Steel and on Finished Product for Selected Actual and Hypothetical Producing Locations Serving New York City*

Location	Transportation Costs Ore	Coal	Finished Product	Total
Fall River (Labrador ore)	$4.56	$6.01	$10.40	$20.97
(Venezuela ore)	3.68	5.63	10.40	19.71
New London (Labrador ore)	4.56	5.79	8.80	19.15
(Venezuela ore)	3.68	5.42	8.80	17.90
Pittsburgh (Mesabi ore)	5.55	1.56	12.40	19.51
Cleveland (Mesabi ore)	3.16	3.85	14.00	21.01
Sparrows Point (Venezuela ore)	3.68	4.26	8.40	16.34
Buffalo (Mesabi ore)	3.16	4.27	11.60	19.03
Bethlehem (Mesabi ore)	5.56	5.06	5.80	16.42
Trenton (Venezuela ore)	3.68	4.65	4.80	13.13

* Source: Isard and Cumberland [11], Table IX p. 257. Methods of calculation and an explanation of the sources are given as a note to Table I (*ibid.*), p. 248.

the purchasing habits of steel consumers were accounted for and various other factors examined, there appeared to be no justification for establishing a New England steel plant.

Despite its negative conclusion, this study clearly illustrates the technique of comparative cost analysis. The economic costs which vary from site to site are isolated and estimated. Then if a region proves to be the point of minimum cost for one or more markets whose total demand is sufficient to justify the new plant, the regional planner is in a position to consider seriously making a positive recommendation.

In the following section, a potential Continental Shelf resource, ilmenite, is examined in the same manner. The ilmenite case is basically a mining problem. It attempts to answer this question: At the present time and with the current cost and price structure, is the mining of offshore ilmenite justified, or is it at a disadvantage relative to exploiting inland sources of the mineral?

2.2.3 The Economic Potential of Ilmenite Recovery from the Continental Shelf Area

(The reader who is not interested in the details of the production process and the cost estimation may quickly glance through the pages of this section, reading carefully only the conclusions. The conclusions on the studies of other Continental Shelf resources are contained in Appendix A.)

(a) Sources of Titanium-Bearing Minerals

The titanium-bearing minerals, ilmenite and rutile, commonly occur in concentrations of heavy minerals in beach sands. These minerals have attracted attention as sources of potential products from the United States Continental Shelf regions. In addition to ilmenite and rutile, these heavy mineral concentrates frequently contain such items as magnetite, monazite, and zircon. Ilmenite ($FeO \cdot TiO_2$) and rutile (TiO_2) are used commercially as sources of titanium dioxide pigment and titanium metal. Magnetite (Fe_3O_4) is a ferrosoferric oxide used as an iron ore. Monazite (Ce, Nd, Pr, La) PO_4 ($+Th_3[PO_4]_4$) is a source of four rare earth metals —cerium, neodymium, praseodymium, and lanthanum. These rare earths exist as orthophosphate salts, sometimes in combination with thorium orthophosphate. Zircon ($ZrSiO_4$) is a zirconium orthosilicate from which zirconium can be extracted for use in the stainless steel industry.[7]

In the analysis which follows, primary attention will be given to the economic feasibility of obtaining offshore ilmenite. This titanium mineral is frequently found on the landward portions of United States beaches, and it is speculated that it occurs in offshore areas as well. No offshore deposits comparable to inland beach deposits have been found, however.

The hydraulic action of waves and surf leads to a concentration of heavy minerals in the rear of the back shore parts of beaches and in areas of contact between the unconsolidated beach sand and the consolidated basal rocks.[8] In addition to landward deposits, longshore currents can concentrate heavy minerals in the offshore areas.[9] Thus it can be speculated that a number of offshore beach sand areas contain concentrates of these heavy minerals, including ilmenite, the mineral of interest in this report.

Of the heavy minerals which are concentrated in this manner, both of the titanium minerals, rutile and ilmenite, are found naturally as separate grains in the beach sands. Of the two minerals, rutile has a richer titanium content, but has been found in much less abundance than ilmenite in the United States.

The two titanium minerals are normally used for different end products, although recent technological advances have enabled one to be substituted for the other at times. The basis of comparison between the two minerals, and the factor which largely determines their eventual end use, is their content of titanium dioxide (TiO_2). In concentrate form, rutile contains 92 to 98 percent TiO_2, while ilmenite concentrate varies from 45 to 65 percent.[10]

Current mining operations occur on the landward portions of beaches. At present, the major source of rutile is an 800-mile strip of beach sands on the east coast of Australia. Production from this area comprises 90–95 percent of the world's rutile production.[11] Australian rutile production reached 300,000 tons in 1967,[12] compared to a United States production of 8,000 tons in 1964, the last year for which data have been reported.[13]

Sizeable rutile deposits are being developed in Sierra Leone, which should eventually prove to have an output capacity in excess of 100,000 tons per year. A proven reserve of 3 million tons of rutile and indicated reserves of more than 30 million tons have been reported.[14] In the United States, limited amounts of rutile were produced in 1964 at Beaver Dam, Virginia, and at Skinner and Vero, Florida.[15] Since 1965, production has occurred only at Beaver Dam. Hence, the United States is highly dependent on imports for its supply of rutile concentrate. In 1967 it imported nearly 167,000 tons.[16]

Ilmenite is geographically distributed much more widely. Significant deposits are mined in Australia, Canada, Finland, Malaysia, Norway, and the United States.[17] United States ilmenite production, which was close to 1 million tons in 1967, took place at Piney River and Hanover County, Virginia; Starke and Highland, Florida; Folkston, Georgia; Tahawus, New York; and Lakehurst, New Jersey.[18]

(b) Industrial Processes in Titanium Recovery

Suction dredging is a common method of mining unconsolidated sand deposits of both ilmenite and rutile. The heavy mineral in the dredge feed is separated from tailings by physical and electro-magnetic methods. The first concentration step is

[7] For more specific information on the physical and chemical properties of these minerals, see Hodgman [6], pp. 1416–1433.
[8] Mero [14], p. 8. [9] *Ibid.*, p. 9. [10] Miller [16], p. 3. [11] Ian Potter [8], p. 6.
[12] *Ibid.* [13] U.S. Bureau of Mines [18], Vol. I, p. 1085. [14] *Ibid.*, Vol. IV, p. 915.
[15] *Ibid.*, Vol. I, p. 1076. [16] U.S. Bureau of Mines [19], Vol. I, p. 1133.
[17] *Ibid.*, p. 1141. [18] *Ibid.*, p. 1134.

carried out in a wet mill, where the heavy mineral concentrate is separated by gravity from the waste.

The second step of the concentrating process depends upon the minerals sought. Ilmenite is a magnetic conductor, due to its iron content, and thus magnetic separators are used to remove the ilmenite from the remainder of the heavy mineral content. Rutile is a non-magnetic electric conductor and it is removed by electrostatic separation.[19]

In order to produce titanium sponge, which is used for the production of titanium metal, titanium tetrachloride is required. Although titanium tetrachloride can be produced from either rutile or ilmenite, rutile is preferred because it has a high titanium content and contains little iron.[20] If iron is present in the ore, as is the case with ilmenite, ferric chloride will form with the titanium tetrachloride. The ferric chloride is currently considered waste.

Ilmenite, then, is used primarily in making titanium dioxide pigment. It was not until 1961 that a commercial process for the production of pigment based on rutile ore was perfected.[21] In 1962, over 55 per cent of this pigment produced was used by the paint industry, while about 16 percent was purchased by the paper industry.[22] Other sizeable users included the manufacturers of floor coverings, rubber, coated fabrics, and printing ink.

In order to produce titanium dioxide pigment, one of two industrial processes is usually followed: the sulfuric acid method or the chlorination method.

Until 1961, the sulfuric acid method was the only sizeable commercial process employed. In this method, titanium concentrate (derived from ilmenite) is digested with sulfuric acid. The resulting titanium and iron sulfates are dissolved in water or dilute sulfuric acid; and in cooling, ferrous sulfate precipitates. Once the iron is filtered out, the solution is heated and hydrated titanium dioxide precipitates. The hydrated titanium dioxide is then calcined to form crystalline titanium dioxide, which is subjected to finishing treatments, filtered, dried, and ground to pigmentary size.[23]

In the chlorination process, the ore is chlorinated and the titanium tetrachloride is oxidized to titanium dioxide under carefully controlled conditions.[24] In this process, rutile is the preferred raw material, although ilmenite-leucoxene-rutile mixtures are also used.[25] In 1964, only 7 percent of the titanium dioxide produced was manufactured by the chlorination process. Fulkerson and Gray point out, however, that most new processing plants currently under construction in the United States will employ the chlorination process.[26] The preference for the newer technology is based upon lower capital costs, lower operating costs, the possibility of a continuous process, and a lesser water pollution problem.

The possibility of pollution from ilmenite digestion in the sulphate process and the chlorination process should be noted. In the former, both sulphuric acid and ferrous sulphate are waste products. These are frequently dumped into rivers, or if the plant location is coastal, into the ocean. Industry sources report that some corrective steps have been taken with regard to river pollution. They contend, however, that in the ocean, the acidity rapidly dissipates and that the addition of iron promotes the growth of plankton which, in turn, leads to an increase in the fish population. In the chlorination process, it is reputed that "the water pollution problem is not as great,"[27] but further information must be collected before this assertion can be validated.

(c) Resources and Equipment Assumptions[28]

In order to evaluate the potential of offshore ilmenite, a comparative cost

[19] Ian Potter [8], p. 5. [20] Fulkerson and Gray [3], p. 6. [21] Ian Potter [8], p. 9.
[22] Fulkerson and Gray [3], p. 29. [23] *Ibid.*, p. 26, and industry sources.
[24] *Ibid.*, p. 26. [25] *Ibid.*, p. 27. [26] *Ibid.*, p. 26. [27] *Ibid.*
[28] A large amount of the cost data used in the analysis was furnished by the Ellicott Machine Corporation, Baltimore, Maryland.

analysis is performed. This analysis compares the cost per ton of recovering ilmenite sand by two types of offshore operations, and by one type of operation on landward beaches. It should be noted from the foregoing section dealing with industrial processes, that when the ore leaves the dredge and enters the concentration process, milling costs and the cost of pigment manufacture are basically the same, irrespective of the process by which ilmenite sand was recovered. Although variations in chemical content of the ore will lead to variations in concentration costs, this factor has been removed in the operation visualized by assuming equal grades and compositions of ore. Therefore, we place emphasis upon dredging costs in the production of ilmenite sand by the several processes and its delivery to the wet mill.

A number of assumptions are necessary in order to perform the analysis. It is assumed that the beach sands mined in each case yield 4 percent heavy minerals and that half of this heavy mineral content is ilmenite. The physical composition of the ores is assumed equal. The remainder of the heavy minerals are not considered. However, the secondary content of heavy minerals is normally recovered. At Tahawus, New York, magnetite and ilmenite are both recovered from ore that contains 18–20 percent titanium dioxide and 34 percent iron.[29] In the Northwest, ilmenite is recovered as a by-product of monazite at Cascade, Idaho, and as a by-product of columbium-tantalum operations at Bear Valley, Idaho.[30] Such by-product relationships could be taken into account by considering in the present analyses the use of additional concentrating equipment.

Although no offshore deposits of ilmenite have yet been located which would yield the 4 percent heavy mineral content assumed, it still is worthwhile, in order to evaluate the resource potential of the Continental Shelf, to compare the mining of equal grades of ilmenite from two distinct environments.

In each case examined, an assumption is made that the deposits are large enough to support a ten-year period of mining. Thus the major capital investment in equipment can be assumed to be fully depreciated, the rate of depreciation being taken at 10 percent. In each of the two dredging operations, a maximum water depth of 50 feet is assumed (slightly greater depths could probably be handled by the same equipment), and the mineral bed thickness is taken to be 7 yards. One cubic yard of sand ore is assumed to weigh 1.35 tons or 2,700 pounds.

Two distinct offshore operations are considered, one using conventional dredging equipment of the type generally employed today, the other using the most modern equipment available, including some which is in prototype form only at the present time (1967). In the landward operation, only existing types of equipment are assumed.

The conventional equipment considered for the offshore operation is an ocean-going diesel-powered dredge with 1,600 ship horsepower. The drilling device is a basket-type cutterhead. The dredge discharge is 16-inch, inside diameter. The maximum dredging depth of the cutterhead is about 70 feet below sea level. A 30-foot dredge tender is required to maneuver the dredge. With an assumed working time of 80 percent per day and a 300-day year due to weather and other environmental conditions, a working year of 5,760 hours is hypothesized.

If we postulate that the offshore ore deposit runs parallel to the coast along a six-mile stretch and is $\frac{1}{2}$ mile wide, the dredge is never more than $\frac{1}{2}$ mile from shore. Delivery is made to the wet mill, which is located on a barge near the shore, a maximum of 3,000 feet from the dredge.

The technologically advanced offshore operation employs what will be referred to here as "super equipment". Again, a 1,600 ship horsepower diesel-powered ocean-going dredge with a 16-inch, inside diameter, discharge pipe is used. Assumptions regarding water depth of operation, sand horizon thickness, and maximum dredging depths are the same as for the conventional equipment. The super equipment, however, has two distinct advantages over the conventional

[29] Miller [16], p. 39. [30] Fulkerson and Gray [3], p. 11.

equipment. Instead of a basket-type cutterhead, a 13-foot diameter dredge wheel is employed. This wheel, equipped with cutter-buckets at specified intervals about its circumference, revolves. Material is held in the bucket until it drops by gravity into the interior of the wheel where it is transported to the dredge by suction. Automatic control equipment is used to regulate the power applied to the bucket. Whereas the normal dredge operator might operate manually at an average efficiency of 66 percent, the automatic control equipment maintains dredging efficiency at close to 100 percent. Such additions as the dredge wheel and automatic control equipment would yield an output two to three times that of the conventional equipment. The advantage factor depends upon the distance of the discharge. Again as in the case of the conventional equipment, the wet mill is on a barge, a maximum of 3,000 feet from the dredge. A 30-foot dredge tender is required to maneuver the dredge. Working time per year is again 5,760 hours.

The land-based operation uses conventional dredging equipment. Such inland operation employs dredges on artificial ponds. In Australia, however, one operation works inland dunes with bulldozers.[31] In the operation considered in the comparative cost analysis, a 900 horsepower electric-powered dredge with a 16-inch, inside diameter, discharge pipe is used. The dredge uses a basket-type cutterhead. Our assumptions on the depth are the same as for offshore operations in order to insure comparability in the analysis. The dredging area is 3 square miles. The dredge's maximum distance from the wet mill is placed at 500 feet, with the wet mill located on barges. Since the movement of the dredge can be controlled by shore-anchored cables, no dredge tender is required.

Since onshore operations are less vulnerable to weather than offshore operations, a working time of 85 percent per day (20.4 hours) for 320 days per year is assumed, yielding a working year of 6,528 hours.

(d) A Comparison of Capital Cost for Ilmenite Recovery Operations by Dredging

The dredging capital costs were computed as follows: A *dredge* of 1,600 ship horsepower required for offshore operations would cost about $500,000. The smaller dredge used for inland operations could be purchased for about 85 percent of that amount, or $425,000. The addition of the super equipment to one of the offshore operations would cost about $210,000. This latter figure includes the cost of the *dredging wheel*, $120,000, and the *automatic control equipment*, $90,000.

Discharge pipe (floating pipe) represents a major expenditure in each of the operations, and is capitalized. Each of the offshore operations would require 3,000 feet of *floating pipe* with appropriate connecting ball-joints. This pipe costs about $24 per running foot, joints included, amounting to a total cost of $72,000. The inland operation would require only 500 feet of such pipe, or a total cost of $12,000. *Pontoons* are required to support the floating pipe. On the average, such pontoons would cost $39 per foot of floating pipe, or a total cost of $117,000 for an offshore operation and of $19,500 for an inland operation. A small *dredge tender*, probably 30 feet long, is required for the offshore operation. This tender could be purchased for $50,000. A summary of the dredging capital costs by type of operation is given in Table 2.2b.

The depreciation rate for dredging capital items varies with the equipment considered. In each case, the analysis assumes for any given item the same depreciation rate regardless of the type of operation hypothesized.

On the basis of industry sources, a 10 percent depreciation rate is considered reasonable for the dredges, the dredging wheel, and the automatic control equipment. As the floating pipe is subject to internal abrasion from the materials transported and external wear from wave motion, a 25 percent depreciation rate is

[31] Ian Potter [8], p. 6.

Table 2.2b Dredging Capital Costs for Selected Items, by Type of Operation

Item	Conventional Equipment, Offshore	Super Equipment, Offshore	Conventional Equipment, Inland
Dredge	$500,000	$500,000	$425,000
Dredge wheel	0	120,000	0
Automatic control equipment	0	90,000	0
Floating pipe ($24 per foot)	72,000	72,000	12,000
Pontoons ($39 per foot)	117,000	117,000	19,500
Dredge tender (300 hp)	50,000	50,000	0
Total	$739,000	$949,000	$456,500

applied. The pontoons are depreciated at a rate of 20 percent, while the dredge tenders are depreciated at a rate of 10 percent. Table 2.2c summarizes these depreciation rates and presents the resulting annual charges for each of the selected capital items by type of operation. It can be seen that for conventional equipment used offshore the total annual depreciation charge is $96,400. It is $117,400 for the super equipment used offshore, and it is only $49,400 for the conventional equipment used inland.

Table 2.2c Depreciation Rates and Annual Depreciation for Selected Capital Items

Item	Depreciation Rate	Conventional Equipment, Offshore	Super Equipment, Offshore	Conventional Equipment, Inland
Dredge	10%	$50,000	$50,000	$42,500
Dredge wheel	10	0	12,000	0
Automatic control equipment	10	0	9,000	0
Floating pipe	25	18,000	18,000	3,000
Pontoons	20	23,400	23,400	3,900
Dredge tender	10	5,000	5,000	0
Total		$96,400	$117,400	$49,400

(e) Comparative Annual Operating Costs for Ilmenite Dredging

The computation of dredge operating costs performed in this analysis considers annual fixed costs and annual variable costs. The fixed costs include annual depreciation charges, interest, taxes, insurance, and storage. Variable costs include labor, fuel, lubrication, maintenance, and repair.

In Table 2.2d annual depreciation charges are listed for each of the operations in Table 2.2c. Interest is calculated at 6 percent of total capital cost for each operation. Taxes are set at $2\frac{1}{2}$ percent of total capital costs. Insurance and storage are estimated at $3\frac{1}{2}$ percent of total capital costs. For the offshore operation using conventional equipment, total fixed costs are thus computed to be $185,080. For the offshore operation employing super equipment, these costs are $231,280. For the inland operation, they are $104,181.

Of the variable costs encountered in the dredging operations, labor costs were assumed to be the same in each type of operation. Three labor shifts are visualized for each type. An operator, a mechanic, and 2 deckmen are required for each of the shifts. In addition to this labor component, one supervisor heads up the entire operation. The wage rates computed were intentionally liberal, as occasionally extra labor is employed. The total wage bill for the 13-man crew as recorded in Table 2.2d might well be spread over additional labor.

The consumption of fuel depends upon the dredging location, as the offshore operations are diesel-powered. The diesel fuel consumption for the offshore dredges was computed on the basis of total horsepower (including both dredge and maneuvering horse power, 2,000 horsepower in total), fuel consumption per horsepower, unit fuel cost, pumping time per year, and the expected load factor.

For the inland operation, the horsepower rating of the dredge was converted to kilowatts (1 horsepower = 0.7455 kilowatt) and then multiplied by an estimated cost per kilowatt and the pumping time per year.

Lubrication costs for the offshore operations were assumed to be 10 percent of total diesel fuel costs. Because of the use of an electric dredge for the inland operation, which entails lower lubrication costs, costs for that operation were arbitrarily set at 60 percent of offshore lubrication costs.

Maintenance and repair costs are estimated at $0.035 per cubic yard of material

Table 2.2d Annual Dredge Operating Costs by Type and Location of Recovery, 1967 Estimates

	Conventional Equipment, Offshore	Super Equipment, Offshore	Conventional Equipment, Inland
Fixed Costs			
Depreciation charges	$96,400	$117,400	$49,400
Interest	44,340	56,940	27,390
Taxes	18,475	23,725	11,413
Insurance and storage	25,865	33,215	15,978
Subtotal	$185,080	$231,280	$104,181
Variable Costs			
Labor	94,500[a]	94,500[a]	94,500[a]
Dredge diesel fuel	60,826[b]	60,826[b]	0
Dredge electricity	0	0	43,800[c]
Dredge tender diesel fuel	2,970[d]	2,970[d]	0
Lubrication	6,380[e]	6,380[e]	3,828[f]
Maintenance & repair	110,880[g]	252,000[h]	190,944[i]
Subtotal	$275,556	$416,676	$333,072
Total	$460,636	$647,956	$437,253
Cubic yards of sand ore dredged per year	3,168,000	7,200,000	6,364,800
Tons of dredged ilmenite per year	85,536	194,400	171,850
Cost per ton of dredged ilmenite	$5.385	$3.333	$2.544

[a]*Labor required*	*Estimated wage bill*
1 supervisor	$12,000
3 operators	24,000
3 mechanics	22,500
6 deckmen	36,000
	$94,500

[b](Total horsepower) (fuel consumption per horsepower) (unit fuel cost) (pumping time per year) (load factor) = (2,000 horsepower) (0.06 gallon/horsepower/hour) ($.11/gallon) (5,760 hours) (.80) = $60,826.

[c](.7455) (dredge horsepower) (electric cost per kilowatt) (pumping time per year) = (.7455) (900 horsepower) ($.01/kilowatt) (6,528 hours/year) = $43,800.

[d](Tender horsepower) (fuel consumption per horsepower) (unit fuel cost) (hours per year in use) = (300 horsepower) (0.06 gallon/horsepower/hour) ($.11/gallon) (1,500 hours/year) = $2,970.

[e](Total fuel cost) (10%) = ($60,826 + $2,970) (10%) = $6,380.

[f]Assumed to be 60% of offshore lubrication costs; ($6,380) (.60) = $3,828.

[g]($0.035) (3,168,000 cubic yards) = $110,880.

[h]($0.035) (7,200,000 cubic yards) = $252,000.

[i]($0.03) (6,364,800 cubic yards) = $190,944.

dredged for diesel-powered dredges. For the electric power dredge used in the inland operation, a slightly lower cost is visualized—namely, \$.03 per cubic yard of material dredged.

Total annual operating cost of the dredging stages of ilmenite recovery are derived in Table 2.2d, by type and location of recovery. Table 2.2d reveals that if each of the three dredges were operated at maximum level for a year, total annual operating costs for the two conventional type dredges would be roughly the same, while the dredge employing the super equipment would encounter additional operating costs of about \$200,000 per year. To derive cost per ton of output, estimates of output levels must be made.

(f) Comparative Dredge Outputs for Ilmenite Recovery

The annual output of each of the dredges considered is the product of the output per hour by dredge type and the number of hours in the working year. For the dredges and dredging environments described in this analysis, it would be expected that the conventional equipment offshore operation would have an output of 550 cubic yards per hour, the super equipment offshore operation an output of 1,250 cubic yards per hour, and the conventional equipment inland operation, an output of 975 cubic yards per hour. Notice that the conventional equipment inland operation has a significantly higher output per hour than the conventional equipment offshore operation, even though dredge capital investments are roughly comparable. This significant output difference is due to the fact that output per hour falls off markedly as the length of the discharge pipe increases, *ceteris paribus*.

When the working time per year is taken into acount, it is found that the conventional equipment would yield 3,168,000 cubic yards per year, the super equipment 7,200,000 cubic yards per year, and the inland equipment 6,364,800 cubic yards per year. These data are recorded in Table 2.2d. Since 1 cubic yard of dredged material weighs 1.35 short tons, these figures can be converted to a tonnage basis.

Assuming that 2 percent of the sand weight is ilmenite—that is, that 50 tons of sand ore are required to recover 1 ton of ilmenite, it can be seen that the offshore conventional equipment will produce 85,536 tons of recovered ilmenite, the super equipment 194,400 tons, and the inland equipment 171,850 tons. Again these data are recorded in Table 2.2d.

The dredging cost of recovering 1 ton of ilmenite can now be evaluated. By use of the conventional equipment, the cost per ton of ilmenite dredged is \$5.385. For the super equipment, the cost is \$3.333. The lowest figure is for the inland equipment, which is \$2.544 per ton ilmenite.

(g) The Concentration Process

As stated previously, it is explicitly assumed in this analysis that the chemical, physical, and mineral contents of the ilmenite sands from each location are identical. Hence, it would be expected that the concentration costs of removing the ilmenite concentrate from the sand ore at these locations would be the same. It is possible that additional washing costs may be encountered in removing ocean salts from the offshore sand, but such an additional cost should be minor.

The concentration processes have been documented elsewhere.[32] Basically, dredge output is pumped to a wet mill, where it is screened to remove oversized particles which are separated off for disaggregation. The material is then forced into a series of spiral concentrators. The heavy mineral content is separated from the tailings by gravitational forces. In one plant, three spiral concentration steps

[32] Grogan, Few, and Hager [4], pp. 205–229; and "How Humphreys Separates Titanium Minerals . . ." [7], pp. 47–49.

are involved, each leading to a finer concentrate.[33] The output of the wet mill is then washed in a cleaner spiral and sent by pipeline up to three miles to the dry mill and final concentrating.

The dry mill recovers the titanium minerals and separates them from the other heavy minerals in the ore. This separation process takes advantage of the conductivity and magnetic properties of the ilmenite.

The cost of the wet mill separation, according to industry sources, is approximately $.12 per ton of sand processed. With a 90 per cent recovery rate, roughly 56 tons of sand would yield 1 ton of ilmenite concentrate after the wet mill process. Thus wet mill operating costs per ton of ilmenite concentrate output would be about $6.72. Dry mill operating costs are estimated by industry sources at $1.00 per ton of output.

(h) Conclusions

As determined in the foregoing analysis, the major cost differences for the three types of operations considered are primarily the cost differences in mining and delivering the sand ore to the wet mill. These are the per ton costs summarized at the bottom of Table 2.2d. These costs indicate that an inland operation has a clear advantage over offshore operations, even when super equipment is used.

Although published ilmenite reserve data are not available, industry sources report that supplies from present domestic sources are adequate. (In the event that such supplies were exhausted, these sources report that lower quality inland ilmenite in Idaho, Wyoming, and Oregon would be exploited before turning to the Continental Shelf.) Moreover, since the chlorination process for the production of titanium dioxide seems to be increasingly preferred to the sulfuric acid method, and since the former employs rutile rather than ilmenite, we do not anticipate any major demand pressures on inland ilmenite deposits unless economical methods for chlorinating ilmenite are developed.

Should offshore deposits of 2.6 percent purity or better be discovered, then a real development potential may come to exist, as indicated by the hypothetical data in Table 2.2e. These data reveal that the per unit dredging cost of production from

Table 2.2e Hypothetical per Unit Dredging Costs for Different Ilmenite Concentrate Levels, Super Equipment, Offshore Operation

Level of Ilmenite Concentrate	Total Dredge Output (in tons)	Ilmenite Concentrate Recovered (in tons)	Total Annual Cost	Dredging Cost per ton of Recovered Ilmenite Concentrate
2.0%	9,720,000	194,000	$647,956	$3.333
2.6	9,720,000	252,720	647,956	2.564
3.0	9,720,000	291,600	647,956	2.222

an offshore deposit containing 2.6 percent ilmenite concentrate by super equipment is equivalent to the per unit dredging cost of production from an inland deposit containing 2.0 percent ilmenite concentrate by conventional equipment. However, *assuming* no drastic change in technology or in consumption pattern, *assuming* that offshore deposits will not exceed 2 percent ilmenite concentration (no sizeable deposits which exceed this richness have been reported), and *assuming* the data provided by industry sources are of a high degree of validity, our tentative conclusion is that there exists no major economic potential for the mining of offshore ilmenite deposits at the present time.

[33] Grogan, Few, and Hager [4], p. 209.

Readings on Comparative Cost Analysis

For the reader interested in probing more deeply into the comparative cost technique, the following references are recommended.

Airov, Joseph, *The Location of the Synthetic Fiber Industry: A Study in Regional Analysis*, New York, John Wiley and Sons, 1959.

Isard, Walter, "Some Locational Factors in the Iron and Steel Industry since the Early Nineteenth Century," *Journal of Political Economy*, 56 (June, 1948).

———, *et al.*, *Methods of Regional Analysis*, Cambridge Mass., The M.I.T. Press, 1960, Chapter 7.

——— and William M. Capron, "The Future Locational Pattern of Iron and Steel Production in the United States," *Journal of Political Economy*, 57 (April, 1949).

——— and John Cumberland, "New England as a Possible Location for an Integrated Iron and Steel Works," *Economic Geography*, XXVI (October, 1950).

——— and Vincent H. Whitney, *Atomic Power, an Economic and Social Analysis*, New York, McGraw-Hill Publishing Company, 1952.

2.3 *Input-Output*

2.3.1 Introduction

In attempting to provide a comprehensive planning framework for a region, an analyst must usually go beyond simple comparative cost studies. Frequently he must examine the complex interrelations within the regional economy. If the planner is interested in selecting industries which might reasonably be promoted in his region, he must concern himself with questions dealing with the input structures of these industries and the local markets for their products. Furthermore, he must be interested in how new industries would affect the operations of other industries in his region and fit into its existing economic structure.

Or perhaps the analyst is concerned with planning beyond mere industrialization. If government or some enterprise has announced plans for a new facility or plant, the analyst may be interested in determining in some consistent manner the potential impact of the new development. He might be interested in determining the new employment and income that might be generated directly and indirectly by this regional addition. He might also wish to know what increases in governmental services might be demanded as a result of the new employment. Finally, he may wish to determine the tax revenues that might be generated, in order to support the expected increase in governmental services to be provided.

It becomes apparent that in order to answer these questions, a relatively comprehensive description of the regional economy is required. The input-output approach does provide a comprehensive quantitative description of the regional economy that is useful for consistent consideration of these issues. Its strength lies in its detailed presentation of the production and distribution characteristics of the industries within the region. It further depicts the nature of the various interrelations among the industrial sectors and between the industrial sectors and other economic components of the region. Given the data provided by an input-output table, the planner can work up consistent and thoughtful answers to the questions faced in comprehensive regional planning.

The input-output approach was largely developed by Wassily Leontief of Harvard University in the 1930's, with application to the national economy. In recent years, it has become a basic tool to the regional analyst and has been successfully applied to problems of the regional economy.

2.3.2 The Input-Output Framework

We begin the presentation of the input-output framework by developing a simple numerical example.[34] Suppose in some regional economy that all economic activity can be divided into three categories or, using traditional input-output terminology, sectors. The region to be analyzed can take any form, be it a group of counties, a standard metropolitan statistical area, a natural region, or a state. It is frequently advantageous to define a region along some political boundaries, since published statistical data can then frequently be used to supplement data from other sources.

With the region defined, it is then necessary to derive the relevant sectors. In this simplified example, the three relevant sectors are (1) agriculture, (2) manufacturing, and (3) trade and services. It should be obvious that more sectors ought to be included, but for illustrative purposes, three will suffice.

Once the economy has been meaningfully sectored, it is necessary to collect the data needed for the input-output formulation. The required information is normally obtained from the available published data and by a survey of firms. In a survey, the analyst is interested in obtaining from each firm data on where that firm's inputs originated over a period of time, say one year. In addition, he is interested in determining the destination of the firm's output. When speaking of origins and destinations in this sense, the analyst concerned with the national economy is interested more in industrial sectors than in geographical regions. However, the regional analyst is interested also in the geographic origins of inputs and destinations of outputs. These origins and destinations will isolate the imports and exports of a region.

It should be remembered that the output of one industry may well be shipped to several types of users. Some of it may be shipped to other industries, where it becomes an input in another industrial process. Some may be shipped directly to final consumers, such as households. This latter category of consumers, whose demand is designated final demand, is treated in a different manner that will become apparent later.

Once the data for firms are obtained, each firm may then be assigned to the relevant input-output sector. Next, within any sector the data for all firms in that sector are processed together with other published and unpublished data that may be available to obtain the relevant flow data for that sector.

Table 2.3a Input-Output Flow Table (in billions of dollars)

Industry Producing \ Industry Purchasing	Agri-culture	Manu-facturing	Trade and Services	**Final Demand**	**Total Gross Output**
Agriculture	1	3	2	6	12
Manufacturing	4	6	4	10	24
Trade and Services	2	3	5	8	18
Total Intermediate Inputs	7	12	11	24	

Consider Table 2.3a which presents various flows within an economy and which is designated an input-output flow table. Beginning with the first column, in that

[34] The simplified example used here is based on an illustration developed by John Cumberland in Isard *et al.* [9], pp. 363–367. This reference is recommended for the reader interested in the mathematical structure of regional input-output models, a topic which will not be treated in this book.

portion of the matrix designated "Industry Purchasing," one finds the sector labeled *Agriculture*. This column indicates the various commodities and services purchased by the agricultural sector over the course of a year for use as inputs. It can be seen that firms and farms within the agricultural sector purchased, during the study year, $1 billion of their inputs from other firms and farms in the agricultural sector. These *intra*sectoral transactions cover, for example, purchases of seed and livestock. Further down the column, it is seen that the agricultural sector purchased $4 billion of inputs from the manufacturing sector and $2 billion from the trade and service sector. These purchases are *inter*sectoral transactions; together with the intrasectoral transactions they reveal the input structure of the agricultural sector. In the second and third columns, dealing with the purchases of inputs of the manufacturing and the trade and services sectors, respectively, the input structure of these two sectors is set forth.

In input-output analysis, this composition of inputs, or input structure, by sector plays a key role. Often the analyst makes a very important and strong assumption concerning this input structure. He assumes that the output of the various sectors and the required inputs are proportional. Thus, if the agricultural sector were to double its output in the next year, that sector would use as inputs not $1 billion from agriculture, $4 billion from manufacturing, and $2 billion from trade and services, but $2 billion from agriculture, $8 billion from manufacturing, and $4 billion from trade and services. With the inputs thus assumed proportionate to the level of output, the input-output analyst explains changes in the level of input use by the sectors in the system once he is able to explain the changes in the level of outputs.

Now consider the rows of the table. Recall that every purchase within the economy must at the same time represent a sale to someone—a sale from production. Sales from production are listed along the rows. For example, in the left-hand tab, the heading "Industry Producing," one again finds the agricultural sector (the first row). This sector ships $1 billion in output to itself, $3 billion to the manufacturing sector, and $2 billion to trade and services. The second row reveals the destination of manufacturing outputs and the third, the destination of trade and service outputs. In effect, then, the input-output formulation represents a double-entry bookkeeping system, revealing both purchases and sales within the economy.

The final demand sector remains to be explained. As already noted, the levels of required inputs of any sector, whether agriculture, manufacturing, or trade and services, are assumed to be linearly dependent upon the level of output in that sector. In a regional economy, it would be unrealistic to attempt to extend the same reasoning to include government and exports (determined by purchasers outside of the region); and often one hesitates to extend it to household consumers. Hence this part of the table is considered to be exogenous (that is, outside the system) and determined by factors other than those one attempts to incorporate in the input-output model. Thus the final demand column may represent exogenously determined purchase decisions by households, government, investors, and firms outside the region. Household decisions to purchase are often viewed as determined to an important extent by some non-economic factor, with purchases made both from family savings and proceeds from the sale of labor. Government output and input levels are frequently determined by political rather than strictly economic decisions. Investment purchases may be geared to long-term production prospects rather than to just the current level of output. Purchases by firms outside the area are often largely determined by their own region's economic conditions rather than those of the study region.

Thus, as can be seen in the final demand column of Table 2.3a, the agricultural sector sold $6 billion of its output to meet the combined demands of households, investment, exports, and government. The manufacturing sector sold $10 billion to final demand, while trade and services sold $8 billion.

At this point, output and input totals can be derived. The gross agricultural output, for example, is $12 billion. The gross value of agricultural inputs is $7 billion. Because it is assumed that the input levels are linearly dependent on the level of output,[35] a further step can be taken which tends to simplify the system. Given the level of output from each sector and the necessary inputs, technical coefficients can be calculated. Each technical coefficient refers to an input per unit of output and is derived by dividing a sector's total purchases of that input by that sector's total output.

For example, consider the agricultural sector. In order to produce $12 billion in agricultural output, the sector requires $1 billion of its own output as input, $4 billion of manufacturing products, and $2 billion of trade and services. Thus, the required inputs per dollar of output in this sector are derived by dividing the value of these purchases by the output of that sector. Hence, the technical coefficient relating agricultural sector output with agricultural sector inputs is $1 billion divided by $12 billion, or 0.083. Similarly, the coefficient relating manufacturing inputs to agricultural output is calculated to be 0.333, and the coefficient relating trade and services input to agricultural output, to be 0.167. In like manner, the coefficients for the other sectors can be calculated. The technical coefficients for the flow data in Table 2.3a are given in Table 2.3b.

Table 2.3b Input-Output Technical Coefficient Matrix

Industry Producing	**Industry Purchasing** Agriculture	Manufacturing	Trade and Services
Agriculture	0.083	0.125	0.111
Manufacturing	0.333	0.250	0.222
Trade and services	0.167	0.125	0.278

The interpretation of Table 2.3b is straightforward. In order to produce $1 of output in the agricultural sector, 8.3¢ in inputs from agriculture, 33.3¢ in inputs from manufacturing, and 16.7¢ in inputs from the trade and services are required. Notice that since final demand is determined exogenously, no technical coefficients are calculated for the final demand sector.

With the technical coefficients in Table 2.3b, it is possible to demonstrate the use of input-output analysis. First, from the magnitude of the technical coefficients, one can pinpoint the sectors which are most closely linked. For example, the greatest percentage of inputs into the agricultural sector come from the manufacturing sector in this hypothetical economy. In the trade and services sector, the agricultural inputs are least important, yet the agricultural input still plays a vital role.

A much more important analytical step can be made, however. Suppose the analyst forecasts that four years hence, because of increased population, exports, and military expenditures, final demand for manufactured goods will rise from the $10 billion listed in Table 2.3a to $15 billion. This would indicate a net increase in the demand for manufactured goods of $5 billion. It also indicates that input purchases by the manufacturing sector must increase to make possible the additional output. If 12.5¢ of agricultural inputs are required for $1 of manufacturing output, then $625 million of agricultural inputs will be required for $5 billion of additional manufacturing output. If 25.0¢ of manufacturing inputs are required for $1 of manufacturing output, then $1,250 million of manufacturing inputs will be re-

[35] This relationship can be viewed conversely; doubling all inputs would in turn double the output.

quired for $5 billion increase in manufacturing output. Finally, if 12.5¢ of trade and service inputs are required for $1 of manufacturing output, then $625 million of trade and service inputs will be required for a $5 billion increase in manufacturing output. Thus, the $625 million of agricultural inputs, the $1,250 million of manufacturing inputs, and the $625 million of trade and service inputs represent the first round of input requirements.

However, the process does not end here. In order to increase agricultural production by $625 million to meet the $5 billion new manufacturing demand, certain amounts of additional inputs into agriculture are required. From Table 2.3b, it is seen that in order to increase agricultural output by $1, there are required 8.3¢ of additional agricultural inputs, 33.3¢ of additional manufacturing inputs, and 16.7¢ of additional trade and service inputs. Thus, to support the new demand for $625 million in agricultural inputs for use in manufacturing, an additional $51,875,000 of agricultural inputs, $208,125,000 of manufacturing inputs, and $104,375,000 of trade and services inputs are required. These constitute part of the second round of input requirements. The other parts of the second-round requirements correspond to the inputs associated with increased output of the manufacturing and the trade and services sectors needed to meet the $5 billion new manufacturing demand.

Once total second round input requirements are calculated, it is easily seen that "third round requirements" are necessary to produce the second-round requirements. The technical coefficients again provide the estimates of third-round requirements. Operating by this round-by-round approach, the analyst eventually discovers, after six or so iterations, that the production increases required by additional rounds become minor. He then terminates the process. Finally, by adding together the increases in production in each industry, required by the several rounds, the analyst determines total effect upon production in the economy, given the initial projected change in final demand for manufacturing output.[36]

There are several important omissions from Table 2.3a. For example, while households are included as a part of the final demand sector, payments to labor for services are not included in that table. These payments could be included in a form similar to the other inputs; that is, they can be listed along a row and represent the value of labor inputs (contributed by the households sector) to the various producing sectors.

In order to make explicit these payments to labor (by each producing sector), as well as other payments (such as taxes to government, outlays for imported goods used as inputs, charges to take account of inventory depletion and depreciation of plant and equipment), we present Table 2.3c, which is an expanded input-output flow table. This table lists these several types of payments in the lower set of rows. It also disaggregates the final demand sector into six columns, one corresponding to every payment row.

With Table 2.3c we can now identify payments to labor (labor inputs). They are listed in the next to last row. For example, wage and salary payments to households by the manufacturing sector are seen to be $5 billion. We also note payments (taxes) to government. For example, tax payments by agriculture are $1 billion. Dollar value of imports (inputs of commodities) from other regions by sector are noted, as are dollar value of imports from abroad. For example, the manufacturing sector used as input $1 billion of goods and services imported from abroad. Finally, payments for inputs obtained by depleting inventories and payments (in the form of depreciation charges) for the services of plant and equipment are noted by sector.

Another major characteristic of an input-output flow table must be pointed up.

[36] The round-by-round process can be rather cumbersome in an input-output table that contains more than three sectors. In larger systems, a mathematical tool, known as the inverse, to be discussed later, is commonly employed.

Table 2.3c An Expanded Input-Output Flow Table for Region A, 1968 (in billions of dollars)

Industry Producing \ Industry Purchasing	Agriculture	Manufacturing	Trade and Services	Final Demand: Government Purchases	Final Demand: Exports to Other Regions	Final Demand: Exports Abroad	Final Demand: Gross Inventory Accumulation	Final Demand: Investment	Final Demand: Households	**Total Gross Output**
Agriculture	1	3	2	1	1	0	1	0	3	12
Manufacturing	4	6	4	1	1	1	1	2	4	24
Trade and services	2	3	5	2	0	0	0	1	5	18
Payments Sectors										
Payments to government	1	2	1	1	0	1	0	0	5	11
Imports from other regions	1	1	0	2	0	1	1	1	1	8
Imports from abroad	0	1	0	1	0	1	1	1	1	6
Gross inventory depletion	0	2	1	1	1	1	0	1	0	7
Depreciation allowances	1	1	1	1	0	0	1	0	1	6
Households	2	5	4	3	0	0	0	1	1	16
Total gross outlays	12	24	18	13	3	5	5	7	21	108

Consider the agriculture sector in Table 2.3c. Total gross output during 1968 was determined to be $12 billion. In the input-output accounting framework all outputs are imputed to some set of inputs. In each processing sector the total gross output must equal the total gross outlays (expenditures) on inputs. Therefore, the total value of inputs into the agriculture sector must also be $12 billion. The inter-industry inputs previously discussed (from the agriculture, manufacturing, and trade and services sectors) account for $7 billion of these inputs. Although the agriculture sector is shown to have no inputs from inventory and imports from abroad, it does employ inputs from other payment sectors (i.e., sectors to which it makes payments for goods and services). It uses $1 billion of imports from other regions, makes $1 billion of tax payments to government, uses up $1 billion worth of capital, and pays $2 billion as wages and other income to households. Thus the total gross outlay, $12 billion, equals the total gross output.

On the output side, Table 2.3c makes possible a disaggregated listing of deliveries to final demand. Specifically listed for each producing sector in its corresponding row are its deliveries to government, to exports to other regions, to exports abroad, to inventory, to investments, and to households. The interpretations of these deliveries are like that of any sale to final demand.

With the addition of the payments sectors and the disaggregation of the final demand sector, it is found that certain payments sectors provide inputs which go directly to final demand. Two of these may be quite large. In the lower right-hand portion of the table, it can be seen that government wage payments to households amount to $3 billion, while household tax payments to government are $5 billion. Unlike the totals for the processing sectors, the totals for corresponding final demand and payments sectors need not be equal. Thus, for example, payments to households in 1968 amounted to $16 billion, whereas final demand purchases by households totaled $21 billion. This difference indicates that households made a substantial portion of these purchases by using up their assets.[37]

As a rule, in a model of this type, technical coefficients are not computed for the rows corresponding to payments and columns corresponding to final demand sectors. Of course, calculations here of labor coefficients corresponding to the Household row, and capital coefficients corresponding to the Investment (capital formation) column, might provide relevant information to the analyst; but it is frequently found that the assumption of constant coefficients is less tenable with reference to these items.

The basic elements of input-output analysis have now been presented in simplified form. It is possible to expand the basic model. In any attempt to build up an input-output table for a region, the sectors to be included are largely determined by the purpose of the study, the characteristics of the regional economy, and the available data. Usually the more the sectors are subdivided, the more precise the analysis that can be made.

To illustrate how an input-output table has been used in a regional study and to point up the types of results which can be expected from an iterative round-by-round approach, consider a study by Isard and Kuenne[38] of the impact of a major development upon an economy. In this study the authors attempted to assess the significance of a new integrated iron and steel works (The Fairless Works) for the Philadelphia-New York industrial region. It was first shown that the growth of certain industries, such as the fabricated metal industries, is dependent upon the existence of nearby iron and steel capacity. By the use of location theory, historical analysis, business interviews, and other information, estimates of induced employment in the fabricated metal industries were made. On the basis of data on value of output per worker in these industries and in integrated iron and steel works, it was

[37] For a complete description of the entries in the payments and final demand sectors, see Miernyk [15]; Isard *et al.* [9], and Chenery and Clark [2].

[38] Isard and Kuenne [12].

Table 2.3d Direct and Indirect Repercussions of New Basic Steel Capacity

Industry	Input Requirements of Initial Steel and Steel Fabricating Activities (in $ thousand) (1)	Minimum Percentage of Input Requirements to be Produced in Area (2)	First Round Expansions in Area (in $ thousand) (3)	Second Round Expansions in Area (in $ thousand) (4)	Third Round Expansions in Area (in $ thousand) (5)	Sum of Round Expansions in Area (in $ thousand) (6)	Total New Employees Corresponding to Round Expansions (7)	Total New Employees in Initial Steel and Steel-Fabricating Activities (8)	Over-all Total of New Employees (9)
1. Agriculture and fisheries	50.0	0	0.0	0	0	0	0		0
2. Food and kindred products	294.6	60	176.8	17,660	8,249	42,492	1,833		1,833
3. Tobacco manufacturers	0.0	0	0.0	0	0	0	0		0
4. Textile mill products	3,864.7	10	386.5	406	39	1,280	142		142
5. Apparel	1,285.6	75	964.2	10,124	3,461	21,155	2,302		2,302
6. Lumber and wood products	5,610.7	5	280.5	93	36	450	64		64
7. Furniture and fixtures	1,753.4	33	578.6	802	198	2,000	234		234
8. Paper and allied products	4,818.7	40	1,927.5	1,674	1,297	6,574	426		426
9. Printing and publishing	425.5	90	383.0	5,929	3,014	14,617	1,667		1,667
10. Chemicals	10,626.4	45	4,781.9	3,599	1,630	12,077	601		601
11. Products of petroleum and coal	10,936.6	25	2,734.2	2,547	1,118	7,634	228		228
12. Rubber products	8,381.5	15	1,257.2	355	102	1,879	169		169
13. Leather and leather products	647.7	20	129.5	679	194	1,371	150		150
14. Stone, clay, and glass products	9,031.7	15	1,354.8	441	139	2,083	268		268
15. Iron and steel	121,170.5	50	60,585.3	13,566	2,965	78,335	6,093	11,666	17,759
16. Nonferrous metals	33,997.4	20	6,799.5	1,667	381	9,063	505		505
17. Plumbing and heating supplies	3,192.4	25	798.1	248	50	1,189	118	3,640	3,758
18. Fabricated structural metal products	3,480.7	40	1,392.3	312	33	1,809	151	1,420	1,571
19. Other fabricated metal products	31,770.9	40	12,708.4	2,146	561	16,121	1,537	10,060	11,597
20. Agricultural, mining, and construction machinery	3,651.3	5	182.6	46	11	251	22	707	729

21. Metal-working machinery	7,389.1	25	1,847.3	270	43	2,210	289	2,705	2,994
22. Other machinery (except electric)	28,463.6	40	11,385.4	2,675	551	15,384	1,486	28,607	30,093
23. Motors and generators	11,265.9	20	2,253.2	226	42	2,560	301		
24. Radios	4,562.2	30	1,368.7	428	101	2,026	192	} 10,392	} 12,312
25. Other electrical machinery	21,773.9	50	10,887.0	2,011	432	13,903	1,427		
26. Motor vehicles	50,530.8	10	5,053.1	742	260	6,421	389	8,770	9,159
27. Other transportation equipment	2,605.5	20	521.1	276	69	958	117	4,605	4,722
28. Professional and scientific equipment	3,221.4	50	1,610.7	801	287	3,123	416		416
29. Miscellaneous manufacturing	5,116.8	60	3,070.1	2,888	982	8,418	845	6,108	6,953
30. Coal, gas, and electric power	7,767.0	50	3,883.5	1,843	2,693	11,079	1,100		1,100
31. Railroad transportation	13,575.8	75	10,181.9	6,010	2,390	21,532	3,308		3,308
32. Ocean transportation	457.3	75	343.0	331	170	1,021	110		110
33. Other transportation	4,179.4	95	3,970.4	8,422	2,836	19,694	2,394		2,394
34. Trade	13,969.8	95	13,271.3	36,585	11,855	83,642	13,874		13,874
35. Communications	1,790.7	90	1,611.6	2,409	1,283	7,305	1,191		1,191
36. Finance and insurance	3,086.2	90	2,777.6	9,472	5,062	25,252	2,329		2,329
37. Rental	3,018.8	95	2,867.9	26,222	9,603	55,680	909		909
38. Business services	5,338.5	95	5,071.6	2,385	2,406	13,384	1,305		1,305
39. Personal and repair services	396.9	95	377.1	14,399	5,088	24,212	4,443		4,443
40. Medical, educational and nonprofit organizations	0.0	90	0.0	9,811	2,160	17,271	4,370		4,370
41. Amusements	0.0	90	0.0	3,677	1,066	6,591	1,100		1,100
42. Scrap and miscellaneous industries	8,388.2	50	4,194.1	2,054	727	7,411	771		771
43. Undistributed	103,638.6	50	51,819.3	5,875	6,019	69,236	7,208		7,208
44. Eating and drinking places	0.0	95	0.0	16,916	3,903	29,551	3,705		3,705
45. Households	348,281.0	82	285,590.4	63,002	80,894	509,578			
Total	903,807.7	—	521,377.2	282,024	164,400	1,177,822	70,089	88,680	158,769

Source: Isard and Kuenne [12], p. 297.

possible to convert the estimates of employment increases into increases in final demand for diverse products, expressed in dollar terms.

Thus, in much the same manner as in the previous example, where a $5 billion increase in demand for manufactured products was projected, increases in final demand were projected here. In this case, the entire set of inputs to be absorbed directly by the steel and steel-fabricating activities represented such increases. They are listed in column 1 of Table 2.3d. The problem then became one of assessing the direct and indirect effects upon the regional economy. One further step was necessary, however, It would have been unrealistic to assume that all direct and indirect demands would have been met by firms within the region. Therefore, estimates of the percentage of these demands to be furnished from within the region were made.

Thus, to derive the first-round requirements, the dollar value of inputs required from each industry was multiplied by the percentage of these inputs expected to be supplied by the region. This is shown in Table 2.3d. As already noted, in column 1 of that table, the input requirements of the initial steel and steel-fabricating activities is shown in thousands of dollars. In column 2, the percentage of these requirements which could be expected to be met from within the region are listed in order. Multiplying column 1 by column 2 gives the first-round expansions expected within the region. These are given in column 3. Thus in sector 10, Chemicals, it was determined that $10,626,400 of chemical inputs would be required by the initial steel and steel-fabricating activities. As the region under examination is a substantial producer of chemical products, it was estimated that 45 percent of these chemical products would come from within the region. Multiplying the two figures indicates that $4,781,880 of these chemical inputs would thus come from the Philadelphia-New York industrial region. In this manner, all first-round effects were derived.

In the manner described earlier, second-round input requirements were calculated. As only a part of these inputs would come from within the region, it was again necessary to multiply these requirements by the percentages in column 2. This procedure yielded the second-round expansions of column 4. As before, the second-round expansion leads to a third round of input requirements, and to a fourth, and so on. It was noted that after calculating for six rounds, the increments in input requirements were converging to negligible magnitudes. Hence, rough extrapolations were made to account for expansions in the infinite number of succeeding rounds.

The several round expansions for each industry were then totaled; the resulting sums are shown in column 6. By use of the output per worker data referred to earlier, these total dollar expansions were converted into new employees by industry. When the number of employees corresponding to the indirect round-by-round calculations were added to the number of steel and steel-fabricating employees initially hypothesized, the total employment impact upon the region was determined. This total impact is shown in column 9 of Table 2.3d.

In the above manner, then, the input-output approach has proved useful in regional analysis. Our illustration, to repeat, employed a round-by-round calculation procedure. However, there is a second way of attacking the problem of making estimates with the use of the input-output technique. This method is best illustrated by using mathematical symbols. Denote the total outputs of the various sectors by $X_1, X_2, \ldots, X_n$; that is, X_1 represents the total output of the first sector, X_2 the total output of the second sector, and so on to X_n, which represents the total output of the nth, or last sector. In general then, X_i can be used to represent the total output of sector i, $i = 1, \ldots, n$. Also X_i, as already noted, is the sum of flows and deliveries along the ith row.

Let the technical coefficient in the ith row and the jth column be denoted by a_{ij}. Both i and j can represent any sector, and a_{ij} reveals the dollars worth of inputs from sector i needed to produce \$1 of the output in sector j. If in an input-output table, one refers, for example, to sector 5 and sector 7, a relevant technical coefficient is $a_{5,7}$. This coefficient shows the value of the output of the fifth sector required to produce one dollar's worth of the seventh sector's output. The total output of the seventh sector has already been designated X_7. Therefore, the seventh sector will purchase goods to the value of $a_{5,7}X_7$ from the fifth sector. The nth sector may also purchase inputs from sector 5, and the value of these inputs is $a_{5,n}X_n$. With these a_{ij} coefficients, the flows of sector five's output to every consuming industry can be calculated.

However, some of the fifth sector's output may be bought by persons in the region who require it, not as an input to their own production processes, but for personal consumption and other purposes. Likewise, some of sector five's output may be purchased by a producer outside of the area covered by the study, so that these purchases do not depend on the level of output of any of the producing sectors in a regional input-output table. As already indicated, purchases of this kind are known as purchases for final demand, and are generally included in a separate section in the table. Although final demand can be divided into demands by households, investors, governments, and exporters, for the moment these various final demands are combined into a single final demand sector. In particular, the final demand for the product of any sector j ($j = 1, \ldots, n$) is designated Y_j.

One can now make a statement about the output of the fifth sector and how this output is allocated among the producing sectors and final demand. Assuming that none of the output is wasted, the following relationship holds:

$$X_5 = a_{5,1}X_1 + a_{5,2}X_2 + a_{5,3}X_3 + a_{5,4}X_4 + \ldots + a_{5,j}X_j + \ldots + a_{5,n}X_n + Y_5$$

The total output of the fifth sector is given on the left-hand side of the equation. On the right-hand side of the equation, all the various uses of this output, which consist of intermediate demand, including the fifth sector's requirements of its own output, and final demand, are given.

Similar equations can be constructed for each sector in the table. It should be noted that the equation given corresponds to a row of flows from the table. Such an equation could, for example, be constructed for the Agricultural row of Table 2.3b. This would read

$$X_1 = 0.083X_1 + 0.125X_2 + 0.111X_3 + Y_1$$

where sectors 1, 2, and 3 are Agriculture, Manufacturing, and Trade and Services, respectively.

If the final demands at some future date are regarded as known, and one wishes to compute the total outputs of the various sectors which would be required to meet the final demands, the solution to the set of equations would provide the answer.

The operation is clearer if the equations are rewritten so that all the unknowns are on one side. For the equation corresponding to the fifth row, we have:

$$X_5 - a_{5,1}X_1 - a_{5,2}X_2 - a_{5,3}X_3 - \ldots - a_{5,j}X_j - \ldots - a_{5,n}X_n = Y_5$$

Notice that on the left-hand side of this equation, the output of the fifth sector, X_5, and the inputs from the fifth sector to the fifth sector, $a_{5,5}X_5$, are both included. Thus, the equation can be written:

$$-a_{5,1}X_1 - a_{5,2}X_2 - a_{5,3}X_3 - \ldots - a_{5,5}X_5 + X_5 - \ldots - a_{5,n}X_n = Y_5$$

This equation can be factored to yield:

$$-a_{5,1}X_1 - a_{5,2}X_2 - a_{5,3}X_3 - \ldots + (1 - a_{5,5})X_5 - \ldots - a_{5,n}X_n = Y_5$$

If we then set down such an equation for each one of our n sectors, each corresponding to a row of our table, we derive a system consisting of n equations and n unknowns, the unknowns being the outputs of the producing sectors. This set of n

simultaneous equations can be solved by algebra to yield the values of the total outputs, X_i, which will satisfy the known final demands, Y_j, given the a_{ij} coefficients.

The computation of the solution of a large number of simultaneous equations can be extremely tedious. It is seen from the above equation that the solution for each X_i depends on the values of all the Y_j and all the $a_{i,j}$. However, this relationship can be expressed in fairly simple form. First we write the set of simultaneous equations in matrix form as follows:[39]

$$\begin{bmatrix} X_1 \\ X_2 \\ \cdot \\ \cdot \\ \cdot \\ X_n \end{bmatrix} - \begin{bmatrix} a_{1,1} & a_{1,2} & \cdots & a_{1,n} \\ a_{2,1} & a_{2,2} & \cdots & a_{2,n} \\ \cdot & & & \cdot \\ \cdot & & & \cdot \\ \cdot & & & \cdot \\ a_{n,1} & a_{n,2} & \cdots & a_{n,n} \end{bmatrix} \begin{bmatrix} X_1 \\ X_2 \\ \cdot \\ \cdot \\ \cdot \\ X_n \end{bmatrix} = \begin{bmatrix} Y_1 \\ Y_2 \\ \cdot \\ \cdot \\ \cdot \\ Y_n \end{bmatrix}$$

where the $X_1, X_2, \ldots, X_n$ form a vector of output values, the $a_{i,j}$'s are arranged as a matrix of technical coefficients (and thus represent an input-output technical coefficient table), and the $Y_1, Y_2, \ldots, Y_n$ form a vector of final demand values.

This formulation can further be reduced to the matrix algebra expression:

$$\overline{X} - A\overline{X} = \overline{Y}$$

where $\overline{X}$ represents the output vector, A the matrix of technical coefficients, and $\overline{Y}$ the final demand vector. By factoring the $\overline{X}$ from this equation, one obtains

$$(I-A)\,\overline{X} = \overline{Y}$$

where I is the identity matrix. (The identity matrix is a matrix with ones along the main diagonal and zeros elsewhere. It has the property that $I\overline{X} = \overline{X}$.) This relationship now gives final demand as a function of the technological coefficients and total output. One can now express total output as a function of the final demands. This transformation is accomplished by multiplying both sides of the previous equation by the inverse matrix of the $(I-A)$ matrix, namely $(I-A)^{-1}$, to obtain:

$$(I-A)^{-1}\,(I-A)\,\overline{X} = (I-A)^{-1}\,\overline{Y}$$

or

$$\overline{X} = (I-A)^{-1}\,\overline{Y}$$

This inverse matrix, $(I-A)^{-1}$, which is obtainable through algebraic manipulations of the $(I-A)$ matrix, is called a matrix of interdependency coefficients. Given in this form, the total output is now a function of the interdependency coefficients and the vector of final demands.

The interdependency coefficients depend only on the $a_{i,j}$'s. Thus, if there are n sectors in the original input-output table, there will be $(n \times n)$ or n^2 interdependency coefficients, two relating each pair of industries.

Let the interdependency coefficients (the elements of the $(I-A)^{-1}$ matrix) be denoted as $\alpha_{i,j}$. Then the ith equation of the previous system of equations can be written:

$$X_i = \alpha_{i,1}Y_1 + \alpha_{i,2}Y_2 + \ldots + \alpha_{i,j}Y_j + \ldots + \alpha_{i,n}Y_n$$

It can now be seen why the $\alpha_{i,j}$ were designated interdependency coefficients. This equation enables one to compute the total output of the ith sector given the final demand for the products of all sectors. It also enables one to find the effect on the total output of the ith sector of a given change in the final demand for any sector. For instance, if the final demand for the products of the second sector rises by \$5 billion, the total output of the ith sector, via all direct and indirect demands, will rise by $\alpha_{i,2}$ times \$5 billion. In this manner, then, with the use of an inverse of an

[39] See Miernyk [15], for a description of matrix algebra and its application to input-output analysis. For a standard discussion on matrix algebra, see Hadley [5], pp. 60–119.

input-output coefficient matrix, which is readily derived by a modern high-speed computer, the impact of a major development, such as an integrated iron and steel works, may also be examined.

However, as already described, the input-output technique has been employed in round-by-round fashion. And there have been numerous other ways in which the technique can and will be employed in connection with a wide range of problems. Its increasing use in future studies is assured because of its ability to provide a comprehensive planning framework involving both consistent description and projection.

Readings on Input-Output Analysis

For the reader interested in probing more deeply into input-output analysis, the following references are recommended.

Chenery, Hollis B. and Paul G. Clark, *Interindustry Economics*, New York, John Wiley and Sons, Inc., 1959.

Evans, W. Duane and Marvin Hoffenberg, "The Interindustry Relations Study for 1947," *The Review of Economics and Statistics*, XXXIV (May, 1952), 97–142.

Hansen, W. Lee, Thayne Robson, and Charles M. Tiebout, *Markets for Califorina Products*, Sacramento, California: State of California Economic Development Agency.

Isard, Walter, *et al.*, Methods of Regional Analysis, Cambridge, Mass., The M.I.T. Press, 1960, Chapter 8.

——and Robert E. Kuenne, "The Impact of Steel Upon the Greater New York-Philadelphia Industrial Region," *The Review of Economics and Statistics*, XXXV (November, 1953), 289–301.

——, Thomas O. Langford, and Eli Romanoff, *The Philadelphia Input-Output Study*, Regional Science Research Institute, Philadelphia, 1969.

Leontief, Wassily, *The Structure of American Economy, 1919–1939*, New York, Oxford University Press, 1951.

————, *et al.*, *Studies in the Structure of the American Economy*, New York, Oxford University Press, 1953.

————, "Input-Output Economics," *Scientific American*, CLXXXV (October, 1951), 15–21.

————, "The Structure of Development," *Scientific American*, CCIX (September, 1963), 148–166.

Miernyk, William H., *The Elements of Input-Output Analysis*, New York, Random House, 1965.

2.4 *The Gravity Model (Spatial Interaction Analysis)*

2.4.1 Introduction

In addition to performing cost and input-output analyses, such as have been described above, the regional planner often encounters the problem of estimating the demand for a specific economic output, in particular, a service. For example, he often must estimate the number of users for the services of a particular highway (i.e., traffic along the highway), or the number of users of a telephone system, of a library or of a cultural development. We know that such estimates are needed for planning many types of facilities and infrastructure. (In the particular context of this book, it will be found to be important in Chapter 4 to forecast the demand for the services to be provided by a recreational complex.) Often in this type of problem, the planner must seek a method for taking into account such diverse variables as population clusters at various points, the distances between these points, and the amount of interaction that might occur among these clusters. Such a method in many situations is provided by a gravity, or in general, a spatial interaction model.

Gravity models (sometimes designated potential models) are a particularly simple form of a class of models known as "spatial interaction models." Spatial interaction models are used to describe the effects at one place of events or conditions at another place. The term "gravity model" is taken from the concept of gravity used in Newtonian physics. There the concept denotes an effect of a body at one place on a body at another place. The concept has been extended into the social science field to denote, say, the effect of the population of one area on the population of another area. Intuitively, one would expect that any such effect on a given area's population would be greater the larger the other area's population. Also, one would expect this effect to be smaller the greater the distance between the two populations concerned.

In the early formulation of the gravity model,[40] it was stated that interactions between any pair of population clusters or cities as measured, for example, by the number of bus passengers in a given period, or the number of telephone calls, were directly proportional to the product of the populations of the cities and inversely proportional to the square of the distance between them.[41] There exists a good deal of empirical evidence to support the view that even such a crude model as this may provide a reasonable approximation to reality.

As already indicated, one of the research problems in which the gravity model has been extensively used is in making traffic projections. In the course of time, it was recognized that the gravity model was being used here to answer two different questions. One was: How many trips originated in a particular area? The other was: How were these trips distributed among the various possible destinations? There has been considerable feeling that the gravity model is more suited to answering the latter question than the former, and as a result, two different kinds of models are generally used to handle these two questions. The first question (How many trips originate in a given area?) is dealt with by what is usually known as a "trip-generation model". The second question (Where do these trips terminate?) is dealt with by what is known as a "trip-distribution model." Gravity models are among the most widely used of the trip-distribution models. Gravity-type concepts are often used for purposes of estimating future travel demands in an area so that highways can be better planned. Trip-generation models usually postulate that the number of trips made per household will depend on such things as household size, income, automobile ownership, and on the population density of the area in which the household lives. If the nature of these quantities is known, or if they can be forecast, then the total number of trips originating in an area can be estimated. These models are generally refined to distinguish between the several kinds of trip by trip purpose, since the determining factors have different effects on different types of trips. For instance, school and work trips will be virtually, if not completely, independent of automobile ownership and household income, whereas social and recreational trips will vary sharply with these factors.

Once the number of trips originating in each zone has been estimated, the trips must be assigned to the various destinations. If gravity models are used for this assignment (known as "trip-distribution"), then one model may be used for all trips originating in an area, or different models may be used for the different types of trips. For instance, one may expect that school trips are very sensitive to distance. In any case, before the assignment, or trip-destination, procedure can be executed, some measure of the relative "attractiveness" of each relevant destination is needed. For example, the attractiveness of a zone for shopping may be measured by the

[40] See, for example, Zipf [20] and [21], and Stewart [17]. On the historical development of the concept, see Carrothers [1].

[41] Some writers suggest that the distance itself, rather than the square of the distance, should be regarded as providing the best predictive answers. This controversy led to one of the first of the many refinements that have been made in the gravity model; namely, the raising of the distance variable to powers other than 2.

number of square feet of floor space in stores in that zone, while the attractiveness of a zone for social trips may be measured simply by its population. The attractiveness of a zone for recreational trips can probably best be measured by some estimate of the amount of recreational facilities in the zone, perhaps with some adjustment for quality of facilities. When used for trip distribution, the gravity model assumes that the trips originating in a given zone which terminate in each relevant zone of destination will be proportional to the attractiveness of the zone of destination and inversely related to its distance from the originating zone.

In the next section, the various ways of using the gravity model will be examined with respect to a specific numerical example. The formulas which relate the various variables will be derived in a form in which they can be readily applied.

2.4.2 Generating the Gravity Model

We begin the development of the model by using simple probability theory.[42] Assume that there is a given region with a population P. Furthermore, assume that this region can be divided into numerous subregions. Take any two subregions i and j. Define P_i to be the population of subregion i and P_j the population of subregion j. Next, assume that the total number of trips within the area is known, and that this number is T. Finally, assume that the inhabitants of the subregions are of the same age, income and occupation structure, and so on. If one wishes to estimate the total number of trips which originate in subregion i and terminate in subregion j, he may designate this number as T_{ij}. If there were no time or cost involved in these trips, then one would expect that of the trips originating in subregion i, the proportion terminating in subregion j would be equal to the proportion of the total population in j—that is, to the ratio P_j/P. Hence, if P were equal to 5,000, and P_j were 1,000, then an individual in subregion i might be expected to make 20 percent of all his trips to subregion j.

This probability-type gravity model can be illustrated by a numerical example. Since it is assumed that the number of trips per person is known, and the distribution of the trips is sought, it is evident that a trip distribution model is to be used.

Table 2.4a Population of Subregions

Subregions	Population
1	100
2	150
3	120
4	140
Total	510

In Table 2.4a, the population of each of four different subregions that make up a greater region is given. In terms of our notation, it is evident that $P_1 = 100$, $P_2 = 150$, $P_3 = 120$, $P_4 = 140$, and $P = 510$. If each person in each region takes 100 trips during a year, then 510 persons make 51,000 trips. The distributions of these trips can be determined in terms of proportions. Consider the trips from subregion 1. These trips can terminate in subregion 1, 2, 3, or 4. As distance is assumed to have no effect at this stage, it would be expected that 100/510 of the trips will begin and terminate in subregion 1. Likewise, 150/510 of the trips will be from subregion 1 to subregion 2, 120/510 from subregion 1 to subregion 3, and 140/510 from subregion 1 to subregion 4. These proportions are recorded in column 2 of Table 2.4b, with the corresponding percentages listed in column 3. Now since

[42] This statement draws heavily upon Isard *et al.* [9], Chapter 11.

Table 2.4b Subregion 1's Trips: Terminations by Subregion

Subregion of Trip Termination	Proportion of Trips Terminating by Subregion (2)	Percentage of Trips Terminating in Subregion (3)	Number of Trips Terminating by Subregion (4)
1	100/510	19.6%	1,960
2	150/510	29.4	2,940
3	120/510	23.5	2,350
4	140/510	27.5	2,750
Total	510/510	100.0%	10,000

we assume that the total number of trips per individual is 100 and that 100 individuals reside in subregion 1, it follows that 10,000 trips originate in subregion 1. Multiplying 10,000 by the percentages listed in column 3 of Table 2.4b yields the number of trips terminating in each subregion as presented in the last column of Table 2.4b. For example, 23.5 percent of all trips (2,350 trips) will be made from subregion 1 to subregion 3.

Although the simple, probabilistic trip-distribution model is interesting, it is rather unrealistic. Travel is not costless. The distance between the various subregions is an important variable. In the real world, it is known, for example, that the number of bus trips between points decreases with an increase in the intervening distance. It is to be expected that considerably more bus trips are made to points two miles away than twenty. Likewise, more bus trips are made to points twenty miles away than two-hundred miles away. The same principle seems to apply to telephone calls, shopping trips, and recreation trips. In fact, since it has been so frequently demonstrated that such interaction decreases with distance, it appears that more realistic estimates can be made if distance is included in the formulation. Hence, the simple probability model will now be reformulated.

We first set down the simple probability model in mathematical terms. It is:

$$T_{12} = kP_1 \frac{P_2}{P}$$

where T_{12} = number of trips made from subregion 1 to subregion 2
k = the number of trips made per person
P_1 = the population of subregion 1
P_2 = the population of subregion 2, and
P = the population of the region

Hence, for the numerical example just examined, one can put the relevant numbers into the formula to obtain:

$$T_{12} = (100)\,(100)\,\frac{150}{510}$$

$$= 10{,}000\,\frac{150}{510}$$

$$= 2{,}940$$

If we now introduce distance as a basic variable to which the number of trips is inversely proportional, the formula takes the familiar form:

$$T_{12} = G\,\frac{P_1 P_2}{d_{12}}$$

Here d_{12} represents the distance between subregions 1 and 2; and G represents a new constant derived from the set of constants in the problem, namely, the number of trips per person, the populations of all the subregions, and the distance between each pair of subregions.[43]

A numerical example can be used to illustrate this new formulation. Again, it will be assumed that all persons in each region are exactly the same, and that each makes 100 trips; i.e., $k = 100$. Four regions will again be considered, each with the same populations as before. The matrix of distances is given in Table 2.4c.

Table 2.4c Distances Between Subregions

From: \ To:	Subregion 1	Subregion 2	Subregion 3	Subregion 4
Subregion 1	2	5	6	8
Subregion 2	5	2	4	3
Subregion 3	6	4	2	5
Subregion 4	8	3	5	2

It should be noted that it has been assumed that the distance from any subregion to itself is positive, and here we have set this distance at 2 miles. Such an assumption is necessary in a formulation in which the number of trips is inversely proportional to distance. Had a zero distance been permitted, the value of the constant G in the above formula would be zero.[44] Accordingly, no trips originating in any given subregion would terminate in other subregions; they would all terminate in the given subregion. By specifying that even for intra-subregional trips some distance is involved, trips to other subregions will be predicted as well.[45]

It may be assumed that the distances are measured from the mid-point of each subregion to the mid-point of every other subregion. However, the distance can also be measured between the centers of population of any two regions, or largest cities, either in miles, travel time, transport cost (economic distance), or whatever is thought to be most appropriate. Now, we may apply the formula to determine the number of trips from subregion 1 to subregion 2. Since $G = .8511$,[46] and P_1, P_2, and d_{12} are 100, 150, and 5, respectively,

$$T_{12} = (.8511)\frac{(100 \times 150)}{5}$$
$$= 2{,}553$$

In similar manner, the other trip predictions can be computed.

One additional remark should be made at this point. In the second formulation,

[43] These constants are, respectively, k, P_1, P_2, P_3, P_4, and d_{11}, d_{12}, d_{13}, and d_{14}. In particular,

$$G = \frac{k}{\frac{P_1}{d_{11}} + \frac{P_2}{d_{12}} + \frac{P_3}{d_{13}} + \frac{P_4}{d_{14}}}$$

In general, with m subregions, the trips from any subregion i to another subregion j can be expressed as:

$$T_{ij} = \frac{kP_i \frac{P_j}{d_{ij}}}{\sum_{j=1}^{m} \frac{P_j}{d_{ij}}}$$

[44] This point follows since one of the terms in the denominator of the formula for G given in the preceding footnote would be infinity for a nonzero population for the subregion.

[45] For a fuller discussion of this technical point, see Isard *et al.* [9], p. 500n.

[46] Since $k = 100$, P_1, P_2, P_3, and P_4 are 100, 150, 120, and 140, respectively, and $d_{11} = 2$, $d_{12} = 5$, $d_{13} = 6$, and $d_{14} = 8$, from footnote 43, we have:

$$G = \frac{100}{\frac{100}{2} + \frac{150}{5} + \frac{120}{6} + \frac{140}{8}} = 0.8511$$

the number of trips made is assumed to be inversely proportional to distance. In certain cases, this may not be so. Persons may be expected to travel farther for recreational trips than for shopping trips or school trips. Such differences in travel patterns can be taken into account by raising the distance variable to some power other than that of unity which is implied by the formula. Generally speaking, one hypothesizes that the distance variable should be raised to some power b which may be viewed as a variable. The formula now takes the more general form:

$$T_{12} = G \frac{P_1 P_2}{d_{12}^b} \qquad \text{(footnote 47)}$$

If the exponent on distance were set at zero, then d_{12}^b would be unity, and distance would have no effect on the trips made. However, if the b exponent were raised to, say, 5, then nearly all trips originating in subregion 1 would terminate in subregion 1, and distance would have an overpowering effect. In most empirical studies which employ this formulation of the gravity model, the appropriate exponent on distance seems to lie in the range between 1 and 3.

Thus it can be seen that the gravity model offers a simple methodology for estimating the possible interaction that can occur between various areas. In a later section of this book, this model is used to estimate recreational demands for various coastal areas. Since the calculations are relatively simple, but tedious, the model has been programmed for use on electronic computers.[48]

Readings on Spatial Interaction Models

The reader interested in examining in more detail the structure of spatial interaction models may refer to the following:

Carrothers, Gerald A.P., "An Historical Review of the Gravity and Potential Concepts of Human Interaction," *Journal of the American Institute of Planners*, XXII (Spring, 1956).

Isard, Walter, *et al.*, *Methods of Regional Analysis*, Cambridge, Massachusetts, The M.I.T. Press, 1960, Chapter 11.

2.5 *Activity Complex Analysis*

2.5.1 Introduction

As has been noted in previous sections, comparative cost analysis appears to be a suitable method of analysis for determining the costs of operation of a single activity at a single site. By employing such a methodology, numerous alternative sites for the activity can be compared in order to find the least cost location. On the other hand, when the interrelations of any one economic activity with all other economic activities is to be investigated, the input-output approach may be appropriate and effective. Frequently, however, the analyst is interested in examining a group (limited set) of interrelated activities in order to find a least cost location for the group. The analyst may realize from his comparative cost analysis that taken singly, none of the industries in the group could compete in his region. And yet he knows that if the demand for the industrial output of each of them could be increased, or if the cost of each one's inputs could be reduced, or both, each might be profitably located in his region.

[47] Using more general notation, $T_{ij} = G \frac{P_i P_j}{d_{ij}^b}$, where i and j refer to any pair of subregions.

[48] A gravity model computer program is presented in Isard, Bassett, Choguill *et al.* [10], Appendix B.

One method of attacking this problem is by means of activity complex analysis. Very often groups of economic activities, when located in proximity to one another, gain economic advantages from production, marketing, and other interrelations. The location of an integrated iron and steel works frequently leads to the establishment nearby of numerous firms manufacturing fabricated metal products. The establishment of a major electronics manufacturer often attracts smaller parts producers whose outputs of components become inputs to the larger firm. Through this process, a complex of related industries may come into existence. The complex concept may be particularly applicable to the iron and steel industries, the electronics industries, the petrochemical industries, aerospace-related industries, and the textile industries. In any one of these groups of industries, say the petrochemical, the per unit cost of output can be reduced or net value of sales increased by the proximity of the interrelated industries. If a metal fabricator uses sheet steel as an input, it is often in his interest to be located close to the steel mill in order to reduce the delivered cost of the required input. The mill itself finds such a situation advantageous for it assures a higher volume demand for its output and hence may well lead to increased output. With increased output from the mill, more economies of scale may be achieved. For these two firms, and others which may be drawn to this mutually advantageous situation, spatial juxtaposition economies occur. Perhaps no single firm could profitably operate in isolation in such a case, yet with the establishment of a complex, all can gainfully produce. One might be interested, then, in finding some method by which meaningful complexes can be selected, and their least cost locations identified. Activity complex analysis appears to be an applicable method for such an investigation.

2.5.2 The Petrochemical Industries

The methodology involved in activity complex analysis can readily be illustrated by an industrial example. The example used here is from a study for the Puerto Rican economy.[49] At the time this study was made, the Puerto Rican economy was relatively undeveloped. An examination of the island's mineral resources revealed little economic potential. However, abundant unskilled labor was present at cheap rates. Although such labor could potentially have found further employment in the textile industry, it was judged highly desirable to identify employment possibilities in other types of industries.

Another advantage that Puerto Rico possessed was its ability to sell output in United States markets free of duty. Still another was its relative proximity to Venezuelan oil, since the cost of shipment of oil from Venezuela to a Puerto Rican port by tanker is low. Thus it was hypothesized that Venezuelan oil might be considered a resource to Puerto Rico, to be considered together with the few other of the island's resources. With these resources identified, the problem then became one of determining a method of linking them together for some type of economic production.

A large number of potential products can be produced from crude oil. This resource can be used to produce gasoline, kerosene, fuel oil and lubricating oil, or the liquid and gas products of hydrogen, methane, ethane, ethylene, propane, propylene, butanes, butylenes, or benzene. Many of these can be used as inputs into other processes, yielding a still larger set of potential products. Methane can be used to generate hydrogen, which can in turn be converted into nitric acid, ammonium nitrate, urea, and finally, fertilizer. Methane is also an input into hydrogen cyanide and acetylene, and ultimately into the synthetic fibers: Orlon, Dynel, and Acrilan. In short, innumerable processes and products are possible.

The complex interrelations of these various products can be presented in a flow chart, each step of which reveals the input arrangement in sequences or successive

[49] Isard, Schooler, and Vietorisz [13].

Table 2.5a Annual Inputs and Outputs for Selected Oil Refinery, Petrochemical and Synthetic Fiber Activities

	Oil Refinery Prototype 1 (1) ...	Oil Refinery Prototype 4 (4) ...	Ethylene Separation Prototype 4 (10) ...	Ethylene Glycol (oxidation) (22) ...	Ammonia from Hydrogen (31)	Ammonia from Methane (32)	Ammonia from Ethylene (33)	Ammonia from Ethane (34) ...	Nitric Acid from Ammonia (43)	Dimethyl Terephthalate (air oxidation) (44) ...	Dacron Polymer (46)	Dacron Staple (47) ...	Ammonium Nitrate from Ammonia (55)	Urea from Ammonia (56)	Nylon Filament (73)
1. Crude oil MM bbl.	−9.428	−9.428													
2. Gasoline, straight-run MM bbl.	+2.074	+1.300													
3. Gasoline, cracked MM bbl.	+1.484	+2.226													
4. Gasoline, reformed MM bbl.		+1.486													
5. Gasoline, polymerized MM bbl.	+0.219	+0.415	+0.029												
6. Naphtha, MM bbl.	+0.660														
7. Kerosene, MM bbl.	+0.943	+0.707													
8. Diesel oil MM bbl.	+1.414	+0.896													
9. Gas oil MM bbl.															
10. Cycle oil MM bbl.	+1.320	+1.980													
11. Heavy residual MM bbl.	+0.943														
12. Coke and carbon 10XMM lb.		+4.033													
13. L.P.G. 10XMM lb.	+6.860	+15.050	+0.508												
14. Hydrogen MM lb.	+0.950	+8.900			−2.000										
15. Methane MM lb.	+12.780	+34.860				−5.500									
16. Ethylene (mixed) MM lb.	+6.510	+17.410	−16.100				−6.290								
17. Ethane (mixed) MM lb.	+9.930	+32.250	−30.190					−5.780							
18. Propylene MM lb.	+3.630	+7.580	−7.580												
19. Propane MM lb.	+2.150	+5.080	−5.080												
20. Butylenes MM lb.															

21. Butanes MM lb.															
22. Pure ethylene MM lb.			+16.100	−8.300											
23. Pure ethane MM lb.			+30.190												
24. Steam MMM lb.	−0.801	−1.402	−0.148	−0.103		−0.023	−0.023	−0.023		−0.030	−0.060	−0.500	−0.007	−0.028	−0.555
25. Power MM kw. hr.	−2.511	−3.999	−0.194	−0.800	−4.640	−5.600	−5.600	−5.600	−1.200	−5.200	−2.500	−12.000	−0.170	−0.340	−16.000
26. Fuel 10XMMM Btu.	−139.000	−242.000		−2.010		−0.450	−0.450	−0.450		−2.800	−1.000			−2.250	
... ...	...	...	...	...	...	...	...	...	...	...	...	...	...	...	...
34. Nitrogen MM lb.				+68.000											
35. Ethylene glycol MM lb.				+10.000							−3.230				−2.200
... ...	...	...	...	...	...	...	...	...	...	...	...	...	...	...	...
39. Ammonia MM lb.					+10.000	+10.000	+10.000	+10.000	−2.860				−2.380	−5.800	
40. HCN MM lb.															
41. Acrylonitrile MM lb.															
42. Methanol MM lb.										−4.000	+3.350				
43. Sulphur MM lb.															
44. Sulphuric acid MM lb.															
45. Nitric acid MM lb.									+10.000				−7.630		
46. Paraxylene MM lb.										−6.800					
47. Dimethyl terephthalate MM lb.										+10.000	−10.100				
48. Dacron polymer MM lb.											+10.000	−10.000			
49. Dacron staple MM lb.												+10.000			
... ...	...	...	...	...	...	...	...	...	...	...	...	...	...	...	...
59. Ammonium nitrate MM lb.													+10.000		
60. Urea MM lb.														+10.000	
61. Carbon dioxide MM lb.														−7.500	
... ...	...	...	...	...	...	...	...	...	...	...	...	...	...	...	...
74. Nylon salt MM lb.															−10.000
... ...	...	...	...	...	...	...	...	...	...	...	...	...	...	...	...
76. Nylon filament MM lb.															+10.000

‡Source: Isard *et al.* [9], pp. 384–385.

chains of products.[50] It was hypothesized that a petrochemical complex might well be competitive if located in Puerto Rico. The activity complex model was then devised to evaluate this hypothesis. The problem involved selecting the most applicable complex from among the various alternatives. The production of synthetic fibers was indicated as a process which made use of sizeable amounts of textile-type labor inputs, a resource that was plentiful in Puerto Rico. An examination of the import-export data of Puerto Rico revealed that nearly all the fertilizer used in Puerto Rico was imported. With the creation of the petrochemical complex, locally produced fertilizer could be substituted for the variety from the United States.

A number of components of the complex were rejected at this stage. For example, ethylene could be ultimately converted into antifreeze. However, since the process required little labor and would produce a product for which there was no local demand, antifreeze production was not considered. Synthetic rubber was rejected, again after market factors were considered.

After a careful examination of potential products, it was concluded that those whose production in Puerto Rico would be most likely to be profitable were gasoline, fuel oil, fertilizer, and synthetic fibers. The next task was to sketch out the structure of a feasible, consistent complex. The structure of a petrochemical complex is characterized by its interrelations among various processes and the steps by which various products are derived. It is thus necessary to define in quantitative terms the extent of these interrelations. Recall that the input-output table reveals the interrelations of all sectors within an economy. In activity complex analysis, however, the investigator is interested in only a few, finely divided sectors. Consequently, a table containing columns and rows for such sectors was constructed. A condensation of the table developed for the Puerto Rican study is presented as Table 2.5a.

This table is somewhat different from the traditional input-output table. Across the top, the headings stand for various activities. Thus activities 1 to 4 might represent various types of oil refineries. Down the left-hand side, the listings refer to commodities which are the outputs and required inputs of the diverse activities. Consider activity 1, designated "Oil Refinery, Prototype 1." The inputs and the outputs listed in this column are expressed in physical terms rather than in the monetary units used in input-output analysis. A plus sign in front of a coefficient signifies that it is an output from the activity, while a negative sign signifies an input. Thus the first column reveals that if inputs of 9.428 million barrels of crude oil, 0.801 billion pounds of steam, 2.511 million kilowatt hours of power, and 1,390 billion Btu's of fuel are fed into Oil Refinery, Prototype 1, the outputs expected will include 2.074 million barrels of straight-run gasoline, 1.484 million barrels of cracked gasoline, 0.219 million barrels of polymerized gasoline, 0.660 million barrels of naphtha, and so on down the column.

Each other column can be interpreted similarly. However, one can go further, and define the interrelations among the columns. The inputs into activity 47, "Dacron Staple" production, include 10,000 million pounds of Dacron polymer. Dacron polymer is produced by activity 46. The inputs of activity 46 include dimethyl terephthalate and ethylene glycol. Ethylene glycol is produced by activity 22. Thus the inputs to the various activities can be traced back across the table to their ultimate origin, the input of crude oil into an oil refinery prototype.

Each ultimate output, such as Dacron staple, is defined at the "unit level." The selection of the unit level is arbitrary. For Dacron staple, the unit level selected was 10 million pounds in order to facilitate computations. Notice, in addition, that although in input-output analysis each sector has a single output, in activity complex analysis each sector is allowed multiple outputs.

Another distinction of complex analysis from input-output analysis is that in

[50] Such a flow chart for the possible products from petroleum is given in *ibid.*, pp. 30–13 and Isard *et al.* [9], pp. 380–381.

the former, alternative processes are permitted. Thus in Table 2.5a, all possible prototype refineries are to be considered in the analysis, with only one to be involved in the final complex selected. The next step of the complex problem, then, is to select from among the possible alternative activities those which would form a viable complex which at its Puerto Rican location could effectively compete in the U.S. market.

Marketing considerations enter into this complex selection process. It was felt that gasoline could be marketed on the mainland, but probably ethylene glycol could not. Thus the ethylene glycol production, as that of other intermediates, was to be restricted to that amount needed within the complex itself. This amount represented inputs directly and indirectly required in the production of synthetic fibers and fertilizer. The level of synthetic fiber production was based upon the estimated demand from mainland sources, while the level of fertilizer production was determined by Puerto Rico's consumption of fertilizer.

A number of alternative programs were considered for the Puerto Rican complex. Consider one of these programs which employed Oil Refinery Prototype 4 (which corresponds to activity 4 in Table 2.5a), and had outputs of Dacron staple, fertilizer, and other standard refinery outputs (gasoline, kerosene, diesel oil, cycle oil, LPG, and Btu). This program is shown in Chart 2.5a, and was designated in

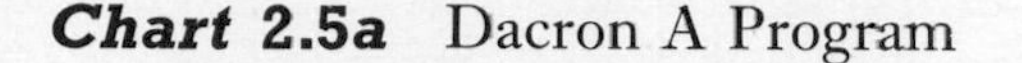

Chart 2.5a Dacron A Program

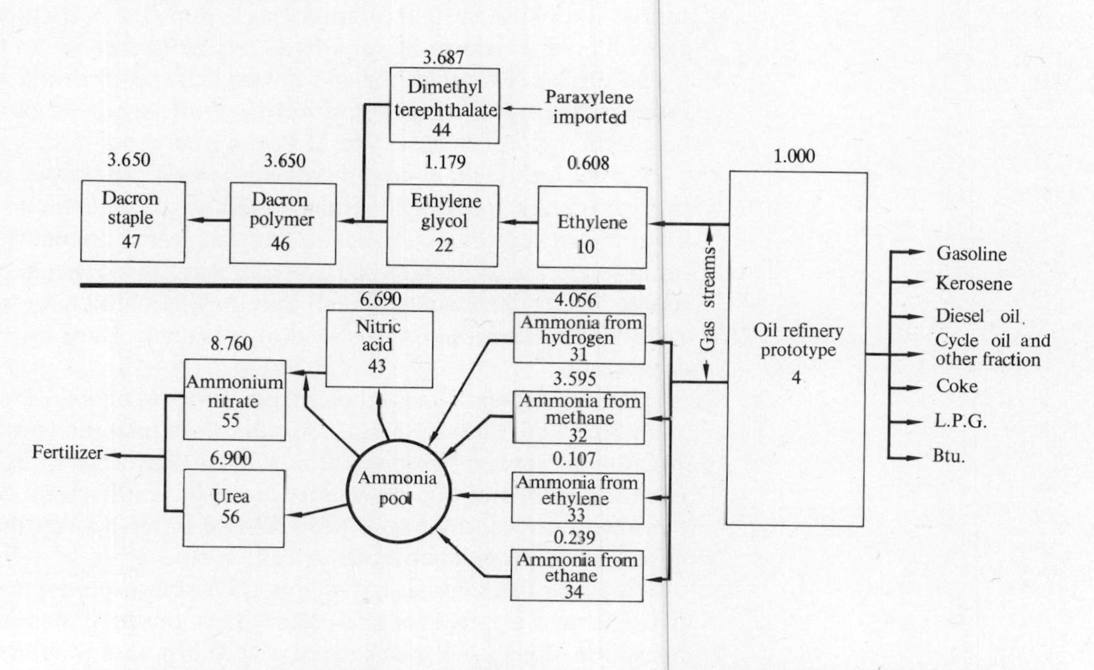

the original study as "Dacron A Program." In Chart 2.5a, the standard refinery outputs are listed on the right-hand side, while the ultimate outputs of Dacron staple and fertilizer are shown on the left.

Consider the chain leading to the output of Dacron staple. The unit level for the Dacron staple production activity was defined as 10 million pounds per year. The number above the Dacron staple cell, 3.650, signifies the multiple of the unit level at which the Dacron staple activity is to be run. Hence a level of 3.650 represents the 36.5 million pounds of Dacron staple production per year. It was judged that this level, when combined with the fertilizer process, would effectively employ the available gaseous outputs of Oil Refinery Prototype 4, when the refinery activity is operated at the unit level. Also, an annual production of 36.5 million pounds of Dacron staple represents a scale of output that could be produced efficiently (at relatively low unit cost) and could be marketed with no great difficulty. Working backwards, Dacron staple production requires the input of Dacron polymer (yielded by activity 46). Again the unit level of the Dacron polymer production activity was defined as that which yields an annual output of 10 million pounds of Dacron polymer. For 3.650 unit levels of Dacron staple production activity, the program shows that the Dacron polymer production activity needs to be operated at 3.650 unit levels (yielding an output of 36.5 million pounds of Dacron polymer per year). The polymer production activity in turn requires steam, power, and fuel, and the raw materials ethylene glycol and dimethyl terephthalate. For example, 3.230 million pounds of ethylene glycol and 10.100 million pounds of dimethyl terephthalate are required by a unit level of the Dacron polymer production activity. The dimethyl terephthalate is produced (via activity 44) from an imported material, paraxylene. For one unit level of output (10 million pounds) of dimethyl terephthalate, the required amount of paraxylene is 6.8 million pounds. In order to fit into the production process for Dacron polymer, the dimethyl terephthalate production activity must be operated at 3.687 unit levels, indicating an annual import of paraxylene amounting to 23.0716 million pounds.

Chart 2.5a also shows that 1.179 unit levels of ethylene glycol production (11.79 million pounds) are required annually. The inputs for the production of ethylene glycol are pure ethylene, steam, power, and fuel. The pure ethylene is obtained from the ethylene separation process, from gas streams given off by the Oil Refinery Prototype #4. In turn, the Oil Refinery Prototype #4, which is programmed to run at unit level, requires crude oil inputs, in particular 9.428 million barrels annually, which are to be imported from Venezuela.

In similar fashion we may go through the set of production activities which are linked to the ultimate output of fertilizer; the sequence of these activities is shown below the bold horizontal line of Chart 2.5a.

Capital and labor requirements for each of the set of activities in the Dacron A program were computed independently. Whereas the material input-output relationships can be assumed to be linear, it was known that the capital and labor input-output relationships cannot be. From the independent computations of labor inputs, it was determined that all told, 5.284 million man-hours of textile labor and 2.229 million man-hours of chemical petroleum labor are required for the Dacron A program.

At this stage of the study a viable set of interrelated industries seems to have been isolated. That is, from a technical standpoint it has been shown that the Dacron A program can operate in Puerto Rico. However, no cost analysis has yet been made. Hence one must next proceed, via the comparative cost approach, to compare this program and other potential programs at a Puerto Rican location and at other competitive locations.

One first specifies a market for the various products of the complex. It was hypothesized in this case that the refinery products market was the Eastern Seaboard, the fiber market was the textile South, and the fertilizer market was Puerto Rico.

The comparative cost procedure for the Dacron A program (and other potential programs as well) compared operations in Puerto Rico with identical operations on the Gulf Coast. It was found, with regard to transportation costs, that after each product was considered, the Dacron A program in Puerto Rico had an overall transport cost disadvantage *vis à vis* the Gulf Coast of $263,000 per year. Chemical-petroleum labor was anticipated to be more expensive in Puerto Rico than on the Gulf Coast by about $1 per hour. This led to a second cost disadvantage, amounting to $2,229,000 per year. However, Puerto Rico did have a major cost advantage over the Gulf Coast with regard to textile-type labor, an advantage that amounted to $4,861,000 per year. Using these factors alone, the relative advantage of Puerto Rico over the Gulf Coast site can be given as:

+ $4,861,000 (textile labor)	− $263,000 (transportation)	− $2,229,000 (chemical-petroleum labor)	= $2,369,000 (cost advantage for Puerto Rico *vis à vis* Gulf Coast)

While there were other cost elements which were found to vary between the two locations, the cost differentials which they generate were minor. Thus the cost advantage is roughly as given.

So far, the assumption has been made that the complexes in both locations were identical. This is unrealistic. If the complex on the United States mainland were split, so that the petroleum refinery operations were on the Gulf Coast (their least-cost location) and the textile fiber operations were in the textile region of the South, then the mainland operations would be much less costly. In that event, the computations show that the Puerto Rican complex would be operating at a net advantage of only $311,000 per annum.

Although many other considerations entered into the Puerto Rican study, involving the evaluation of many different types of programs, the above discussion suffices to illustrate how the activity complex analysis can be used to derive specific decisions relating to the planning process. As the complex analysis needs to encompass only a relatively few activities compared to a full blown input-output analysis, much finer sectoring of the relevant activities can be considered. More important, scale factors can be derived which can be used to by-pass the linearity assumptions of input-output analysis with regard to the specific activities under consideration. Furthermore, certain basic externalities can be encompassed in the analysis.

2.5.3 Activity Complex Analysis Applied to Recreation

With the complex analysis methodology established in terms of an industrial complex, it is now possible to extend the methodology to recreation.

First, we consider a set of activities which are closely related in one or more major ways. Such a set of activities are the marine-oriented recreational activities. Their major relationship involves the common use of facilities, such as parking area, breakwaters, dredged channels and basins, docks, moorings, ramps, shore protection, construction, and so on. The development of any one of these marine-oriented recreational activities by itself would require a large portion of the capital investment that is needed for the entire complex. By sharing the annual fixed charges on this capital investment, each activity in the complex is able to operate at a much lower unit cost. Sharing labor and other direct service inputs leads to other savings for each activity when a complex of spatially juxtaposed activities is operated.

Unlike the petrochemical complex, the recreational complex does not possess one type of basic interrelationship. It does not involve that type of technical interdependence encompassing a series of products where, except for the final product, each in turn becomes an input into the next product yielded in a sequence of activities. On the other hand, the recreational complex does possess another type of basic interrelationship not strongly involved in the petrochemical complex. Recall that the demand for any particular product of the petrochemical complex has only a minor connection to the demand for other products in the complex; i.e., the demands for the products are relatively independent. In the recreational complex, on the other hand, the demand for one or more types of recreational activities to be supplied at some site may be highly dependent on the presence of demand for other types of recreational activities at that site. For example, the demand for party boat

Table 2.5b Summary of Costs and Revenues of Marine-Oriented Recreational Complexes at Three Sites and at Three Scales of Operation

	Site I: Jones River			**Site II: Island Creek**			**Site III: The Nook**		
	400 Boats	600 Boats	800 Boats	400 Boats	600 Boats	800 Boats	400 Boats	600 Boats	800 Boats
Total capital and planning costs	$2,035,381	$2,831,164	$3,670,705	$1,827,019	$2,601,306	$3,356,824	$1,690,433	$2,437,511	$3,172,584
Total annual ecological costs	3,065	4,986	7,040	4,100	6,670	9,419	9,160	14,900	21,040
Total annual costs excluding ecological costs	453,543	625,362	787,600	434,905	601,949	760,183	427,407	595,232	754,968
Surplus of annual revenues over annual costs	98,275	195,191	297,448	116,913	218,604	324,691	124,411	225,321	329,906
Percent of return on investment	4.82%	6.90%	8.10%	6.40%	8.40%	9.67%	7.63%	9.24%	10.40%

recreation activity to be supplied at some location cannot be estimated independently of the demands for closely related recreational activities.

In the case study to be made later,[51] we specifically do not examine the consequences of changing the composition of recreational activities in the complex. Ideally, this step should be made; but the data available and our knowledge are limited in terms of a detailed breakdown of consumer demand for recreational activities. As a result, we are unable to estimate how gross revenues of a recreational complex changes with changes in the composition of demand. We do not have sufficient knowledge of elasticities of demand for recreational activities to perform the finer analysis of gross revenues which would be required. Hence, this part of an ideal complex analysis is not covered in our case study.

However, a second major aspect of complex analysis is examined. This aspect is associated with the investigation of the economic desirability of different sizes of complexes at different locations. In the case study to be presented later, we examine three scales of marina operation at three different sites at Plymouth Bay, in the vicinity of Duxbury, Massachusetts. Table 2.5b summarizes the findings.[52] *Given the various assumptions of the study*, there are major gains to be derived from larger scales of operation. For example, the rate of return for a 400-boat facility at the Jones River site is only 4.92 percent. An 800-boat operation at that site is estimated to yield an 8.11 percent return on investment. This pattern is also the same at the Island Creek site and at The Nook. A complex at The Nook is most desirable at all three scales of operation. However, it might well be that when several sites are being examined for a development, the most advantageous site for the smaller complexes can absorb the larger complexes only with sharp increases in investments and/or with sharply rising ecological costs. Under those circumstances, other sites which would not require undue increases in capital investments and ecological costs with increase in size of complex might be optimal for the larger complexes.

To sum up, in this section on activity complex analysis, we have pointed out the major aspects to which the investigator must be sensitive. First, fine technical and marketing linkages may exist among a series of operations, as in the petrochemical case. Under these circumstances, different compositions of production processes and final products, oriented to a single or a few resources, must be considered. Second, it is necessary to go beyond a mere examination of the economies at different scales for any single activity. It is often appropriate and necessary to look at the scale of interrelated activities, and, by so doing, to evaluate possible locations in terms of the scale economies of the whole set of activities. This point is well illustrated with respect to both the petrochemical and recreational complexes. Third, there is a need to examine how total revenues of a complex change as the mix of activities changes, when the demands for the services of these activities are highly interdependent. This aspect is still to be developed by means of a case study.

Readings on Activity Complex Analysis

For the reader interested in probing more deeply into activity and industrial complex analysis, the following readings are recommended.

Isard, Walter, *et al.*, *Methods of Regional Analysis*, Cambridge, Mass., The M.I.T. Press, 1960, Chapter 9.

———, and Eugene W. Schooler, "Industrial Complex Analysis, Agglomeration Economies, and Regional Development," *Journal of Regional Science* I (Spring, 1959).

———, Eugene W. Schooler, and Thomas Vietorisz, *Industrial Complex Analysis and Regional Development*, Cambridge, Mass., The M.I.T. Press, 1959.

[51] See Chapter 5.

[52] The details of this study are given in Section 5.10. There the required coefficients and magnitudes are derived. Table 2.5b summarizes the totals derived.

Bibliography

1. Carrothers, Gerald A.P., "An Historical Review of The Gravity and Potential Concepts of Human Interaction," *Journal of the American Institute of Planners*, XXII (Spring, 1956).
2. Chenery, Hollis B. and Paul G. Clark, *Interindustry Economics*, New York, John Wiley and Sons, Inc., 1959.
3. Fulkerson, Frank B. and Jerry J. Gray, *The Titanium Industries and Their Relation to the Pacific Northwest*, U.S. Department of the Interior and Bonneville Power Administration, Report 7-G, Portland, Oregon, 1964.
4. Grogan, Robert M., William G. Few, and Charles R. Hager, "Milling at Du Pont's Heavy Mineral Mines in Florida," in *Milling Methods in the Americas*, Nathaniel Arbiter (ed.), New York, Gordon and Breach Science Publishers, 1964, pp. 205–229.
5. Hadley, G., *Linear Algebra*, Reading, Mass., Addison-Wesley Press, 1961.
6. Hodgman, Charles D. (ed.), *Handbook of Chemistry and Physics*, 38th edit., Cleveland, Ohio, Chemical Rubber Publishing Company, 1956.
7. "How Humphreys Separates Titanium Minerals at New Highland Plant," *Mining World* (November, 1955).
8. Ian Potter and Company, "The Australian Mineral Sands Industry: An Investment Review" (processed), Melbourne, 1966.
9. Isard, Walter, *et al.*, *Methods of Regional Analysis: An Introduction to Regional Science*, Cambridge, Mass., The M.I.T. Press, 1960, Chapter 7.
10. ———, Kenneth E. Bassett, Charles L. Choguill, John G. Furtado, Ronald M. Izumita, John Kissin, Richard H. Seyfarth, and Richard Tatlock, *Report on Ecologic-Economic Analysis for Regional Development: Some Initial Explorations with Particular Reference to Recreational Resource Use and Environmental Planning*, Regional Science and Landscape Analysis Project, Department of Landscape Architecture—Research Office, Graduate School of Design, Harvard University, December, 1968.
11. ———, and John H. Cumberland, "New England as a Possible Location for an Integrated Iron and Steel Works," *Economic Geography*, XXVI (October, 1950), pp. 245–259.
12. ———, and Robert E. Kuenne, "The Impact of Steel Upon the Greater New York-Philadelphia Industrial Region," *The Review of Economics and Statistics*, XXXV (November, 1953), pp. 289–301.
13. ———, Eugene W. Schooler, and Thomas Vietorisz, *Industrial Complex Analysis and Regional Development*, Cambridge, Mass., The M.I.T. Press, 1959.
14. Mero, John L., *The Mineral Resources of the Sea*, Amsterdam, Elsevier Publishing Company, 1965.
15. Miernyk, William H., *The Elements of Input-Output Analysis*, New York, Random House, 1965.
16. Miller, Jesse A., *Titanium: A Materials Survey*, U.S. Bureau of Mines Information, Circular 7791, 1957.
17. Stewart, John Q., "Empirical Mathematical Rules Concerning the Distribution and Equilibrium of Population", *Geographical Review*, XXXVII (July 1947).
18. U.S. Bureau of Mines, *Mineral Yearbook, 1964*, Vols. I, III, and IV.
19. U.S. Bureau of Mines, *Mineral Yearbook, 1967*, Vols. I, II, and III.
20. Zipf, George K., *Human Behavior and the Principle of Least Effort*, Reading, Massachusetts, Addison-Wesley Press, 1949.
21. ———, "The P_1P_2/D Hypothesis of the Intercity Movement of Persons," *American Sociological Review*, XI (October, 1946).

Interviews

E.I. DuPont de Nemours and Company. Personal Interviews with Robert M. Grogan, Chief Geologist, and Joseph Shrawder, Manager, Pigment Division, Wilmington, Delaware. February 7, 1967.

Ellicott Machine Corporation. Personal interview with Helmut Guenschel, Sales Engineer, Baltimore, Maryland. March 8, 1967.

National Lead Company. Personal interview with A. R. Reiser, Titanium Division, New York, New York. January 31, 1967.

Titanium Metals Corporation of America. Personal interview with William P. Cloyes, New York, New York. January 31, 1967.

U.S. Bureau of Mines, Personal interview with John Stamper, Titanium Commodity Specialist, Washington, D.C. March 22, 1967.

Natural Resources in Regional Analysis

3.1 *Introduction*

Natural resources may be defined as those *natural conditions* and *raw materials* which man uses to meet his needs and improve his net welfare. In general, some form of man's activities must be applied to these natural conditions and raw materials to convert them into actual goods and services. It follows from this definition that the supply of natural resources is not a fixed quantity, but rather a supply which becomes greater and more varied with every scientific and technological advance by man. Because the type and supply of natural resources are a function of man's ability to develop them, alternative natural resource development policies will inevitably exist, with some alternatives being more desirable than others.

In the preceding chapter several methods for evaluating the *economic* consequences of alternative development policies were described. The purpose of this chapter is to begin to explore a systematic means for projecting the *environmental* consequences of alternative development policies. The following sections first describe how natural resources are interrelated in the natural environment, and then how these interrelationships may be considered in regional planning procedures. Hopefully, with information on both the economic and environmental effects of alternative development policies, regional planning agencies will be more effective in their efforts to achieve their stated goals and objectives.

3.2 *Natural Resource Classification*

In considering the environmental consequences of natural resource development, it is useful to identify first three classes of natural resources based on their renewability (potential for replacement).

The first type of natural resources are *non-renewable resources*; i.e., fossil fuels and mineral deposits, or those types of raw material for which the rate of renewal is so slow as to be negligible. Man can use these non-renewable resources rapidly or slowly, efficiently or inefficiently, but their total quantity, particularly the quantity in high-grade deposits, is limited.

The second type of natural resources are *flow resources*, including solar radiation, wind and tides, and water in the hydrologic cycle. These resources have a continuing supply in nature and their process of renewal is not affected by man, although the quantity or quality of the resource may be diminished in local areas. For example, air pollution may reduce the amount of solar radiation received in an area, but the supply itself is not permanently affected.

The third type of natural resources are *naturally renewable resources*, including all living organisms capable of growth and reproduction. Naturally renewable resources are unique in that their rate of renewal depends both on the physical environment and on the magnitude of the propagating stock. For these resources there conceivably exists some optimum rate and manner of use.

Although classifying resources according to their renewability is only one of several methods of classification, it does help us understand the possible effects of man's activities on the natural environment.[1] From the previous description it can be seen that naturally renewable resources are the most sensitive to changes in environmental conditions and therefore are the most susceptible to man's activities which affect the environment. However, to project these effects it is necessary to understand the natural environment as a complex set of interrelated processes and conditions, rather than as isolated elements functioning independently of one another. The study of ecology provides a basis for systematically describing these interrelationships and projecting the consequences of man's activities.

3.3 *Ecology and Natural Resources*

Ecology is usually defined as the study of the relation of organisms or groups of organisms to their environment. Because ecology is concerned especially with the biology of groups of organisms and with functional processes on land, in the oceans, and in fresh waters, it is appropriate to define ecology more broadly as *the study of the structure and function of natural systems.*[2] The study of the structure and function of natural systems is, then, the key to understanding how man can effectively use elements of the natural environment (natural resources) to meet his own needs while managing the natural systems for future generations.

ECOSYSTEMS

In studying the structure and function of natural systems it is useful to subdivide the natural environment into two main components: living organisms and their nonliving environment. These two components are inseparably related and interact upon each other to produce an exchange of materials between living and nonliving states. Any area of nature where these two components are interacting to produce an exchange of materials is referred to as an ecological system or ecosystem. The following section briefly describes the components of an ecosystem and how they are functionally related. The reader should refer to various ecology texts for a further explanation and discussion of these concepts.[3]

The two components of an ecosystem are, as stated above, living organisms and nonliving substances. Nonliving substances (*abiotic*) are the basic inorganic and organic compounds of the environment, such as water, carbon dioxide, oxygen, calcium, nitrogen and phosphorus salts, amino acids, and so on. In terms of natural resource types, nonliving substances are classed as either *stock resources* (mineral deposits), which have no means of renewal, or *flow resources* (water in the hydrologic cycle, oxygen), which are in continuous supply.

The living (*biotic*) component of an ecosystem is subdivided into three parts: (1) producers, (2) consumers, and (3) decomposers.

(1) *Producers* are autotrophic organisms (autotrophic = "self-nourishing"), primarily green plants, which are able to manufacture food from simple inorganic substances by the process of photosynthesis. These organisms provide the basic food for an ecosystem.

(2) *Consumers* are heterotrophic organisms (heterotrophic = "other-nourishing"), chiefly animals, which consume other organisms or particles of organic matter. *Primary consumers*, called herbivores, feed directly on living plants or plant remains. *Secondary consumers*, called carnivores, feed on the primary consumers, etc.

(3) *Decomposers* are also heterotrophic organisms and include primarily bacteria

[1] For further discussion of natural resources and natural resources classification, see Cain [1], pp. 56–60. Also see Schaefer and Revelle [9].

[2] See Odum [7]. [3] *Ibid.*, pp. 10–42 and Clarke [27], p. 16.

and fungi. These organisms perform the unique function of breaking down the complex compounds of dead protoplasm (dead plants and animals). In the process of decomposition, decomposers absorb some of the products as nutrients and release simple substances usable by producers.

The three living components of an ecosystem comprise the *naturally renewable resources*: living organisms capable of growth and reproduction, with the rate of renewal depending on the physical environment and the magnitude of the propagating stock. To summarize the ecosystem concept, Chart 3.3a is included to show the functional relationships of the component parts.

Chart 3.3a The Ecosystem Structure

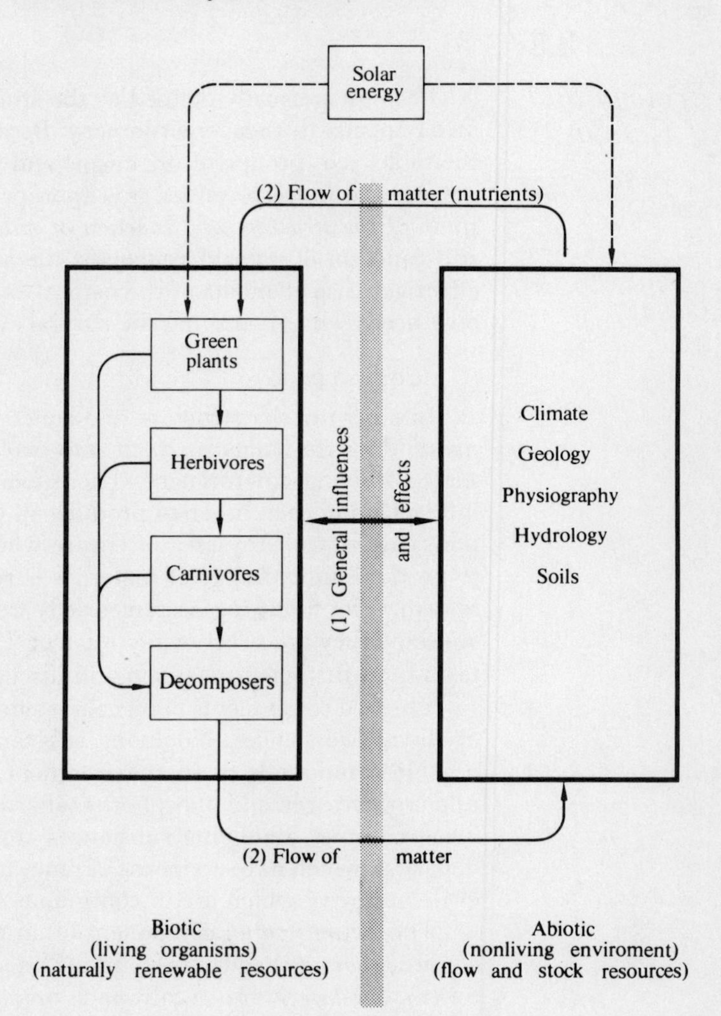

Chart 3.3a can be regarded as a simplified description of the natural environment "in action": living organisms and the nonliving environment interacting to produce a flow of energy and matter. The functional relationships expressed in this diagram between the biotic and abiotic components are somewhat arbitrarily divided into two parts: (1) the general influences and effects that each component exerts on the other, and (2) the actual exchange of matter between living and nonliving states. The exchange of matter between living and nonliving states is actually a part of the whole pattern of influences and effects which exist between organisms and their environment. However, it is separated here for purposes of explanation.

Plants, for example, incorporate nonliving materials (nutrients) into living tissue by the process of photosynthesis. Conversely, plants die and are decomposed into nonliving materials. This process involves the actual exchange of materials between living and nonliving states. However, plants also affect the nonliving environment by modifying climate, and in turn are affected by climate. This type of interrelationship does not involve the exchange of matter, but is nevertheless of equal functional importance. An illustration of these interrelationships is the growth of marine organisms (plants and animals). The amount of dissolved nutrients and oxygen available in the marine environment affects the growth rate of the organisms. The growth of the plants depletes the supply of nutrient salts. The respiration of the animals consumes oxygen and increases the amount of carbon dioxide in the water. In this example the nonliving environment receives materials from the organisms and loses material to them as they grow.

Other examples of organism-environment exchanges could be cited. Furthermore, important functional relationships also exist within each component. For example, animals and plants modify their own living environment by consuming each other as food. In the following section several of the many ecological principles which operate within the context of the ecosystem concept will be explained further. In each case the ecosystem concept will serve as the overall framework for relating the various areas of investigation.

In view of the description of the ecosystem concept, it is useful to review the purpose of this chapter outlined earlier; that is, to begin to explore a systematic means for projecting the environmental consequences of alternative development policies (natural resources development). Given the three classes of natural resources described earlier, and given the structure of the ecosystem, it is clear that the decision to use one element of the natural environment for man's purposes may have consequences in other, seemingly unrelated, areas. In fact, the effects of a development decision may ultimately incur costs to other economic activities. It is this linkage between the natural environment and economic activities which will be the focus of Chapter 4.

In the following section (Section 3.4) two ecological principles which operate within the ecosystem will be specifically described for use in regional analysis. Section 3.6 then illustrates how a particular set of interrelationships are quantified, after the development of a conceptual framework in Section 3.5.

3.4 *Ecological Principles in Regional Analysis*

This section develops two ecological principles. The principles outlined here and applied in Section 3.6 and Chapter 5 are oriented toward the analysis of a specific set of economic activities (recreational) in relation to a specific set of ecological subsystems. While they are important for the recreational development programs considered later, there is no assurance that they represent the most important interrelationships in the ecosystem. Theoretically, this problem of identifying the most significant interrelationships could be partially solved by constructing a descriptive ecological framework similar to the input-output framework already developed for describing the economy of a region (Section 2.3). Such an ecologic framework would quantitatively describe in a comprehensive fashion the diverse functional relationships which exist between the elements of an ecosystem, as already set forth. A start at such a framework is presented in the following section.

FOOD CHAIN

One useful ecological principle is the food chain. This principle refers to the process whereby living organisms obtain food energy by consuming other organisms. At the base of the food chain are green plants which produce food energy through the process of photosynthesis. This process combines solar energy (sunlight) and nonliving materials to form organic matter (potential energy). This first step is indicated in Chart 3.3a as the autotrophic component. All other living organisms (animals) either consume plants directly to satisfy their food requirements, or consume other animals, all of which use plants as their original source of food energy.

Chart 3.3a outlines the food chain and shows the relationships between autotrophic organisms, heterotrophic organisms, and the inflow of solar energy. The various levels of the food chain are designated *trophic levels*, and organisms whose food is obtained from plants by the same number of steps are said to belong to the same trophic level. Thus, green plants belong to the first trophic level, primary consumers (herbivores) to the second trophic level, secondary consumers (carnivores) to the third trophic level, and so on. A given species may occupy one or more than one trophic level according to the source of energy actually assimilated. Chart 3.4a illustrates the basic structure of the food chain and summarizes the terminology associated with it.

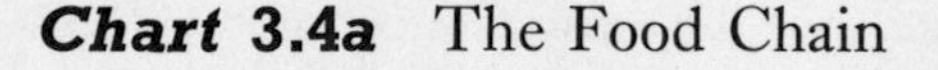

Chart 3.4a The Food Chain

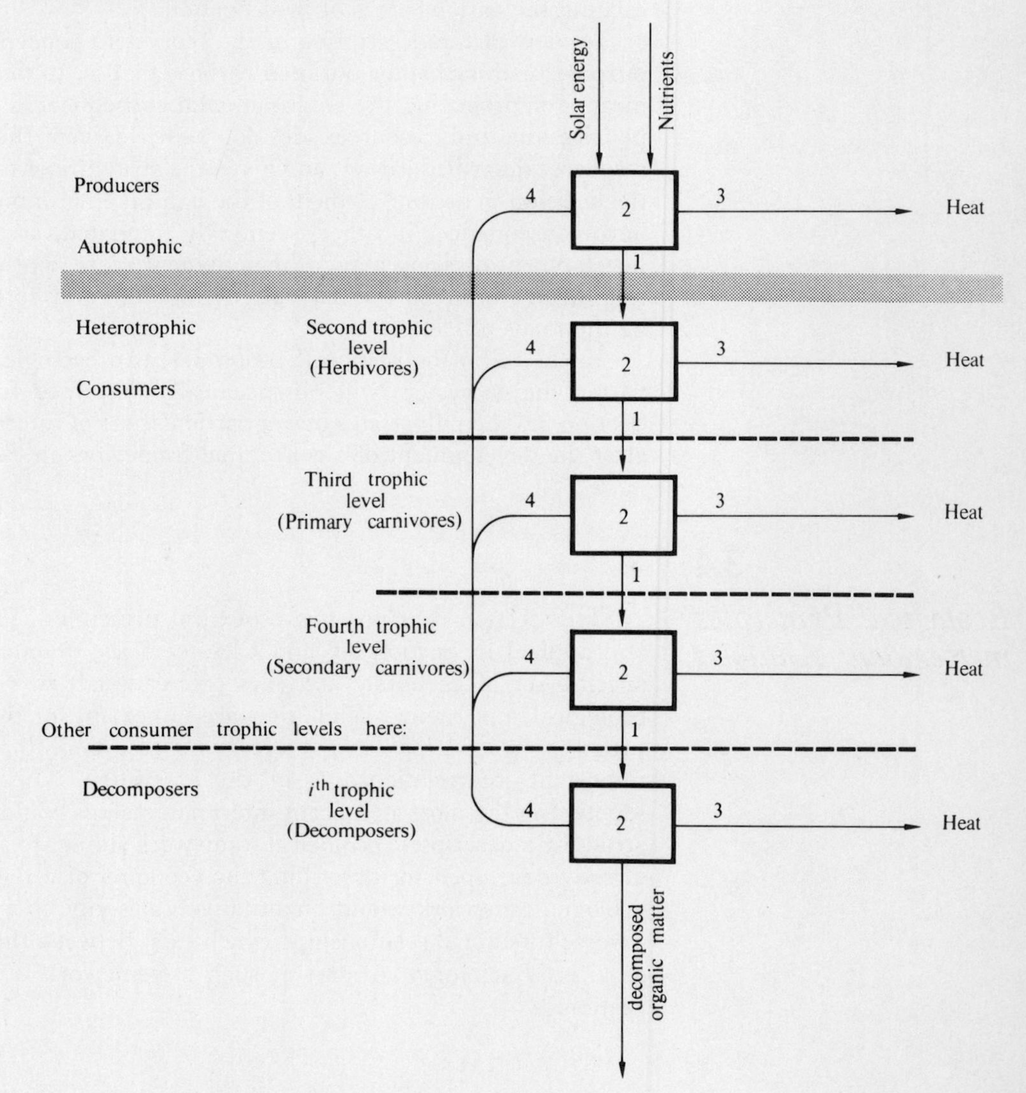

The four major processes in the food chain are indicated in Chart 3.4a. Other interrelationships exist, but for purposes of explanation only the four major ones are described. The first process (labeled process 1 on Chart 3.4a) is the transfer of food energy from its source in plants through the various trophic levels. The food energy is transferred in the form of living tissue at each step. At each trophic level, organisms convert part of the food energy assimilated into body tissue (process 2 on Chart 3.4a). The remainder of the food energy is converted by the process of respiration into body heat and dissipated into the surrounding environment (labeled process 3 on Chart 3.4a). Processes 2 and 3 represent the total energy flow through a trophic level (production of living tissue plus respiration). The fourth major process involves the transfer of dead organic matter from each trophic level back to the abiotic environment via decomposers (labelled process 4 on Chart 3.4a).

The significance of the food chain for regional planning lies in its description of the functional relationships which exist between the living organisms of an ecosystem.[4] The rate at which food energy flows through the ecosystem and the paths that it follows are both elements of the food chain principle which, if fully described, allow the planner to assess the effects of man's interference via an economic activity. If, for example, the by-product of an economic activity reduces the rate of photosynthesis (production of organic matter) in a particular area, then the effects of those by-products upon organisms which consume the green plants can also be estimated, using food chain data such as that presented in Section 3.6.

BIOGEOCHEMICAL CYCLES

The study of the functional relationships which exist within the ecosystem can also be approached through a consideration of the flow of abiotic materials. Chemical elements (abiotic materials) of the natural environment tend to circulate in ecosystems in characteristic paths from the nonliving environment to organisms and back to the nonliving environment. This cycling of chemical elements between living and nonliving states is referred to as "inorganic-organic" cycles, or *biogeochemical cycles*. This type of cycle was referred to previously in Chart 3.3a where the actual exchange of materials between living and nonliving states is an integral part of the ecosystem concept.

The chemical elements vary in their importance to living organisms. Some elements, such as carbon, hydrogen, oxygen, and nitrogen, are needed in relatively large quantities. Other elements are required in very minute quantities; e.g., iron and copper. Regardless of the degree of need, though, these chemical elements must be available for the growth of living organisms and must be continuously resupplied in a usable form.

The cycling of chemical elements between living and nonliving states is directly affected by the activity of living organisms. Plants and animals in their normal life processes utilize these elements to form living protoplasm (living tissue). For example, nitrogen, in the form of nitrates, becomes a part of the protoplasm of plants and animals through protein synthesis. Thus, nitrogen is incorporated into living organisms by the activity of living organisms themselves. In a reverse manner the decomposition of protoplasm returns nitrogen to the abiotic environment. Decomposer organisms (bacteria) reduce proteins to their component elements and in the process obtain food energy for their own respiratory processes.

The chemical elements of an ecosystem can be divided into various compartments or pools. For ecological purposes it is useful to consider primarily two types of pools: (1) the nonbiological pool where the elements are not available to organisms, and (2) the biologically available pool where chemical elements are directly available to plants. The rate of circulation of chemical elements between these two pools depends on certain biological and nonbiological mechanisms. For example, nitrogen in the atmosphere (nonbiological pool) is not directly usable by plants and animals although it is present in large quantities. However, nitrogen is converted into a biologically available form (nitrates) by the action of certain organisms

[4] Food chains are not isolated sequences, as the reader might initially be led to believe. The term "food web" may be more appropriate terminology for the interlocking pattern food chains form in an ecosystem.

(nitrogen-fixing bacteria and algae) and certain physical processes (lightning: electrification). Conversely, it is returned to the unavailable form by denitryfying bacteria. Thus the cycle between the biological state and the "geo" nonliving state is complete in a circular manner for this element, as it is for other elements.

3.5 *A Proposed Method for Describing Natural Systems and a Framework for Data Collection*

3.5.1 The Use of the Input-Output Framework to Depict Interrelations among Ecologic Variables

Section 3.4 contains some broadly outlined general ecological principles which are basic for the comprehensive analysis of the effects of a specific set of economic activities (e.g., recreational activities) upon the ecosystem. We now wish to proceed beyond these statements and develop a conceptual framework for describing in a detailed, quantitative form the key interrelationships of an ecosystem. We shall follow the input-output, or more strictly, the activity analysis (programming) format developed by economists, regional scientists, and applied mathematicians.

Recall that the input-output framework was presented in Section 2.3 of this book in order to describe and analyze the complex interrelationships between economic sectors (industries) which comprise a regional economy. The framework was developed in the form of a table, which attempts to indicate the dependence of the activity level of any economic sector on the activity levels of other sectors. Each economic sector is represented by both a row and a column in the table. In the column corresponding to a particular sector, the table shows its requirements or inputs from other sectors. The requirements for a particular sector's products (or output) by other sectors are shown in its row.

The variables in the economic sectors, such as level of production by industries and land uses by economic activities, have more frequently than not been measured in dollars. The variables in the ecologic sectors include amounts of abiotic substances such as water, nutrients or light; or amounts of organisms such as phytoplankton, winter flounder, and the like. Diverse units of measurement are used for these variables but these different units of measurement are not a problem. In fact, there is no reason to use the same units to measure all the variables in the typical input-output table, even if this is feasible. The important thing is that each variable be measured in a consistent manner. For example, steel and coal can both be measured in dollars or tons; or one can be measured in dollars and the other in tons. In the latter case we can speak meaningfully about an input coefficient which states the tons of coal required per dollar output of steel. However, when we involve non-economic variables which cannot be measured in dollar terms, measurements must necessarily be made in terms of physical units.

An example of how an input-output framework can be used is shown in Table 3.5a. Assume that we are concerned with winter flounder production. We know that flounder consume algae, annelida, mollusk tips, crustaceans, and a small amount of other organic matter. We also know that each of these marine animals have food sources, mainly organic detritus. Each of these items are listed both in the rows and the columns of the table. We can indicate flounder production by placing a + sign in the cell formed by the intersection of the flounder row and column. We can then indicate the food inputs to flounder production by placing a − sign in the cells formed by the row of each food input and the column for flounder. Similarly, we can indicate the production of each of the direct flounder food sources. For example, the production of annelida would be indicated by a + sign in the column and row for annelida and a − sign in the column for annelida and row for its food source, detritus. We may also expand this table to include the production of other commodities from the ecosystem—cod, for example, which

Table 3.5a Winter Flounder Production Linkage Submatrix

⋮	…	Marine Plants (including Algae)	Algae	Miscellaneous Foods (assumed to be Plants)	Detritus	Annelida	Mollusca	Crustacea	Winter Flounder	…
Marine plants (including algae)		+			—					
Algae			+						—	
Miscellaneous foods (assumed to be plants)				+						
Detritus					+	—	—	—		
Annelida						+			—	
Mollusca							+		—	
Crustacea								+	—	
Winter flounder									+	
⋮										

may or may not use the same direct or indirect inputs as flounder. In this way, we may proceed to build an interrelationship or "linkage" table or matrix which indicates the relationships between an activity and all of its related activities which directly or indirectly provide inputs to it.

If we have the data on the quantitative relationships among ecological components—for example, flounder and its food sources—we can establish the amounts of inputs required per unit level of output at that level for which the data were collected. If this can be accomplished for all the ecological components listed in a table, then the regular input-output procedures mentioned in Section 2.3 can be utilized. We would then have a means by which we could begin to analyze the consequences to the ecological system of proposed changes in one or more of the related components or variables.

Certainly, one would like to be able to put numbers into all the cells of an interrelationship table. Unfortunately, at present this is not possible. There are major data deficiencies; to a considerable extent, research can overcome many of them. There are also conceptual difficulties. However, it should be possible to develop conventions similar to those used in economics and regional science which would enable us to overcome the conceptual difficulties which arise in the attempt to apply input-output methods to the study of the environment. Meanwhile, it is in fact quite reasonable to attach numerical values to some of the entries in the table. For example, according to Riley, Stommel, and Bumpus,[5] marine phytoplankton production by photosynthesis depends on, among other things, the concentration of dissolved phosphate in the water. This relationship between an organism and an abiotic substance takes a definite mathematical form. As long as the concentration of phosphorus is less than a particular amount (0.55 mg. of atomic phosphorus as phosphate per cubic meter of water), phytoplankton production is assumed to be directly proportional to the amount of phosphorus present as

[5] Riley, Stommel, and Bumpus [8].

phosphate.[6] This proportionality can be directly entered into the table; for every unit of phytoplankton produced, a definite amount of phosphorus (in the form of phosphate) is required. This is recorded in the table by entering this amount in the row for phosphorus and the column for the phytoplankton production by photosynthesis. This number is more informative than a mere minus sign would be, but has to be approached with caution for a number of reasons. In the first place, the relationship holds only if the concentration of phosphorus is less than 0.55 mg. of atomic phosphorus as phosphate per cubic meter of water. In the second place, the quantitative effect of an increase in the amount of dissolved phosphate will depend on the actual levels of several other variables, including turbidity and incident radiation. That is, the effect of a given increase in phosphate concentration will be reduced with increasing levels of turbidity. Therefore, in computing numerical values for the interrelation coefficient between two variables, typical values of all other variables have to be assumed.

Even when it is not possible to estimate quantitative coefficients, however, the use of a linkage table, such as we outline, may serve to pinpoint the effects which should be considered before action on any development proposal is taken. In some cases it will be clear that some of the direct effects will be quantitatively slight, so that they may be ignored, while others will be important. A decision-maker may be able to pick out those elements from the table which are likely to matter, and then use the table to help trace out the likely effects of a given course of action.

One of the assumptions that the input-output format makes is that each sector produces a single product and uses a single process. Of course, in both the economy and the natural environment, this is an over-simplification. In both the economic and ecologic systems it is quite common for several products to be produced by a single activity or organism. In economics this "simplifying" assumption can be avoided by using an activity analysis or programing format, where we distinguish between *commodities* and *processes*. Each commodity is represented by a row and may be produced by one or more processes. Each process is represented by a column and may be associated with the production of one or more commodities. In what follows we adopt a similar format and distinction for the ecologic system.

3.5.2 Construction of the Table

(a) Delineation of Regions

In order to construct an interrelations table for planning purposes, a meaningful sectoring of the ecological processes and commodities is needed. First, we begin with the subdivision of geographical areas into regions of similar environmental conditions. Each region is characterized by definite ecological processes and physical flows which are mutually dependent and operate to maintain life and regenerate vital nutrients. Thus we are led to identify such major regions as LAND and MARINE.

Next, we must recognize explicitly that the various regions are interrelated by ecological processes. We have already mentioned in Section 3.4 several ecological concepts which deal with interrelationships within and between regions. As pointed out, the study of "food chain" relationships can provide an understanding of energy flows not only between organisms but also between regions. So also can the study of "biogeochemical cycles" which traces the flow of abiotic substances essential for organic growth through more or less circular paths between organisms and the several regions of the environment. Table 3.5b illustrates how interrelationships between regions can be displayed in a manner helpful for their description and analysis.

[6] *Ibid.*, p. 43.

Table 3.5b Interrelationships among Regions

	Land (i zones)	Marine (j zones)	Air (k zones)
Land (i zones)	Effect of land processes on land processes	Effect of marine processes on land processes	Effect of air processes on land processes
Marine (j zones)	Effect of land processes on marine processes	Effect of marine processes on marine processes	Effect of air processes on marine processes
Air (k zones)	Effect of land processes on air processes	Effect of marine processes on air processes	Effect of air processes on air processes

The table postulates three main regions based upon gross similarities of environmental conditions: land, marine, and air. The three regions may be further subdivided into zones, each having a high degree of identity in terms of geographical location and ecological processes. For example, the marine region might be subdivided into two subregions: open water and intertidal, as proposed in Table 3.5c. In turn, each of these subregions may be further subdivided into zones of similar environmental conditions, depending on the requirements of the particular problem being investigated.

Table 3.5c Subdivision of Marine Region into Zones

			MARINE				
			Intertidal		**Open Water**		
			Zone A	Zone B	Zone C	Zone D	Zone E
MARINE	**Intertidal**	Zone A					
		Zone B					
	Open Water	Zone C					
		Zone D					
		Zone E					

(b) Sector Organization within a Zone

In our basic framework each zone's sectors are to be divided into *ecologic* and *economic*. After considerable research and experience over the years, a highly useful standard classification of economic sectors has evolved.[7] For the ecologic sectors, however, there exists no such standard classification system. Since our framework requires a classification of ecologic sectors, we put forth the following system. This system, however, is based only on a brief review of work by various natural scientists, and must be considered most tentative.

[7] Such a classification has been essential for input-output analysis. See Isard *et al.* [4], Chapter 8.

The ecologic sectors are divided into two main groups:

1. the abiotic
2. the biotic

This division reflects the interdependency between the environment (abiotic factors) and organisms referred to in Section 3.3. The *abiotic* grouping is organized into the following categories:

a. Climate
b. Geology
c. Physiography
d. Hydrology
e. Soils

The *biotic* grouping is organized into:

a. Plants
b. Animals

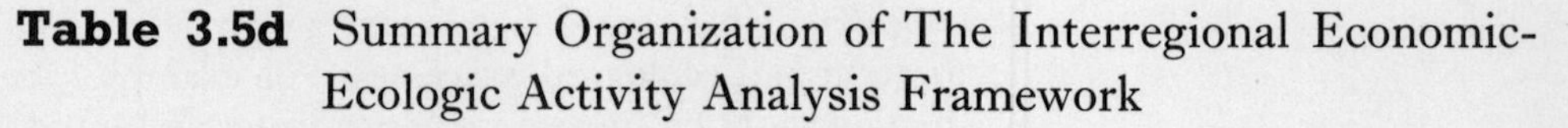

Table 3.5d Summary Organization of The Interregional Economic-Ecologic Activity Analysis Framework

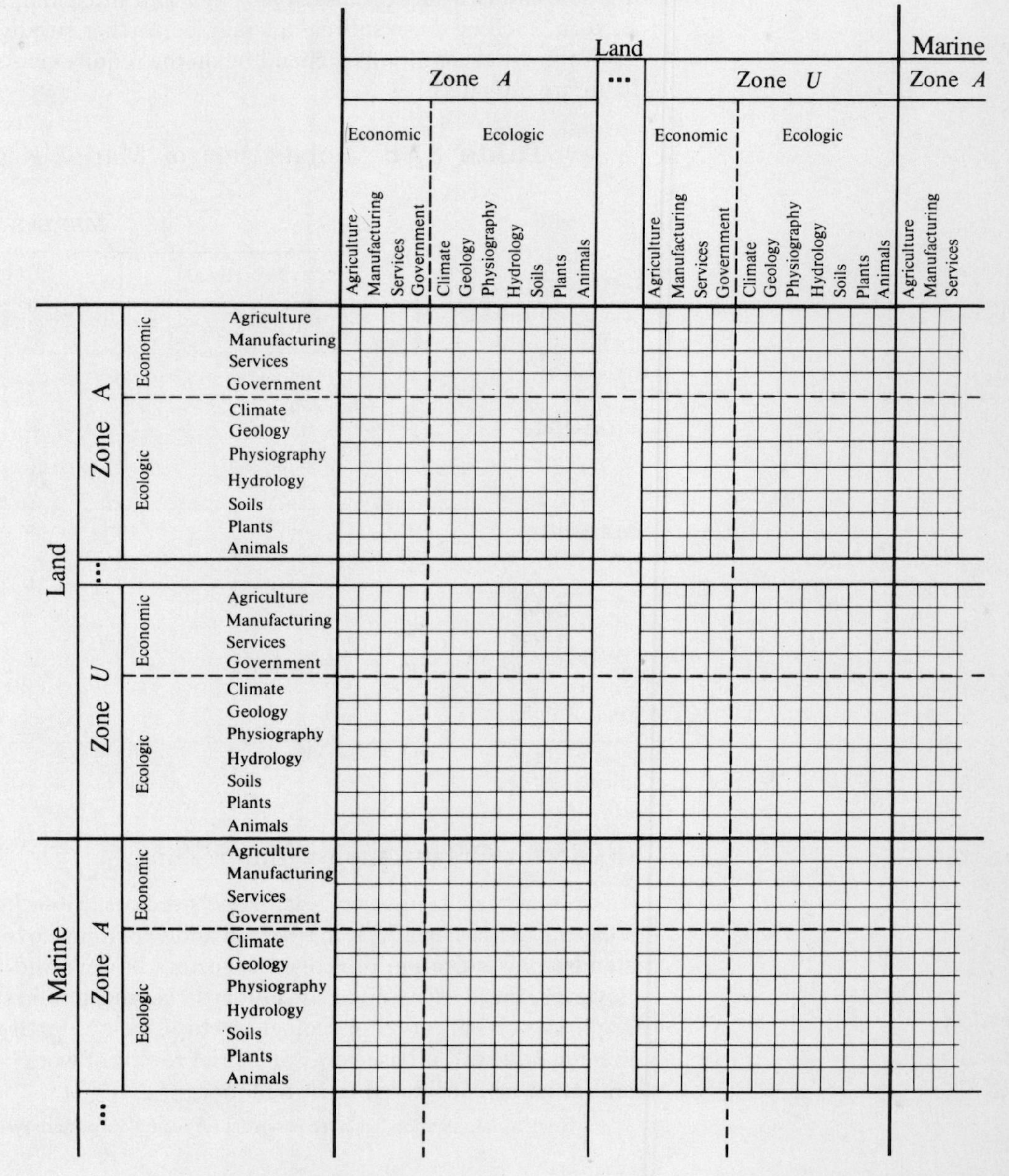

The latter grouping distinguishes essentially between autotrophic and heterotrophic categories. *Autotrophic*, or *producer*, organisms are able to build up complex organic substances from simple abiotic substances through the fixation of light energy (photosynthesis). The great majority of these autotrophic organisms are green plants. *Heterotrophic* organisms exist through the utilization, rearrangement, or decomposition of the complex materials which the autotrophic organisms produce. They also produce abiotic substances usable by the autotrophic organisms. The heterotrophic organisms are often further subdivided into *consumers* and *decomposers*. Table 3.5d summarizes the organization of our framework.

3.5.3 A Numerical Ecological Classification System

Governmental agencies concerned with the description of national and regional economies have found it useful to establish a standard classification system for economic activities. This system is known as the Standard Industrial Classification (S.I.C.) system.[8] The Standard Industrial Classification was developed for use in the classification of establishments by type of activity in which they are engaged. The basic aim is to facilitate the collection, tabulation, presentation, and analysis of data relating to establishments and to promote uniformity and comparability in the presentation of statistical data collected by various agencies of the United States Government, state agencies, trade associations, business, and private research organizations. The Standard Industrial Classification purports to cover the entire field of economic activities: agriculture, forestry, and fisheries; mining; construction; manufacturing; transportation, communication, electric, gas, and sanitary services; and government.

In this classification system each industry is given a number. The first digit indicates the economic level at which the industry operates. Thus industries whose S.I.C. number begins with 0 are primary agriculture activities. Industries whose S.I.C. number begins with 1 are mineral extraction activities; those beginning with 2 are raw materials processing; those beginning with 3 are manufacturing activities; and those with higher first digits are trade and service type activities. The second digit of a S.I.C. number refers to the broad classification within the first digit level. Thus group 29 refers to the petroleum industry. Further digits are added to give a finer classification—for instance, 2911 is petroleum refining. A general classification using up to seven digits has been developed, but the system is flexible, and as many digits may be used as are needed. For instance, if 2911 refers to petroleum refining, a further digit could be added to describe the particular refining process used.

Keeping in mind the Standard Industrial Classification system, we propose the following classification system to facilitate the numerical referencing and tabulation of the ecological processes and commodities with which we shall be concerned. The first major division of the table into the major environmental regions, Land and Marine, can be designated by the letters L and M respectively.[9] Therefore, the numerical designations for all land activities, both ecologic and economic, will be preceded by the letter L, while all activities on or within the marine environment will be preceded by the letter M. To designate zones within these general regions, we can place a superscript (or subscript) after the letter L or M. Further zoning within these superscript zones can be accomplished by adding additional superscripts. For example, if we designate land in general as L, we may designate the New England land area and the Great Lakes states as L^N and L^G, respectively.

[8] U.S. Bureau of the Budget [10].

[9] In what follows, we shall not be explicitly considering AIR or other major regions of the environment. However, the conceptual framework we propose can easily be extended to these major regions.

Within the New England area, we may designate a Boston subarea as ${}^{b}L^{N}$, and a Worcester subarea as ${}^{w}L^{N}$.

Within each major environmental region in the table, there are two basic classifications of activities: *ecological* and *economic*. The economic classification uses the Standard Industrial Classification mentioned in the first part of this section with the appropriate prefix designating the economic activity's environmental and geographic location. For example, if a petroleum refining activity, Standard Industrial Classification number 2911, is located in the Boston land area, then using the zoning method just suggested, this petroleum refining activity can be designated ${}^{b}L^{N}$ 2911.

We propose a digital system for classifying ecological processes and commodities. To avoid confusion with the Standard Industrial Classification numbers, the ecological classification numbers will be preceded by the letter X. As indicated in Section 3.5.2, the environmental information is classified into abiotic and biotic groups: that is, climate, geology, physiography, hydrology, and soils; and plants and animals, in that order. Most of the ecosystem data with which we will be concerned can be classified under one of these headings. The first digit of the classification number indicates the environmental heading under which the information is classified. Accordingly:

1 indicates climate
2 indicates geology
3 indicates physiography
4 indicates hydrology
5 indicates soils
6 indicates plants
7 indicates animals.

Therefore, soils in the Boston area of our hypothetical example would be classified under ${}^{b}L^{N}$X 5.

To classify further within these main environmental headings, more digits are added. Pending work within this framework to develop conventions which impart specific and significant meaning to the use of additional digits, we employ additional digits to differentiate: (1) among major plant and animal categories; (2) among plant and animal types within any of these major categories; and (3) among the various organic materials produced by the functioning or death of any one of the plant and animal types. For example, animals can be classified as herbivores; carnivores; parasites; scavengers; decomposers, or organisms which utilize dead organic matter to produce decomposed matter; and transformers, or organisms which transform decomposed organic matter into abiotic substances. Therefore, herbivores are classified as 71, while decomposers are classified as 75. Various types of herbivores are classified by designating herbivore type 1 as 711, herbivore type 2 as 712, and so on. Products produced by herbivore type 1, or animal 711, can be designated by a fourth digit; thus its feces could be designated as 7111, while its bones and teeth could be designated as 7115. The number 0 has been used to indicate a nonspecified classification. For example, bones and teeth of animals in general, nonspecified into classes or types, are referred to as 7005, while bones and teeth of herbivores in general are referred to as 7105.

If we employ the fourth digit to designate herbivore products, for example, we may have more than 9 different herbivore types to designate by the third digit. In order to handle this problem, we have used a hyphen to isolate this kind of digit. Thus product 1 of a herbivore type 12 can be designated 71-12-1. In this case, the entire number 12 is regarded as the third digit. In order to distinguish a process from a commodity, the letter *P* can be added before the classification number of the primary commodity produced by the process.

Table 3.5e Summary of The Economic-Ecologic Commodity Classification System

	Classification number	Commodity
LAND - L; Land zone A - L^A; Economic	S.I.C. numbers	Agricultural products
		Mineral products
		Textile products
		.
		.
LAND - L; Land zone A - L^A; Ecologic - X	1	Climatic
	2	Geologic
	3	Physiographic
	4	Hydrologic
	5	Soils
	6	Plants
	60	Unspecified types of plants (all types)
	61	Green plants
	610	Unspecified types of green plants (all types)
	611	Green plant type 1
	6111	Product 1 from green plant type 1
	6112	Product 2 from green plant type 1
	62	Parasite plants
	63	Saprophytes types of animals
	7	Animals
	70	Unspecified
	71	Herbivores
	710	Unspecified types of herbivores
	711	Herbivore type 1
	7111	Product 1 from herbivore type 1
	7112	Product 2 from herbivore type 1
	72	Carnivores
	73	Parasite animals
	74	Scavengers
	75	Decomposers
	76	Transformers
⋮	⋮	⋮
LAND ZONE U - L^U		
MARINE - M; Marine Zone A - M^A		

Table 3.5e summarizes the Economic-Ecologic Commodity Classification System to date. Table 3.5f lists those ecological commodities that we have currently considered in this report.

Table 3.5f Ecologic Commodities Currently Considered

Classification Number	Commodity Name
LX 21	Phosphate rocks—volcanic apatite
LX 22	Phosphate rocks—guano deposits and fossil bones
LX 23	Phosphate rocks—uplifted sedimentary rocks
LX 24	Particulate phosphate
LX 42	Dissolved phosphate—in streams
LX 51	Dissolved phosphate—in soils

Table 3.5f (cont.)

Classification Number	Commodity Name
LX 6001	Dead plant matter
LX 610	Green plants
LX 62	Parasite plants
LX 7001	Animal feces
LX 7004	Dead animal matter
LX 7005	Bones and teeth
LX 710	Herbivores
LX 721	Primary carnivores
LX 722	Secondary carnivores
LX 73	Parasite animals
LX 74	Scavengers
LX 75	Decomposers—decomposing bacteria
LX 7501	Decomposed organic matter
LX 76	Transformers—phosphatizing bacteria
MX 11	Light—incident solar radiation at the ocean surface
MX 31	Bay or estuary water area
MX 32	Intertidal and subtidal shoal water area
MX 410	Particulate phosphate—in estuarine waters
MX 411	Particulate phosphate in estuarine waters at 14 mg. P per m^2
MX 420	Dissolved phosphate in ocean water
MX 421	Dissolved phosphate in ocean water at 19 mg. P per m^2
MX 43	Dissolved organic phosphorus at 6 mg. P per m^2
MX 44	Water transparency—extinction coefficient
MX 51	Muddy and sandy bottom area
MX 52	Solid material and firm bottom area
MX 53	Phosphates in shallow marine sediments
MX 60	All marine plants
MX 6001	Detritus—dead plant matter (in gm.)
MX 6002	Detritus—particulate food for mussels (in mg. P per m^2 per day)
MX 610	Marine green plants
MX 612	Algae
MX 61–10	Plankton[a]
MX 61–11	Phytoplankton (in lb.)
MX 61–12	Phytoplankton—existing population stock (in gm. C per m^2)
MX 61–13	Phytoplankton matter (in gm. C per m^2)
MX 61–14	Phytoplankton produced by photosynthesis
MX 61–15	Phytoplankton matter utilized in respiration
MX 62	Marine parasite plants
MX 7001	Feces
MX 7004	Dead animal matter
MX 7005	Bones, shells, and teeth
MX 710	Marine herbivores
MX 711	Zooplankton
MX 712	Herbivorous invertebrates—annelida
MX 713	Herbivorous invertebrates—mollusca
MX 714	Herbivorous invertebrates—blue mussel
MX 715	Herbivorous invertebrates—mussel population (in mg. P per m^2)
MX 7151	Ingested phosphorus by mussel population
MX 7152	Feces by mussel population
MX 7153	Pseudofeces by mussel population
MX 7154	Dead mussels
MX 7155	Mussel gametes
MX 716	Herbivorous invertebrates—soft-shelled clam
MX 717	Herbivorous invertebrates—crustacea
MX 718	Herbivorous invertebrates—miscellaneous
MX 719	Herring
MX 720	Primary carnivores
MX 721	Carnivorous invertebrates—large gastropods
MX 722	Small fish
MX 723	Winter flounder
MX 724	Marine secondary carnivores
MX 725	Cod
MX 73	Marine parasite animals

Table 3.5f (cont.)

Classification Number	Commodity Name
MX 74	Marine scavengers
MX 7202	Marine bird droppings
MX 75	Decomposers—decomposing agents such as bacteria, etc.
MX 7501	Decomposed organic matter
MX 76	Transformers—phosphatizing bacteria, etc.

[a]Plankton comprises both plant and animals, and strictly speaking should not be classified under plants. See Section 3.6.6.

3.6 *Derivation of some Ecological Interrelation Coefficients*

3.6.1 Introduction

This section is concerned with the derivation of ecological-type coefficients which are to be used in the interrelations table referred to in Section 3.5. In order to analyze a real situation we have selected the Plymouth Bay area in Massachusetts as a case study area. Therefore, the coefficients derived in this section have evolved from interrelations relevant to the case study area. The interrelations studied thus far are: the "food chain" production requirements for winter flounder, cod and shellfish; the production relations between a producer organism (namely, phytoplankton) and the abiotic environment; the tracing of an essential element, phosphorus, in its cycle of involvement within organisms and the abiotic environment; and the quantification of a part of this cycle, the phosphorus transformations by the mussel population within an estuarine environment.

The Plymouth Bay area, like the entire New England coast, provides a traditional and increasingly important recreation resource for the region's inhabitants and visiting tourists. Also, because of its access to the Atlantic, its cities and commerce have grown significantly. Such growth often seems to conflict with environmental quality and the well-being of those economic activities which depend on the maintenance of natural environmental quality.

We begin this part of the study by examining the requirements or inputs to one of these environmentally sensitive industries—namely, recreational sportfishing. In the New England area the sportfishing activity depends on two main fish species, winter flounder and cod. In order to understand the relative abundance of these fish, we investigate their production requirements in terms of their direct food sources as well as their ultimate plant food sources. Thus we begin by listing in summary form the production requirements for winter flounder, cod, and shellfish. Appendix B gives a more detailed description of these requirements and the procedures used for estimating them.

3.6.2 Winter Flounder Production

It was found that winter flounder (*Pseudopleuronectes americanus*) requires food inputs of ten times the weight of the winter flounder produced. Therefore, 1,000,000 pounds of winter flounder requires 10,000,000 pounds of food. This food is divided into five inputs as listed in Table 3.6a.

Putting this into activity analysis format, and defining a unit level of the winter flounder producing activity as that level which yields 1 million pounds of winter flounder output, we obtain per unit level of this activity the following required inputs:

3.36 units of annelida

2.73 units of algae
2.30 units of mollusca
.71 units of crustacea
.90 units of other miscellaneous foods

where the unit of each of these inputs is also 1 million pounds, and an input of .04 units of bay or estuary water area, where the unit of bay or estuary water is 1 million acres.

Table 3.6a Requirements for Winter Flounder Production

Output	
Winter flounder	1,000,000 lb.
Food Inputs	
1. Annelida (*polychaeta*)	3,360,000
2. Algae	2,730,000
3. Mollusca	2,300,000
4. Crustacea	710,000
5. Other miscellaneous foods	900,000

Also, a requirement of 40,000 surface acres of bay or estuary area was estimated for the production of 1,000,000 pounds of winter flounder.

Annelida, mollusca, and crustacea require detritus as food at a consumption ratio of about 10 to 1. Therefore, the 3.36 million pounds of annelida (required by 1 million pounds of winter flounder) in turn require 33.6 million pounds of detritus, the 2.3 million pounds of mollusca require 23 million pounds of detritus, and the 0.710 million pounds of crustacea require 7.1 million pounds of detritus.[10] The marine bottom area requirements of these bottom-dwelling herbivorous invertebrates were estimated as follows:

1 unit of annelida production requires .007550 units of muddy and sandy bottom (equal to 25,000 acres for 3,360,000 pounds of annelida)
1 unit of mollusca production requires .002265 units of muddy and sandy bottom (equal to 5,200 acres for 2,300,000 pounds of mollusca)
1 unit of crustacea production requires .007550 units of muddy and sandy bottom (equal to 5,400 acres for 710,000 pounds of crustacea)

The area requirements for algae and the other miscellaneous foods (assumed to be plants) were estimated as follows:

1 unit of algae requires .000008 units of intertidal and subtidal shoal water (equal to 22 acres for 2,730,000 pounds of algae)
1 unit of other miscellaneous foods (assumed to be plants) requires .000008 units of muddy and sandy bottom (equal to 7.2 acres for 900,000 pounds of miscellaneous foods)

Detritus was estimated to be produced by marine plants at a 1 to 1 ratio.[11] Each unit of detritus-producing marine plant was estimated to require .000008 units of intertidal and subtidal shoal water.[12]

As already stated, this transfer of food energy from its source in plants through a series of consumer organisms is known as the food chain. Thus, in the foregoing

[10] The total of these detritus requirements is thus 63.7 million pounds.

[11] Thus 63.7 million pounds of detritus required 63.7 million pounds of marine plant which when added to the 2.73 million pounds of algae and 0.9 million pounds of other plant food directly consumed by 1 million pounds of winter flounder yield 67.33 million pounds of plant-type food directly and indirectly required by 1 million pounds of winter flounder.

[12] The 67.33 million pounds of plant-type food noted in the previous footnote therefore require 540 acres of intertidal and shoal subtidal waters.

Table 3.6b Food Chain for Winter Flounder Production in Activity Analysis Format

Classification Number	Commodity	Units	Production						
			PMX 60 Marine Plants (including Algae)	PMX 612 Algae	PMX 6001 Detritus	PMX 712 Annelida	PMX 713 Mollusca	PMX 717 Crustacea	PMX 723 Winter Flounder
MX 31	Bay or estuary water area	acres							−.04
MX 32	Intertidal and subtidal shoal water area	acres		-8×10^{-6}					
MX 51	Muddy and sandy bottom area	acres	-8×10^{-6}			-7550×10^{-6}	-2265×10^{-6}	-7550×10^{-6}	
MX 60	Marine plants (including algae)	lb.	+1		−1				
MX 612	Algae	lb.		+1					−2.73
MX 6001	Detritus	lb.			+1	−10	−10	−10	
MX 712	Annelida	lb				+1			−3.36
MX 713	Mollusca	lb.					+1		−2.30
MX 717	Crustacea	lb.						+1	−.71
MX 723	Winter flounder	lb.							+1

we have quantitatively related flounder production back to its plant sources. These relationships are indicated in the food chain flow diagram for flounder production, Chart 3.6a, and are put into activity analysis format in Table 3.6b. For further materials on the derivation of the data see Appendix B.

Chart 3.6a Food Chain Flow Diagram For Winter Flounder Production

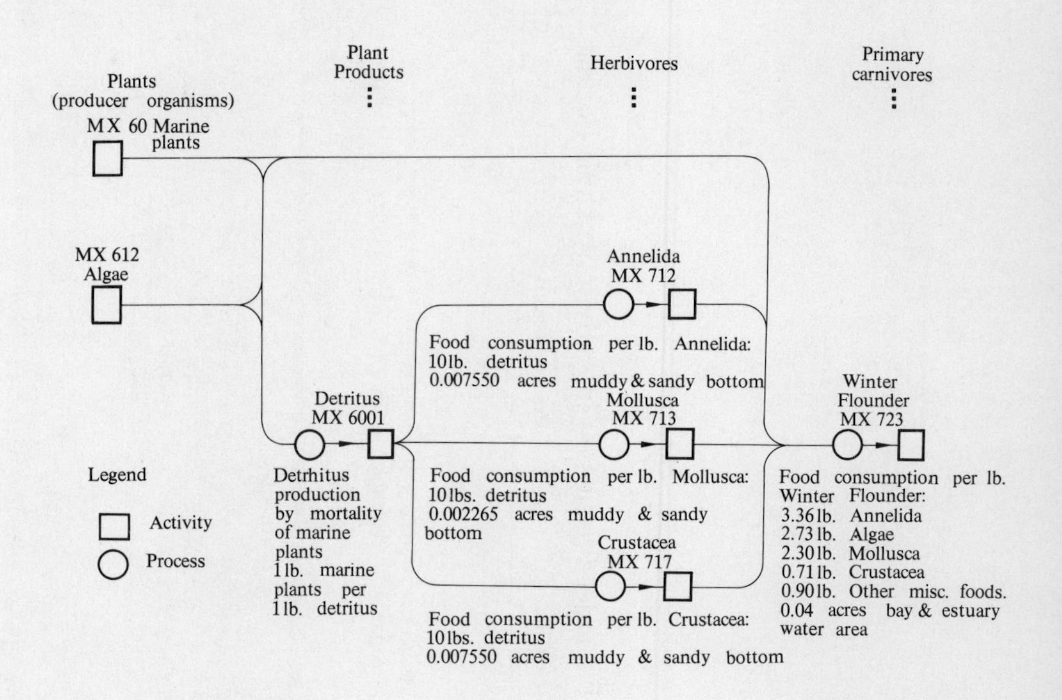

3.6.3 Cod Production

The production requirements of cod (*Gadus morhua*) were estimated in a similar manner as those for winter flounder. The cod's food chain has one more link than the winter flounder's food chain, in that cod eat predatory crustaceans and gastropods (carnivorous invertebrates) and small fish which, like the winter flounder, eat primarily small herbivorous invertebrates. Thus cod are termed secondary carnivores. It is estimated that the production of 1,000,000 pounds of cod requires 1,167,500 pounds of herring, 8,333,000 pounds of carnivorous invertebrates, and 1,667,500 pounds of small fish. Therefore, every unit level of cod production activity requires inputs of:

8.333 units of carnivorous invertebrates
1.167 units of herring
1.667 units of small fish

In a similar manner the inputs for carnivorous invertebrates, small fish, and herring production were estimated. These are tabulated in Table 3.6c.

As previously noted, a unit level production of herbivorous invertebrates requires 10 units of detritus.

Thus, by multiplying out the steps of the food chain, we see that cod requires roughly 1,011 times its weight in plant matter, while the flounder requires roughly 100. Also, the cod requires about 10 times as much herbivorous invertebrates as does the flounder, and thus requires about 10 times the bottom acreage. This is, however, only an approximation, for we do not know at present whether the cod

Table 3.6c Requirements for Production of Selected Flounder Foods

Unit Level Output of		
Carnivorous invertebrates	requires 10 units of	Herbivorous invertebrates
Small fish	requires 10 units of	Herbivorous invertebrates
Herring	requires 10 units of	Plankton (plant source)

food (other than herring) has the same preference for annelida as the flounder. If the cod food has a smaller propensity to consume (less intense preference for) annelida than winter flounder, then the total acreage requirements for cod may be smaller.

The food chain requirements for cod production are shown in the flow diagram, Chart 3.6b, and in activity analysis format in Table 3.6d. For further materials on the derivation of the data, see Appendix B.

Chart* 3.6*b Food Chain Flow Diagram For Cod Production

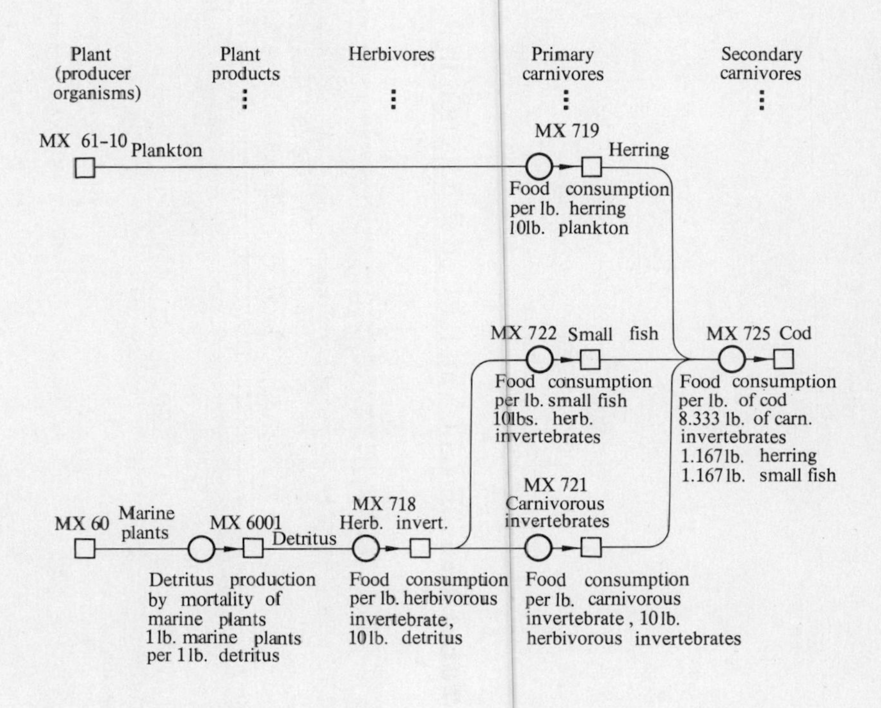

3.6.4 Shellfish Production

The production requirements of two shellfish, native to Plymouth Bay and the New England area, were estimated in a similar manner. These are the soft-shelled clam (*Mya arenaria*) and the blue mussel (*Mytilus edulis*). The soft-shelled clam, in particular, provides a recreation and food resource which is uniquely identified with the New England region. Because shellfish are relatively stationary, these filter-feeding bivalves are often used as environmental indicators of pollution levels, nutrient levels, and so on. Mussels are also of indirect value to man in that they play a major role in the cycling of phosphorus within the estuarine system. Though mussels are a relatively small component of the estuarine ecosystem, they

Table 3.6d Food Chain for Cod Production in Activity Analysis Format

			Process							
Classification Number	Commodity	Units	PMX 61-10 Plankton Production	PMX 60 All Marine Plant (incl. Plankton) Production	PMX 6001 Detritus Production	PMX 718 Herbivorous Invertebrate Production	PMX 719 Herring Production	PMX 722 Small-Fish Production	PMX 721 Carnivorous Invertebrate (Large Gastropod) Production	PMX 725 Cod Production
MX 61–10	Plankton	lb.	+1				−10			
MX 60	All marine plants (including plankton)	,,		+1	−1					
MX 6001	Detritus	,,			+1	−10				
MX 718	Herbivorous invertebrates (miscellaneous)	,,				+1		−10	−10	
MX 719	Herring	,,					+1			−1.167
MX 722	Small fish	,,						+1		−1.667
MX 721	Carnivorous invertebrates (large gastropods)	,,							+1	−8.333
MX 725	Cod	,,								+1

have been shown to be quite important to the ecosystem as a biogeochemical agent. In filtering the water to obtain their food, mussels ingest huge quantities of suspended particulate matter which they then deposit in the form of pseudofeces. This sedimented matter is utilized by bacteria and other organisms which reprocess it into dissolved phosphate, an essential and often limiting commodity for plant production. This particular function of the mussel population will be covered later as a part of the phosphorus cycle.

It is estimated that a unit level of production of soft-shelled clams and of blue mussel each requires 10 units of detritus. Again, one unit (pound) of detritus is taken to be produced by the mortality of one unit (pound) of marine plant. It was also estimated that the production of a pound of soft-shelled clams requires .000033 acres of muddy and sandy estuary bottom, while the production of a pound of blue mussel requires .000042 acres of estuary bottom, either firm or solid material.

The food chain requirements for soft-shelled clam and blue mussel production are shown in activity analysis format in Table 3.6e. For further information on the derivation of the data, see Appendix B.

Table 3.6e Food Chain for Shellfish Production in Activity Analysis Format

Classification Number	Commodity	Units	PMX 6001 Detritus Production	PMX 716 Soft-Shelled Clam Production	PMX 714 Blue Mussel Production
MX 51	Muddy and sandy bottom area	acres		-33×10^{-6}	
MX 52	Firm Estuary bottom or solid material	,,			-42×10^{-6}
MX 6001	Detritus	lb.	+1	−10	−10
MX 716	Soft-shelled clam	,,		+1	
MX 714	Blue mussel	,,			+1

3.6.5 Estimating Coefficients in Phytoplankton Production: the Relationships of a Producer Organism to the Abiotic Environment

(a) Phytoplankton Production Equation

As already mentioned, food chain studies relate various levels of consumer organisms to their ultimate plant food sources. It is the purpose of this section to describe the derivation of the coefficients showing the relationships between a producer organism and the abiotic conditions of its environment. Although detritus from land, shallow water plants, and algae provide significant food sources in Continental Shelf and estuarine situations such as Plymouth Bay, phytoplankton is acknowledged as the main producer plant in the marine regions.

Riley, Stommel, and Bumpus[13] point out that the abundance and seasonal distribution of both phytoplankton and zooplankton in any region can be fairly closely predicted by means of a formula based on certain important limiting factors of the environment and physiological coefficients determined from labora-

[13] Riley, Stommel, and Bumpus [8].

tory experimentation. In simplified and non-mathematical form the formula they devised for estimating phytoplankton production is as follows:

rate of change of phytoplankton (density per unit time)	=	rate of photo-synthesis	−	rate of respir-ation	−	rate of "grazing" (loss to herbivores)	−	rate of sinking below eu-photic zone

Mathematical equations are developed to explain this distribution. The authors point out that these equations are essentially in agreement with the facts and have as their basis the assumptions that (1) any marine population is quantitatively controlled by the processes that increase or decrease the organic content of the population, and (2) the rates of the processes are determined by a complex of environmental factors that acts by affecting the physiology of the organisms and their physical dispersal.

Photosynthesis was found to be limited by, and therefore largely a function of, temperature, light, and phosphate concentration. Respiration is largely determined by temperature. The zooplankton "grazing pressure" was determined from data obtained in laboratory cultures and knowledge of the concentration of herbivores. Although the computation is complex, the loss, if any, from the sinking of phytoplankton plant cells below the euphotic zone (the depth below which light is ineffective for plant growth) can be determined from physical oceanographic data. In general, observations were within 25 percent of the values predicted. This is regarded as remarkably close considering the complexity of the situation.[14]

From this work on the quantitative ecology of plankton, it is possible to derive coefficients relating the environmental factors and the growth of plankton which can be used in the interrelations matrix. The following material deals with the derivation of these coefficients. The non-mathematical formula for estimating the production of phytoplankton is stated by Riley, Stommel, and Bumpus in equation form as:

$$\frac{dP}{dt} = P\,(P_h - R_p - G) \qquad \text{Equation } 1^{15}$$

in which the rate of change of the total population P depends on the coefficients of photosynthesis P_h, respiration R_p, and grazing G. Relating these physiological coefficients to environmental conditions yields the equation:

$$\frac{dP}{dt} = P\left[\frac{KI_o}{kL}(1-e^{-kL})\ A''V_p - R'e^{sT} - WH\right] \qquad \text{Equation } 2^{16}$$

in which P_h of equation (1) $= \dfrac{KI_o}{kL}(1-e^{-kL})A''V_p$

R_p of equation (1) $= R'e^{sT}$
and G of equation (1) $= WH$

Equation 2 contains six fundamental environmental factors: (1) incident solar radiation, I_o; (2) the extinction coefficient for the penetration of visible light, k; (3) temperature, T; (4) the total quantity of herbivorous zooplankton, H; (5) the quantity of phosphate; and (6) the depth of the mixed layer. The last two factors do not appear in the equation *per se* but are used to determine derived values; namely, V_p, which is the ratio of actual phosphorus (as phosphate concentration) to that level of phosphorus (as phosphate concentration) which when exceeded has no further positive effect on phytoplankton production; and A'', which is that proportion of the phytoplankton which is net loss due to the sinking of the phyto-

[14] Odum [7], p. 335.
[15] Equation numbers are those used in the monograph by Riley, Stommel, and Bumpus [8].
[16] *Ibid.*

plankton below the euphotic zone. Another derived value, L, is defined as the depth at which the mean radiation is 0.0015 gm. cal. per cm^2 per min. (approximately 0.5 per cent of the radiation at the surface in the summer). Certain constants were derived: the photosynthetic constant, K; the coefficient of respiration at 0°C, R'; the coefficient of the increase in the respiratory rate with temperature, s; and the grazing constant, W. Thus equation 2 completely restates equation 1 in a way that enables physiological coefficients to be calculated numerically from the environmental data.

In computing the coefficients for phytoplankton production for activity analysis format we have separated equation 1

$$\frac{dP}{dt} = P\,(P_h - R_p - G)$$

into 3 parts: (1) the gross production of phytoplankton matter by photosynthesis; (2) the loss of phytoplankton matter due to respiration (which may be regarded as a phytoplankton maintenance cost); and (3) the loss of phytoplankton matter due to grazing by zooplankton. The third part, namely zooplankton grazing of phytoplankton, corresponds to the production of zooplankton and thus is a food chain relationship, dependent on the availability of phytoplankton. Accordingly, phytoplankton are treated as an input to the production of zooplankton, to be indicated by a negative coefficient in the row for phytoplankton and the column for zooplankton.

(b) Gross Production of Phytoplankton by Photosynthesis

The gross phytoplankton production by photosynthesis (designated as Q) equals its photosynthetic coefficient (P_h) times the quantity of phytoplankton present (P). That is:

$$Q = P \times P_h \qquad \text{Equation } 3^{17}$$

P is the quantity of phytoplankton present in the column of ocean water under each square meter of ocean surface. That is, P is the grams of phytoplankton carbon in a column of ocean water the surface of which is 1 square meter in area and the depth of which extends to the limit of the euphotic zone, or that depth beyond which light penetration is not effective in producing photosynthesis. Henceforth, P will be expressed in grams of phytoplankton carbon per square meter, with the implicit understanding that it relates to the column just described. P_h is the photosynthetic coefficient and is expressed as the grams of phytoplankton carbon produced per day per gram of phytoplankton population. Therefore, the gross phytoplankton production is expressed as grams of phytoplankton carbon produced per day per square meter.

The gross production of phytoplankton by photosynthesis is further developed into the expression

$$Q = P\left[\frac{KI_o}{kL}\,(1-e^{-kL})V_p\right] \qquad \text{Equation 4}$$

which relates gross phytoplankton production to its environmental factors. Notice that the expression in the brackets is from the first part of equation (2) if we ignore losses due to phytoplankton sinking below the euphotic zone. That is, we assume that the reduction factor, A'', is equal to unity. This assumption is felt to be justifiable in the shallow water situation of the case study area.

It will be seen that the output depends on the level of existing phytoplankton population, P; incident solar (surface) radiation, I_o; relative phosphate concentration, V_p; and the extinction coefficient for the penetration of visible light, k. All these are regarded as variable in principle, but in order to estimate interrelations

[17] This equation number and the following refer solely to this report.

coefficients, we assume typical values for each except that one whose coefficient is being estimated.

To estimate the coefficients, we have derived the following values for the parameters of equation 4 from the data presented in Riley, Stommel, and Bumpus. We chose values which, as far as it was possible to determine, were applicable to the Plymouth Bay Area. (These values can be modified as more accurate data are assembled.)

$K = 2.5$ (Riley, Stommel, and Bumpus, p. 44)
$k = .13$ (Riley, Stommel, and Bumpus, p. 11)
$I_o = 0.2$ gm. cal. per cm^2 per min. (Riley, Stommel, and Bumpus, p. 10)
$L = 41$ meters (derived from $I_z = I_o e^{-kz}$)[18]
$V_p = \frac{.16}{.55} = .30$, where the concentration of phosphorus (as phosphate) is taken to be .16 mg. of atomic phosphorus per m^3 during the winter months (Riley, Stommel, and Bumpus, p. 17) and where .55 is the level of concentration of phosphorus (as phosphate) beyond which higher concentration has no effect on phytoplankton growth.
$P = 3.98$ gm. C per m^2

P has been derived from the three surface phytoplankton concentrations of the Coastal and Slope Water areas listed on page 45 of Riley, Stommel, and Bumpus. These were averaged and multiplied by the depth of the euphotic zone, L, to give the total phytoplankton in the euphotic zone under 1 square meter of ocean surface. It is assumed that the vertical distribution of phytoplankton is uniform.

Using these values for the parameters of equation 4, one can then estimate the input-output coefficients. If the input and output for a unit area are computed, the ratio of the input to output will yield the input-output coefficient. When the numerical values for the parameters given above are inserted into equation 4

$$Q = 3.98\left[\frac{(2.5)\,(0.2)}{(.13)\,(41)}(1 - e^{-(.13)(41)})\,(0.3)\right].$$

Taking $e^{-5.33}$ to be zero, Q is approximately .1120 grams of carbon per day per square meter. The ratios: P/Q, I_o/Q, k/Q and V_p/Q were then estimated.

$$\frac{P}{Q} = \frac{3.98}{.1120} = 35.54$$

$$\frac{I_o}{Q} = \frac{0.2}{.1120} = 1.79$$

$$\frac{k}{Q} = \frac{0.13}{.1120} = 1.16$$

[18] The symbol k represents the extinction coefficient of light in seawater; i.e., the proportion of the light entering a layer of water 1 meter thick which is absorbed in that layer. Then, if I_z is the intensity of radiation at a depth z, we have

$$k = -\frac{dI_z}{dz}\,/I_z$$

so that

$$I_z = \frac{1}{k}\Big/ -\frac{dI_z}{dz}$$

Hence

$$I_z = I_o e^{-kL}$$

The depth below which light penetration is not effective in producing photosynthesis is known as the limit of the euphotic zone. This depth is designated by the symbol L and is defined as the depth at which the mean daily radiation I is .0015 gm. cal. per cm^2 per min.
Therefore, at depth L

$$I_L = I_o e^{-kL}$$

$$.0015 = (.2)e^{-(.13)(L)}$$

$$L = 41 \text{ meters}$$

$$\frac{V_p}{Q} = \frac{0.3}{.1120} = 2.68$$

The third ratio describes the relationship between the extinction coefficient for the penetration of visible light, k, to the production of phytoplankton Q. However, unlike P, I_o, and V_p in which an increase in these variables results in an increase in the output, it can be seen from equation 4 that an increase in k results in a decrease in phytoplankton Q. This relationship raises a problem in developing an appropriate coefficient to be placed in the phytoplankton production column in a table in which it is understood that an increase in an input level is associated with an increase in output. The extinction coefficient for the penetration of visible light, k, is a measurement describing the transparency of water; that is, an increased value of k indicates a reduced transparency of the water, and thereby a reduced quantity of effective light and decreased production of phytoplankton. In order to enter a coefficient describing a direct relationship between water transparency and the production of phytoplankton into the table, we let t, designating water transparency, be equal to $1/k$. We then estimate the ratio Q to be:

$$\frac{t}{Q} = \frac{1/k}{Q} = \frac{1/.13}{.1120} = 68.68$$

We thus have a quantitative relationship between water transparency and phytoplankton in which an increase in t results in an increase in phytoplankton production.

The fourth ratio is not an input-output coefficient, because it merely associates a phytoplankton output magnitude with a ratio.[19] But this is not what we are interested in. Rather, we are interested in the *quantity* of phosphorus present as phosphate. If the amount of atomic phosphorus in phosphate per cubic meter is 0.16 mg., and the euphotic zone is 41 meters deep, then there are 41×0.16 mg. or 6.56 mg. or .0066 gm. of phosphorus as phosphate in an area of 1 square meter in the euphotic zone. Thus the coefficient for phosphorus [in the form of phosphate] in grams per unit area is

$$\frac{.0066}{.1120} = .0589$$

The coefficient of approximately 35.54 for the number of units of phytoplankton required to produce one unit of phytoplankton illustrates a problem which may arise with an excessively rigid application of input-output methodology. In fact, 1 gram of phytoplankton is produced daily for every 35.54 grams of phytoplankton present, so that, using the normal definition of input-output coefficients, a coefficient of 35.54 is derived. However, the 35.54 grams of phytoplankton are not consumed; a stock of this size is simply required to permit the production of the additional gram. This phytoplankton stock requirement is illustrated in Table 3.6f by placing both a plus and a minus in front of the phytoplankton stock coefficient. The usual use of input-output techniques for projection purposes implies that the necessary inputs are consumed in the production process; where this is not so, the projection techniques must be modified. Furthermore, the coefficients for incident radiation and phosphorus (as phosphate) concentration similarly imply that a certain quantity of radiation must fall on the water and that a certain quantity of phosphorus must be present for a particular amount of phytoplankton to be produced; the coefficients do not imply that these quantities are necessarily used up.

On account of these difficulties in interpreting input-output coefficients in the case of the strictly ecological relationships, we consider that, for our purposes,

[19] Recall that V_p is defined as the ratio of an actual concentration of phosphorus (as phosphate) to that concentration of phosphorus (as phosphate) beyond which there is no further effect on phytoplankton growth.

partial derivatives of equation 4 may be at least as useful and relevant as pure input-output coefficients. These partial derivatives are:

$$\frac{\delta Q}{\delta P} = I_o K V_p \frac{1}{kL}(1-e^{-kL})$$

$$\frac{\delta Q}{\delta I_o} = PKV_p \frac{1}{kL}(1-e^{-kL})$$

$$\frac{\delta Q}{\delta(\text{phosphorus})} = PI_o K \frac{1}{.55kL}(1-e^{-kL})$$

$$\frac{\delta Q}{\delta k} = PI_o KV_p \frac{1}{k^2 L}(1-e^{-kL}-kLe^{-kL})$$

Inserting the numerical values previously derived for the Plymouth Bay area into these partial derivative expressions yields the following values:

$\frac{\delta Q}{\delta P}$ = .0281 gm. C per day per gm. C of the existing population

$\frac{\delta Q}{\delta I_o}$ = .5600 gm. C per day per gm. cal. per cm² per min. of surface radiation

$\frac{\delta Q}{\delta(\text{phosphorus})}$ = .6788 gm. C per day per mg. at. P conc. per m³ up to the concentration of .55 mg. at./m³

$\frac{\delta Q}{\delta k}$ = −.8615 gm. C per day per % increase in the extinction coefficient

Table 3.6f Gross Production of Phytoplankton by Photosynthesis

Classification Number	Commodity	Units	Process PMX 61-14 Gross Phytoplankton Production by Photosynthesis
MX 11	Light: incident solar radiation at ocean surface	gm. cal. per cm² per min.	−1.79
MX 420	Phosphorus (as dissolved phosphate): in ocean water below 0.55 mg. at. per m³	mg. at. per m²	−0.06
MX 420	Phosphorus (as dissolved phosphate): in ocean water above 0.55 mg. at. per m³	mg. at. per m²	−0.00
MX 44	Water transparency: $t = 1/k$		−68.68
MX 61–12	Phytoplankton: existing population stock	gm. C per m²	±35.54
MX 61–14	Phytoplankton produced by photosynthesis	gm. C per m² per day	+1.00

It will be noted that the partial derivatives of phytoplankton production with respect to P, I_o, and k are all simply the reciprocals of the input-output coefficients. This is because the expressions for the partial derivatives are exactly the same as equation 4 for Q divided by I_o, P, and k, respectively. (In the last case, this is an approximation, obtained by assuming e^{-kL} to be equal to zero.) This identity between the input-output coefficients and the reciprocals of the partial derivatives, means that, for the variables concerned, average and marginal requirements are the same, so that there is no practical difference between using input-output coefficients and using interrelationship coefficients derived from partial derivatives. However, pure input-output coefficients have implications which the latter interrelationship coefficients do not have; hence, the latter may be considered preferable. For the present, however, until further research is conducted, we continue to use the pure input-output coefficients.

The coefficients for the gross production of phytoplankton by photosynthesis are presented in input-output format in Table 3.6f.

(c) Phytoplankton Matter Loss due to Respiration

The phytoplankton loss due to respiration (designated as D_r) equals the phytoplankton's respiratory coefficient (R_p) times the quantity of phytoplankton present (P). That is:

$$D_r = P \cdot R_p$$

The quantity of phytoplankton present, P, is expressed in grams of phytoplankton carbon per square meter; and the phytoplankton respiratory coefficient, R_p, is expressed as the grams of phytoplankton carbon consumed per day per gram of phytoplankton carbon. Therefore, the phytoplankton matter loss is expressed as grams of phytoplankton carbon consumed per day per square meter.

The phytoplankton matter loss due to respiration is further developed into the expression

$$D_r = P[R'e^{sT}]$$

The expression inside the brackets (the respiratory coefficient) corresponds to the second term within the brackets in equation 2 of Riley, Stommel, and Bumpus. The respiratory loss depends on the level of the existing phytoplankton population, P, and temperature, T. R', S, and e are constants.

The values for the variables P and T are again derived or taken from Riley, Stommel, and Bumpus.

$P = 3.98$ gm. C per m^2 (as derived previously)
$T = 2°$ to $17°$C (Plymouth Bay area; Riley, Stommel, and Bumpus, pp. 13–14)
$R' = 0.0175$ (Riley, Stommel, and Bumpus, p. 55)
$e = 2.7183$
$S = 0.069$ (Riley, Stommel, and Bumpus, p. 55)

Using these values we would like to compute the interrelations coefficients. However, respiratory loss of a given phytoplankton population is not independent of temperature. The respiratory loss of a given phytoplankton population increases exponentially with temperature. Therefore, a single coefficient on respiratory loss cannot be derived. One way of handling this problem is to derive coefficients for respiratory loss at several temperatures. Therefore, at a known temperature, the quantitative relationship between phytoplankton abundance and phytoplankton utilized in respiration can be established.

Water temperature in our case study area ranges roughly from 2°C to 17°C.

Hence, the coefficients which express the grams carbon of phytoplankton consumed in respiration per day per gram carbon of phytoplankton matter are:

$$\frac{D_r}{P} @ 2^\circ = \frac{P[R'e^{2s}]}{P} = .0201$$

$$\frac{D_r}{P} @ 7^\circ = \frac{P[R'e^{7s}]}{P} = .0281$$

$$\frac{D_r}{P} @ 12^\circ = \frac{P[R'e^{12s}]}{P} = .0400$$

$$\frac{D_r}{P} @ 17^\circ = \frac{P[R'e^{17s}]}{P} = .0565$$

These coefficients are presented in activity analysis format in Table 3.6g.[20]

Table 3.6g Utilization of Phytoplankton Matter by Respiration

Classi-fication Number	Commodity	Units	Process: Utilization of Phytoplankton Matter by Respiration P1MX 61-15 @ 2°C	P2MX 61-15 @ 7°C	P3MX 61-15 @ 12°C	P4MX 61-15 @ 17°C
MX 61–13	Phytoplankton (as consumed in respiration)	gm. C per m²	−.0201	−.0281	−.0400	−.0565
MX 61–15	Phytoplankton (as maintained after respiration)	gm. C per m² per day	+1.00	+1.00	+1.00	+1.00

(d) Herbivorous Zooplankton Production

As mentioned previously, the production of zooplankton is treated as a plant herbivore food chain relationship, dependent on the availability of phytoplankton. Herbivorous zooplankton are largely filter-feeding organisms, filtering phytoplankton from the water as their food source. Hedgpeth[21] estimates herbivorous zooplankton daily percentage increase by weight (designated g_H) at 10, and their daily percentage loss by respiration (designated r_H) at 4. Therefore, herbivorous zooplankton can assimilate 14 percent $(g_H + r_H)$ of their weight daily and the percentage of the food assimilated which can be built into new tissue is roughly 70 percent $\left(\frac{100\, g_H}{g_H + r_H}\right)$. These data thus suggest that the phytoplankton input per unit production of herbivorous zooplankton is 100/70 = 1.4.

The percentages developed above are for phytoplankton food assimilated by the zooplankton. Normally, when phytoplankton is scarce, the total quantity of ingested phytoplankton is assimilated by the zooplankton; but when phytoplankton are abundant, such as during a phytoplankton spring flowering, much food is wasted. This surplus food is eliminated in the form of fecal matter and partially assimilated plant matter which supply part of the requirements of many of the bottom-dwelling organisms. This phytoplankton detritus is therefore also a product of zooplankton grazing, and represents the difference between the total amount of phytoplankton that the zooplankton filter and the amount of phytoplankton that the zooplankton assimilate.

[20] Strictly speaking, the +1.00 output corresponding to commodity *MX* 61-15 should be replaced by the positive amounts of Btu. and other commodities which are the outcomes (outputs) of phytoplankton matter utilization in respiration.

[21] Hedgpeth [3], p. 39.

Riley, Stommel, and Bumpus indicate that as long as physical conditions remain constant, herbivorous zooplankton tend to filter a constant volume of water per unit time regardless of the quantity of phytoplankton in the water. Thus a grazing constant, W, can be defined as the ratio of the volume of water filtered per unit time per unit zooplankton to the volume of water contained in the column of 1 square meter of ocean surface. (This column is the unit volume used for recording phytoplankton population.) Thus the factor G in equation 1 of Riley, Stommel, and Bumpus, which represents the fraction of the phytoplankton population consumed in unit time by the herbivore zooplankton population H, may be stated as WH. Stating the relation in the converse way, the amount of phytoplankton consumed in unit time by a unit quantity of zooplankton is WP. (Recall that P is the phytoplankton population contained in the column of 1 square meter of ocean surface.) Furthermore, if the zooplankton assimilated all the food they consume, WP would equal the assimilation rate A_H. However, when the ingested phytoplankton exceeds the amount assimilated, it is better to state

$$A_H = W(P-P')$$

where P' is the amount of phytoplankton that is consumed but not assimilated, or the amount of phytoplankton detritus produced by zooplankton grazing. It then follows that

$$P' = \frac{WP-A_H}{W}$$

If we insert in this formula our present data, we should arrive at a value for P', the phytoplankton detritus produced by zooplankton grazing, measured in grams carbon per square meter.

We have

$$P = 3.98 \text{ gm. C of phytoplankton per m}^2$$
(as previously defined and derived)

$$g_H = 10\%$$
$$r_H = 4\%$$

For New England coastal waters, Riley, Stommel, and Bumpus (p. 145) have found the zooplankton population to be 16.6×10^{-9} grams carbon per cubic centimeter; that is

$$16.6 \times 10^{-3} \text{ grams carbon per cubic meter}$$

If we make the simplifying assumption (as in Riley, Stommel, and Bumpus, p. 109) that the phytoplankton and zooplankton each have a uniform vertical distribution, the maximum depth of which coincides with the depth of the euphotic zone (designated as L), and if $L = 41$ meters as previously derived, then

$$H = (16.6 \times 10^{-3})\,(41) = .68 \text{ gm. C per m}^2$$

Since A_H is the assimilation rate of zooplankton in grams carbon consumed per unit zooplankton per unit time it is seen that

$$A_H = (g_H + r_H)\,(H)$$

Therefore $A_H = (.10+.04)\,(.68) = .095$ grams carbon consumed per square meter of zooplankton population per day.

The grazing constant, W, has been defined as the ratio of the volume of water filtered per unit time per unit zooplankton to the volume of water contained in the column of 1 square meter of ocean surface. Then, postulating the case in which the phytoplankton and zooplankton each have a uniform vertical distribution, the maximum depth of which coincides with the depth of the euphotic zone, the grazing constant, W, may be designated by

$$W = \frac{W'}{L}$$

in which L (as previously stated) is the length of a column of water of unit area extending to the lower limit of the euphotic zone, and W' is the length of a column of similar surface area filtered by a unit quantity of zooplankton in unit time.[22]

The filtering action of the herbivorous zooplankton population is assumed by Riley, Stommel, and Bumpus (p. 109) to vary with their respiration rate.[23] They have developed a filtering factor, w, in which

$$w = (23.5 \times 10^6)R_H$$

where w is cubic centimeters of water filtered and R_H is grams carbon used up in the respiration process per unit time by any given quantity of zooplankton.

Hedgpeth has estimated that the daily loss by zooplankton respiration is about 4 percent of their weight.[24]

$R_H = (.04)\,(H) = (.04)\,(.68) = .03$ gm. C per m^2 column of zooplankton per day

Therefore, $w = (23.5)\,(.03)\,(10^6) = .71 \times 10^6$ cc. water filtered by 1 square meter column of zooplankton population per day

Or $w = .71$ cubic meter of water filtered by 1 square meter column of zooplankton population per day

Hence, $W' = .71$ meter (a column of water 1 square meter in area and 0.71 meter deep)

and, if $W = \dfrac{W'}{L}$, $W = \dfrac{.71}{41} = .017$

Therefore, if $P' = \dfrac{WP - A_H}{W}$

$$P' = \frac{(.017)\,(3.98) - .095}{.017}$$

or

$$P' = \frac{.067 - .095}{.017}$$

which is less than zero. This is impossible. Assuming our data are correct, P, the phytoplankton population, and H, the zooplankton population, are known values; and the zooplankton respiration is assumed to be maintained, thereby fixing the grazing constant. Hence, the variable which must change is the growth of the new zooplankton matter, g_H; and P' must equal zero.

Substituting $(g_H + r_H)H$ for A_H, we have

$$\begin{aligned} H\,(g_H + r_H) &= WP - WP' \\ .68\,(g_H + .04) &= .017\,(3.98) - .017\,(0) \\ .68 g_H &= .067 - .027 \\ g_H &= .059 \end{aligned}$$

Therefore, for a phytoplankton population of 3.98 grams carbon per square meter and a zooplankton population of .68 grams carbon per square meter, the daily percentage increase by weight of herbivorous zooplankton is 5.9.

This result suggests a change in the estimation of the phytoplankton input needed for unit production of zooplankton since this input coefficient depends on the percentage of assimilated food which is built into new tissue; that is $\left(\dfrac{100\,g_H}{g_H + r_H}\right)$. This new percentage, at $g_H = .059$ and $r_H = .04$, is 59 percent. Therefore, the phytoplankton input per unit level of zooplankton production is $100/59 = 1.7$, for our case study situation of a phytoplankton population of 3.98 grams carbon per

[22] Riley, Stommel, and Bumpus [8], p. 109. [23] *Ibid.*, p. 127. [24] Hedgpeth [3].

square meter, and a zooplankton population of .68 grams carbon per square meter.

The coefficients for the phytoplankton requirements for zooplankton production are presented in activity analysis format in Table 3.6h.

Table 3.6h Phytoplankton Requirements for Zooplankton Production

Classification Number	Commodity	Units	Process PMX 711 Food Consumption by Zooplankton
MX 61–11	Phytoplankton @ 3.98 gm. C per m^2	grams	−1.7
MX 711	Zooplankton @ .68 gm. C per m^2	grams	+1.00

3.6.6 Plankton Production as a Combination of Phytoplankton and Zooplankton

According to the section on the cod production food chain, one of the cod's direct food inputs, herring, requires inputs of plankton for its production. Plankton is a generalized expression for the mixture of phytoplankton and zooplankton in the ocean. Hence, having derived the production coefficients for phytoplankton and zooplankton, we should be able to relate these coefficients to plankton production (availability) and thereby to the cod food chain relationships. First, however, the units of measurement must be made consistent, for while in Table 3.6d plankton production is expressed in pounds, in Table 3.6h phytoplankton production is expressed in grams carbon. In order to convert a unit weight of phytoplankton in grams carbon to a unit weight of phytoplankton in pounds, we need to know the percentage of carbon in phytoplankton organic matter. Riley, Stommel, and Bumpus discuss this conversion problem with reference to estimating phytoplankton abundance by colorimetric measurement of the pigment content of the phytoplankton cells. They state, "The result was an average estimate of 0.035 mg. of phytoplankton organic matter per unit of plant pigments. . . . On this basis it was further estimated that the carbon content would average about 0.017 mg. per pigment unit. In the paper that follows the latter will be used frequently as a convenient conversion factor."[25]

If we accept the statement that there is 0.035 mg. of phytoplankton organic matter per unit of pigment and 0.017 mg. of carbon content per unit of pigment, we may take phytoplankton organic matter to be roughly 50 percent carbon. With this percentage factor we can create a "dummy" row and column in the activity analysis table, Table 3.6i, which enables us to convert grams of phytoplankton carbon to pounds of phytoplankton in dry weight. For every unit output of phytoplankton in grams, we can state an input of 0.50 phytoplankton in grams carbon. And knowing that there are 454 grams in a pound, we can further state that for every unit output of phytoplankton in pounds, we require an input of 227 units of phytoplankton in grams carbon. Thus we obtain rows and columns for phytoplankton in the common unit, the pound. Likewise, using the relationship in Table 3.6h, we can express zooplankton in the common unit, the pound.

Next we need to state the mixture of phytoplankton and zooplankton which can

[25] Riley, Stommel, and Bumpus [8], p. 27.

Table 3.6i Plankton, Phytoplankton and Zooplankton Production

Classification Number	Commodity	Units	Process: PMX 61-14 Gross Phytoplankton Production by Photosynthesis	Utilization of Phytoplankton Matter by Respiration: P1MX 61-15 @ 2°C	P2MX 61-15 @ 7°C	P3MX 61-15 @ 12°C	P4MX 61-15 @ 17°C	PMX 61-11 Phytoplankton in Pounds (Dummy Unit Conversion Process)	PMX 61-10 Plankton	PMX 711 Food Consumption by Zooplankton
MX 11	Solar radiation	gm. cal. per cm^2 per min.	−1.79							
MX 420	Phosphorous (as phosphate) in ocean water below 0.55 mg. at. per m^3	mg. at. per m^2	−0.06							
MX 42	Phosphorous (as phosphate) in ocean water above 0.55 mg. at. per m^3	mg. at. per m^2	−0.00							
MX 44	Water transparency: $t = 1/k$		−68.68							
MX 61–11	Phytoplankton @ 3.98 gm. C per m^2	lb.						+1.00	−0.86	−1.7
MX 61–12	Phytoplankton stock	gm. C per m^2	±35.54							
MX 61–13	Phytoplankton (as consumed in respiration)	gm. C per m^2		−.0201	−.0281	−.0400	−.0565			
MX 61–14	Phytoplankton (as produced by photosynthesis)	gm. C per m^2 per day	+ 1.00					−227		
MX 61–15	Phytoplankton (as maintained after respiration)	gm. C per m^2 per day		+1.00	+1.00	+1.00	+1.00			
MX 61–10	Plankton	lb.							+1.00	
MX 711	Zooplankton @ .68 gm. C per m^2	lb.							−0.14	+1.00

be taken to comprise a unit output of plankton. If we know that the amount of phytoplankton under 1 square meter of ocean surface in the Plymouth Bay region is 3.98 grams carbon (refer to the value of P above) and that the zooplankton population is 0.68 grams carbon per square meter (refer to the value of H, above) then we can calculate that for a unit level of plankton production, which corresponds to the output of 1 gram of plankton, we need inputs of 0.86 gram of phytoplankton and 0.14 gram of zooplankton. Hence, we are able to relate the production of phytoplankton and zooplankton, combined as plankton, to the production of cod through its food chain requirements. The production of phytoplankton and zooplankton and their combination as plankton is summarized in activity analysis format in Table 3.6i.

3.6.7 The Phosphorus Cycle

Thus far we have been concerned with the food chain relationships of certain marine organisms which are considered useful to man. We have related their production quantitatively to the availability of previous levels of food animals and finally to the availability of the basic animal food, green plants. We also have described roughly the quantitative relationship between the availability of key components of the abiotic environment and the production of a marine green plant, phytoplankton.

The study of ecosystems, or regions with their living and non-living parts, may be approached not only from the consideration of the organisms, but also from that of the abiotic environment. In other words, we may study not only organisms in their environmental relationships, but also the basic non-living environment in relation to organisms. Of the 90 odd elements known to occur in nature, between 30 and 40 are known to be required by living organisms. Some elements such as carbon, hydrogen, oxygen, and nitrogen are needed in large quantities; others are needed in small, or even minute, quantities. Whatever the need may be, essential elements (as well as non-essential elements) appear to have definite biogeochemical cycles. That is, as mentioned in Section 3.4, there are chemical elements which circulate in the biosphere in diverse paths from the environment to organisms and back to the environment.

Materials move from the environment into the bodies of plants and animals as the latter grow, return to the environment when plants and animals die and decompose, and in some instances undergo complicated transformations and translocations in the environment before they are again taken up by living organisms. These abiotic materials are not equally abundant in the different phases of their cycles, nor do the various steps take place at uniform rates. Biogeochemical investigations have shown that materials of critical concern to plants and animals may accumulate in certain places which represent points of stagnation in the cycles. Nutrient substances may thus be withdrawn from circulation for long or short periods of time. A relatively temporary stagnation is represented by the organic matter in the soil or on the bottom mud of water bodies. The nutrient minerals contained in this organic matter are unavailable for plant growth until the material decomposes. In many soils this retardation of the cycle is beneficial because the formation of humus in the soil has valuable physical effects in addition to providing a slow, steady release of nutrients.

The gradual accumulation of nutrient materials in the deep sea is an example of a long-term stagnation of the nutrient cycles. The many cubic miles of peat, lignite, and coal buried in the earth's crust represent stagnations in the carbon cycle for hundreds of millions of years. A similar stagnation in the calcium cycle is represented by the deposits of chalk, limestone, and coral material.

Great differences exist in the total supply of the various building materials

Chart 3.6c Flow Diagram of the Phosphorus Cycle

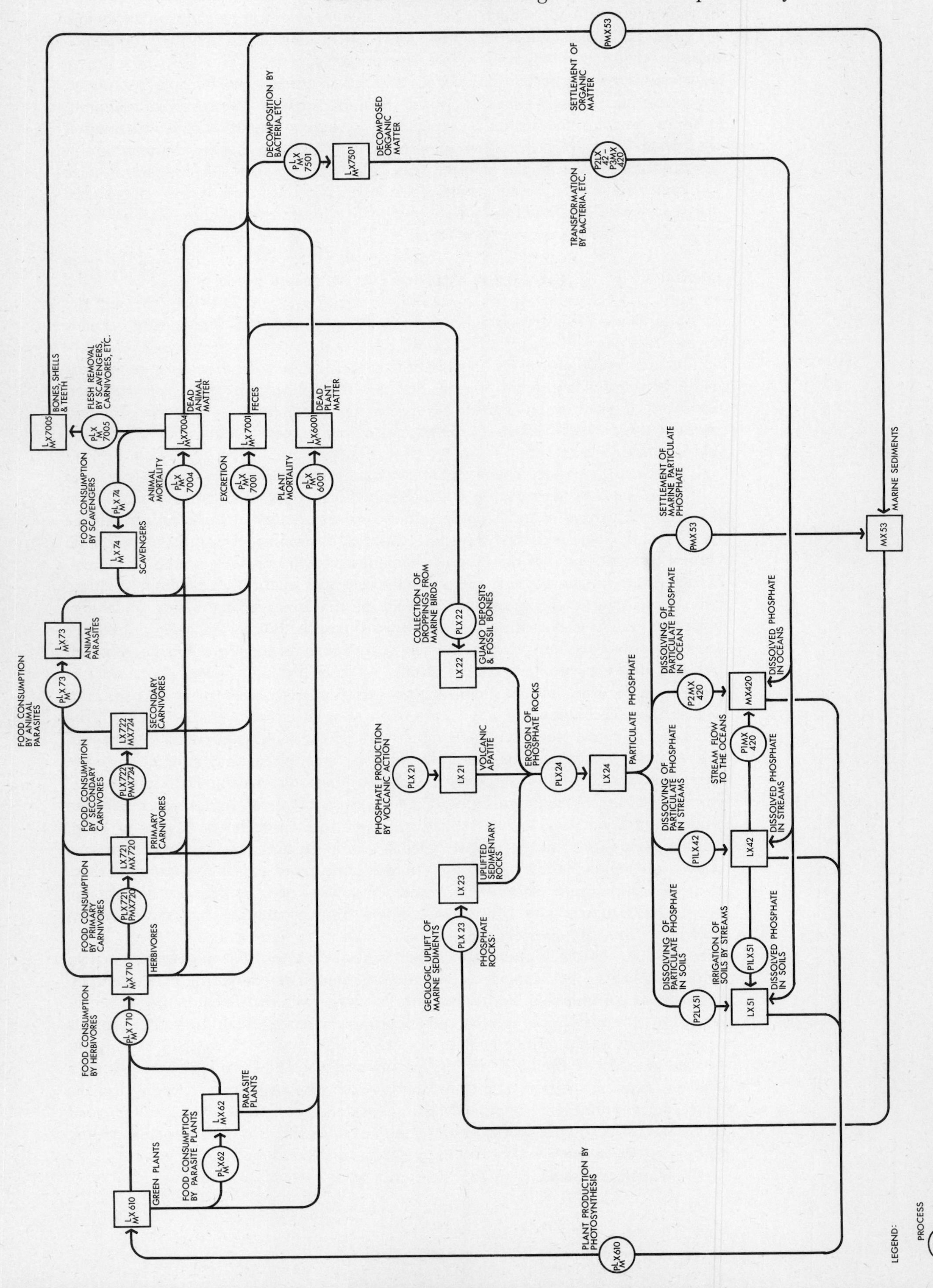

needed by plants and animals as well as in their availability. When stoppages occur in the cycles of elements likely to be scarce in *available* form, such as nitrogen and phosphorus, critical conditions may arise. An inexhaustible supply of nitrogen exists in the earth's atmosphere, but this represents a reservoir that can be drawn upon only slowly by certain physical and biological agents. Phosphorus, in contrast, is a rare material; only about $\frac{1}{700}$ of the earth's crust is composed of this element. A supply of phosphate from the rocks and deep sea sediments can be obtained at only a very slow rate. The most ready sources of phosphorus are the products of decomposition of the bodies of organisms. Therefore, study of the phosphorus cycle not only establishes linkages between regions, environmental components, and organisms but also provides knowledge of critical points in the environment which may limit plant and animal production.

Chart 3.6c is a flow diagram of the phosphorus cycle.[26] A main part of the cycle illustrates the flow of phosphorus from the dissolved phosphate in the soils, streams, and seawater to plants and animals by absorption, and then, through the decomposition of these plants and animals, back to the soils, streams, and oceans as dissolved phosphate.

Phosphorus as phosphate is involved in organic matter first by green plants through the photosynthetic process. Its involvement in animals is accomplished first by the consumption of plant matter by herbivores and plant scavengers, and through the consumption of these animals by successive levels of other animals (carnivores). This sequence of consumption of organic matter originally synthesized by plants through successive levels of animals is a food chain.

The release of the phosphorus that has been built into the bodies of plants and animals involves two steps: first, the organic matter must be *decomposed* into soluble form and subsequently into inorganic form, and second, the resulting inorganic material must be *transformed* into compounds which can be absorbed by green plants. Living organisms are required to carry out practically every one of these steps of decomposition and transformation. Fungi are especially active in decomposing organic matter on land; bacteria are prominent in damp soil and in the water environment. These microorganisms not only work on the surfaces of solid material but also attack dissolved organic matter.

This cycle, as it involves phosphorus being either locked up in organisms or available as dissolved phosphate, is not one hundred percent efficient. Some of the phosphorus in organic material is eroded from the land and washed by streams into the sea where part of it is deposited in the shallow sediments and part is lost to the deep sediments; in the latter case it is taken out of use for organic production.

The reservoirs of phosphorus for the cycle are the rocks and other deposits which have been formed in past geological periods. These are gradually eroding, releasing phosphates to the ecosystem, as well as to the ocean sediments. The means of returning phosphorus to the cycle may presently be inadequate to compensate for the loss. Because of gradual loss of phosphorus, to the deep sea sediments, actions by man and natural organisms to maintain phosphorus within the system may be extremely important.

The phosphorus flow diagram has also been transformed into linkage matrix form. See Table 3.6j. In this table, a format is adopted which distinguishes between *commodities* and *processes* as discussed in Section 3.5.1. Each commodity is represented by a row. Each process is represented by a column. Each process has inputs and outputs of commodities, though in general, a process will have only one output. Each commodity may be produced by one or more processes. An output of a process is indicated by a + in the column corresponding to the process, and the row corresponding to the commodity produced. An input to a process is indicated by a − in the column corresponding to the process and in the row corresponding to the commodity being used in the operation of the process.

[26] Adapted from Odum [7], p. 34.

Table 3.6j The Phosphorus Cycle in Linkage Matrix Format

			CLASSIFICATION NUMBER	COMMODITY \ PROCESS	PLX 21 PHOSPHATE PRODUCTION BY VOLCANIC ACTION	PLX 24 EROSION OF PHOSPHATE ROCKS	P1LX 42 DISSOLVING OF PHOSPHATES IN STREAMS	P1LX 51 IRRIGATION OF SOILS BY STREAMS	P1MX 420 STREAM FLOW OF DISSOLVED PHOSPHATES TO OCEAN	PMX 410 TRANSPORT BY STREAMS OF ERODED SOILS CONTAINING PARTICULATE PHOSPHATE TO OCEAN	P1MX 6001 TRANSPORT BY STREAMS OF DEAD PLANT MATTER TO OCEAN	P1MX 7001 TRANSPORT BY STREAMS OF FECAL MATTER TO OCEAN	P1MX 7004 TRANSPORT BY STREAMS OF DEAD ANIMAL MATTER TO OCEAN	P1MX 7005 TRANSPORT BY STREAMS OF BONES & TEETH TO OCEANS	P2LX 51 DISSOLVING OF PHOSPHATES IN SOILS	PLX 610 PHOTOSYNTHESIS (PLANT PRODUCTION)	PLX 62 FOOD CONSUMPTION BY PARASITE PLANTS	PLX 6001 PLANT MORTALITY	PLX 710 FOOD CONSUMPTION BY HERBIVORES	PLX 721 FOOD CONSUMPTION BY PRIMARY CARNIVORES	PLX 722 FOOD CONSUMPTION BY SECONDARY CARNIVORES	PLX 73 FOOD CONSUMPTION BY PARASITE ANIMALS	PLX 74 FOOD CONSUMPTION BY SCAVENGERS	PLX 7001 EXCRETION	PLX 7004 ANIMAL MORTALITY	PLX 7005 FLESH REMOVAL BY CARNIVORES, SCAVENGERS, ETC.	PLX 7501 DECOMPOSITION BY DECOMPOSERS	P2LX 42 PHOSPHATE PRODUCTION BY TRANSFORMERS
					LAND REGION																							
					ABIOTIC											BIOTIC												
					GEOLOGY		HYDROLOGY								SOILS	PLANTS			ANIMALS									
LAND REGION	ABIOTIC	GEOLOGY	LX 21	PHOSPHATE ROCKS: VOLCANIC APATITE	+	−																						
			LX 22	" : GUANO DEPOSITS & FOSSIL BONES		−																						
			LX 23	" : UPLIFTED SEDIMENTARY ROCKS		−																						
			LX 24	PARTICULATE PHOSPHATE		+	−			−					−													
		HYDROLOGY	LX 42	DISSOLVED PHOSPHATE: IN STREAMS			+	−	−							−												+
		SOILS	LX 51	" : IN SOILS				+							+	−												+
	BIOTIC	PLANTS	LX 610	GREEN PLANTS												+	−	−	−									
			LX 62	PARASITE PLANTS													+	−	−									
			LX 6001	PLANT PRODUCTS: DEAD PLANT MATTER							−							+									−	
		ANIMALS	LX 710	HERBIVORES															+	−		−		−	−			
			LX 721	PRIMARY CARNIVORES																+	−	−		−	−	±		
			LX 722	SECONDARY CARNIVORES																	+	−		−	−	±		
			LX 73	PARASITE ANIMALS																		+		−	−			
			LX 74	SCAVENGERS																			+	−	−	±		
			LX 7001	ANIMAL PRODUCTS: FECES								−												+			−	
			LX 7004	" : DEAD ANIMAL MATTER									−										−		+	−	−	
			LX 7005	" : BONES & TEETH										−												+		
			LX 75	DECOMPOSERS: DECOMPOSING BACTERIA, ETC.																							±	
			LX 7501	DECOMPOSED ORGANIC MATTER																							+	−
			LX 76	TRANSFORMERS: PHOSPHATIZING BACTERIA, ETC.																								±
MARINE REGION	ABIOTIC	HYDROLOGY	MX 410	PARTICULATE PHOSPHATE: IN ESTUARINE WATERS						+																		
			MX 420	DISSOLVED PHOSPHATE: IN OCEAN WATERS					+																			
		SUBSTRATE	MX 53	PHOSPHATES: IN SHALLOW MARINE SEDIMENTS																								
	BIOTIC	PLANTS	MX 610	MARINE GREEN PLANTS																								
			MX 62	PARASITE PLANTS																								
			MX 6001	DETRITUS: (DEAD ORGANIC MATTER-LARGELY PLANTS)							+																	
		ANIMALS	MX 710	MARINE HERBIVORES																								
			MX 720	PRIMARY CARNIVORES																								
			MX 724	SECONDARY CARNIVORES																								
			MX 73	PARASITE ANIMALS																								
			MX 74	SCAVENGERS																								
			MX 7001	ANIMAL PRODUCTS: FECES								+																
			MX 7202	" : MARINE BIRD DROPPINGS																								
			MX 7004	" : DEAD MARINE ANIMAL MATTER									+															
			MX 7005	" : BONES, SHELLS & TEETH										+														
			MX 75	DECOMPOSERS: DECOMPOSING AGENTS AS BACTERIA, ETC.																								
			MX 7501	DECOMPOSED ORGANIC MATTER																								
			MX 76	TRANSFORMERS: PHOSPHATIZING BACTERIA, ETC.																								

Code	Process	Subsystem	Region																			
PLX 23	GEOLOGIC UPLIFT OF MARINE SEDIMENTS	GEOLOGY	MARINE REGION – ABIOTIC																	-		
P2MX 420	DISSOLVING OF PHOSPHATES IN OCEAN	HYDROLOGY	MARINE REGION – ABIOTIC																		+	-
PMX 53	SETTLEMENT OF MATERIALS CONTAINING PHOSPHATE TO MARINE SEDIMENTS	SUBSTRATE	MARINE REGION – ABIOTIC					-	-		-						-			+		-
PMX 610	PHOTOSYNTHESIS (PLANT PRODUCTION)	PLANTS	MARINE REGION – BIOTIC																+		-	
P2MX 6001	MARINE PLANT MORTALITY	PLANTS	MARINE REGION – BIOTIC														+	-	-			
PMX 62	FOOD CONSUMPTION BY PARASITE PLANTS	PLANTS	MARINE REGION – BIOTIC															+	-			
PMX 710	FOOD CONSUMPTION BY HERBIVORES	ANIMALS	MARINE REGION – BIOTIC													+		-	-			
PMX 720	FOOD CONSUMPTION BY PRIMARY CARNIVORES	ANIMALS	MARINE REGION – BIOTIC												+	-						
PMX 724	FOOD CONSUMPTION BY SECONDARY CARNIVORES	ANIMALS	MARINE REGION – BIOTIC											+	-							
PMX 73	FOOD CONSUMPTION BY PARASITE ANIMALS	ANIMALS	MARINE REGION – BIOTIC										+	-	-	-						
PMX 74	FOOD CONSUMPTION BY SCAVENGERS	ANIMALS	MARINE REGION – BIOTIC						-			+										
P2MX 7001	EXCRETION	ANIMALS	MARINE REGION – BIOTIC								+	-	-	-	-	-						
PMX 7202	EXCRETION BY MARINE BIRDS	ANIMALS	MARINE REGION – BIOTIC							+					-							
PLX 22	COLLECTION OF DROPPINGS	ANIMALS	MARINE REGION – BIOTIC							-												
P2MX 7004	MARINE ANIMAL MORTALITY	ANIMALS	MARINE REGION – BIOTIC						+			-	-	-	-	-						
P2MX 7005	FLESH REMOVAL BY CARNIVORES, SCAVENGERS, ETC.	ANIMALS	MARINE REGION – BIOTIC					+	-			±		±	±							
PMX 7501	DECOMPOSITION BY DECOMPOSERS	ANIMALS	MARINE REGION – BIOTIC			+	±		-		-						-					
P3MX 420	PHOSPHATE PRODUCTION BY TRANSFORMERS	ANIMALS	MARINE REGION – BIOTIC		±	-															+	

Code	Process																					
PLX 23	GEOLOGIC UPLIFT OF MARINE SEDIMENTS																			+		
P2MX 420	DISSOLVING OF PHOSPHATES IN OCEAN																					
PMX 53	SETTLEMENT OF MATERIALS CONTAINING PHOSPHATE TO MARINE SEDIMENTS																					
PMX 610	PHOTOSYNTHESIS (PLANT PRODUCTION)																					
P2MX 6001	MARINE PLANT MORTALITY																					
PMX 62	FOOD CONSUMPTION BY PARASITE PLANTS																					
PMX 710	FOOD CONSUMPTION BY HERBIVORES																					
PMX 720	FOOD CONSUMPTION BY PRIMARY CARNIVORES																					
PMX 724	FOOD CONSUMPTION BY SECONDARY CARNIVORES																					
PMX 73	FOOD CONSUMPTION BY PARASITE ANIMALS																					
PMX 74	FOOD CONSUMPTION BY SCAVENGERS																					
P2MX 7001	EXCRETION																					
PMX 7202	EXCRETION BY MARINE BIRDS																					
PLX 22	COLLECTION OF DROPPINGS																				+	
P2MX 7004	MARINE ANIMAL MORTALITY																					
P2MX 7005	FLESH REMOVAL BY CARNIVORES, SCAVENGERS, ETC.																					
PMX 7501	DECOMPOSITION BY DECOMPOSERS																					
P3MX 420	PHOSPHATE PRODUCTION BY TRANSFORMERS																					

3.6.8 The Phosphorus Flow Through a Mussel Population

The previous section on the phosphorus cycle describes the linkages that take place within a generalized phosphorus cycle. In the analysis of specific ecosystems, the generalized phosphorus flow diagram and linkage matrix help to locate the restrictions, reservoirs, and suppliers of this key nutrient for the production and maintenance of a well-balanced environment. As indicated in the section on shellfish production, mussels play an important role in the cycling of phosphorus within the estuarine system.

Phosphorus flows through a mussel population are discussed in a monograph by Edward J. Kuenzler.[27] As he states, his study was undertaken to determine the rate at which phosphorus flows through a population of the mussel *Modiolus demissus dillwyn*, located in an estuarine, intertidal salt marsh near Sapelo Island, Georgia, and to evaluate the effect on the ecosystem of this nutrient flow through the mussel.

He has found in this and a previous study[28] that *Modiolus* represents a typical filter-feeding lamellibranch, ingesting some of the particular matter from sea water, but rejecting the rest in the form of pseudofeces. The pseudofeces, which is rich in phosphorus, other minerals, and vitamins, is thus retained in the marsh instead of being carried out by the tide to accumulate as deep sea sediments. A good fraction of the phosphorus contained in the pseudofeces is returned to the water phase as dissolved phosphate or dissolved organic matter through the action of important marsh-mud populations such as crabs, snails, polychaetes, nematodes, and bacteria. The phosphorus, therefore, becomes available for organic production.

Kuenzler was able to calculate that the turnover time of particulate phosphorus in the water, due solely to the action of the mussel population, was only 2.6 days. That is, the mussels removed from the water every two and one-half days a quantity of phosphorus equal to the average amount present in the particles in the water (estimated, at his study area, to be about 14 milligrams per square meter). The turnover time of phosphorus within the mussel population itself was 115 days. Therefore, although the mussels are a relatively minor component of the marsh in terms of biomass and energy flow, they have a major effect on the biogeochemical cycling and retention of valuable phosphorus. To put it another way, Kuenzler's study demonstrated that the mussel population is more important to the ecosystem as a biogeochemical agent than as a transformer of energy.

Although Kuenzler's study concerned itself with *Modiolus demissus*, which does not occur in abundance in Plymouth Bay, the assumption that his phosphorus flow figures would also be valid for estimating magnitudes for other mussel species, such as *Mytilus edulis*, was confirmed by Dr. John M. Teal of the Woods Hole Oceanographic Institute. Kuenzler's study measured the mussel population by its standing crop of phosphorus, or by the total dry weight of phosphorus present at any one time. This was found to be 37.2 mg. phosphorus per square meter, the body fraction comprising 67 percent, the shell 30 percent, and the liquor 3 percent. The quantities of phosphorus present in natural marsh water measured in mg. phosphorus per square meter were: particulate, 14; phosphate, 19; and dissolved organic, 6. It was found that the amount of phosphorus entering into the mussel population by its filtration was a total of 5.480 mg. phosphorus per square meter per day. This was comprised of 5.410 mg. as particulate matter and 0.070 mg. as phosphate. Of the 5.410 mg. of particulate matter, 0.775 mg. phosphorus per square meter per day was ingested by the mussel population as food material—that is, organic detritus—leaving 4.63 mg. of particulate matter not ingested as food. This amount plus the 0.070 mg. of dissolved phosphate make up the 4.700 mg. phosphorus per square meter per day which was rejected in the form of pseudofeces.

[27] Kuenzler [5], pp. 410–412. [28] *Ibid.* [6].

Table 3.6k Phosphorus Flow through a Mussel Population

PHOSPHORUS FLOW THROUGH A MUSSEL POPULATION IN INPUT - OUTPUT FORMAT

MARINE REGION		CLASSIFICATION NUMBER	COMMODITY	UNITS	PMX 7151 INGESTION BY MUSSEL POPULATION	PMX 421 DISSOLVED PHOSPHATE PRODUCTION BY MUSSEL POPULATION	PMX 7155 GAMETE PRODUCTION BY MUSSEL REPRODUCTION	PMX 431 DISSOLVED ORGANIC PHOSPHORUS PRODUCTION BY MUSSEL POPULATION	PMX 7154 DEAD MUSSEL PRODUCTION BY MUSSEL MORTALITY	PMX 7152 FECES PRODUCTION BY MUSSEL EXCRETION	PMX 7153 PSEUDOFECES PRODUCTION BY MUSSEL POPULATION		PMX 715 GROWTH OF GAMETES INTO MUSSELS	P3MX 420 RETURN TO WATER PHASE AS DISSOLVED PHOSPHATE BY ORGANISMS SUCH AS CRABS, BACTERIA, ETC.	PMX 610 GREEN PLANTS PRODUCTION BY PHOTOSYNTHESIS	
ABIOTIC SECTOR	HYDROLOGY	MX 411	PARTICULATE MATTER @ 14 mg.P./M^2	mg.P./M^2 DAY	-4.63											
		MX 421	DISSOLVED PHOSPHATE @ 19 mg.P./M^2	"	-0.07	+.260								+	-	
		MX 431	DISSOLVED ORGANIC @ 6 mg.P./M^2	"				+.023								
BIOTIC SECTOR	PLANTS	MX 610	GREEN PLANTS												+	
		MX 6002	DETRITUS (FOOD FOR MUSSELS, SUSPENDED AS PARTICULATE MATTER)	mg.P./M^2 DAY	-0.78											
	ANIMALS	MX 715	MUSSEL POPULATION: MEASURED BY PHOSPHORUS CONTENT	mg.P./M^2	±37.20	±37.20	±37.20	±37.20	±37.20	±37.20	±37.20		+			
		MX 7151	PHOSPHORUS INGESTED BY MUSSEL POPULATION	mg.P./M^2 DAY	+5.48	-.260	-.011	-.023	-.021	-.460	-4.70					
		MX 7152	MUSSEL PRODUCTS: FECES	"						+.460				-		
		MX 7153	" PSEUDOFECES	"							+4.70			-		
		MX 7154	" DEAD MUSSEL	"					+.021					-		
		MX 7155	" GAMETES	"			+.011						-			
		MX 76	PHOSPHATIZING AGENTS SUCH AS CRABS, SNAILS, NEMATODES, BACTERIA, ETC.											±		

(Column header group: MARINE REGION — BIOTIC SECTOR; PROCESS)

The losses and elimination rates of the mussel population from its food utilization measured in mg. phosphorus per square meter per day are as follows: mortality, .021; spawned gametes, .011; dissolved organic, .023; phosphate, .260; and feces, .460. These phosphorus flows through the mussel population are indicated on the flow chart diagram, Chart 3.6d. They are recorded in activity analysis format in Table 3.6k.

***Chart* 3.6d** Diagram of the Phosphorus Flow Through a Mussel Population

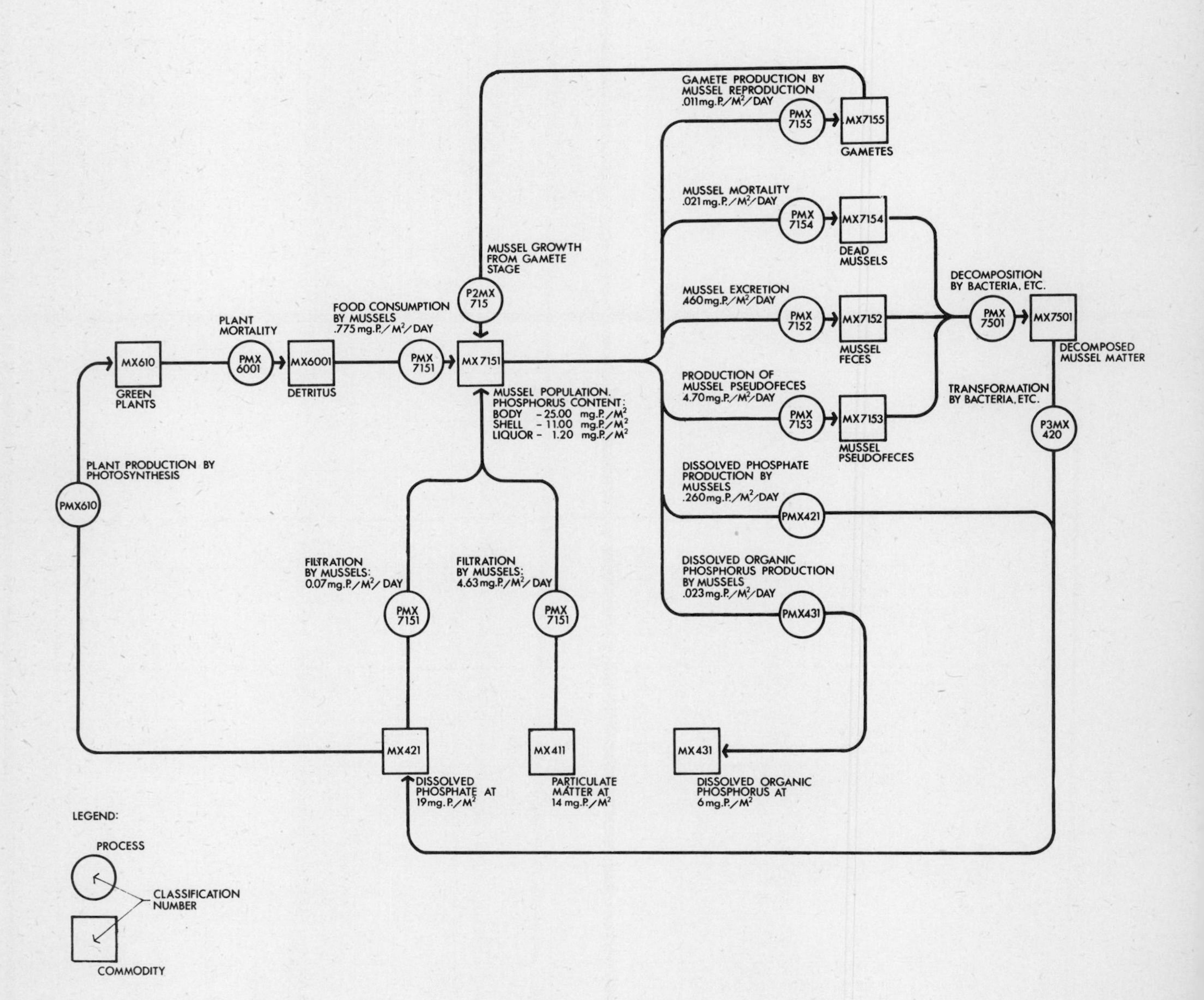

Bibliography

1. Cain, Stanley A., *Conservation: The Developing Ecological Sciences of Resource Management*, Second National Congress on Environmental Health, Proceedings, 1961, pp. 56–60.
2. Clarke, George L., *Elements of Ecology*, New York, John Wiley and Sons, Inc., 1954.
3. Hedgpeth, Joel W. (ed.) *Treatise on Marine Ecology and Paleo-ecology*, Vol. 1, Chapter 3, "Concepts in Marine Ecology," Geological Society of America, New York, 1957.

4. Isard, Walter, *et al.*, *Methods of Regional Analysis: An Introduction to Regional Science*, Cambridge, Mass., The M.I.T. Press, 1960, Chapter 7.
5. Kuenzler, Edward J., 'Phosphorus Budget of a Mussel Population," *Limnology and Oceanography*, 6 (1961).
6. ———, "Structure and Energy Flow of a Mussel Population in a Georgia Salt Marsh", *Limnology and Oceanography*, 6 (1961).
7. Odum, Eugene P., *Fundamentals of Ecology*, 2nd ed., W.B. Saunders, Company, Philadelphia, 1959.
8. Riley, Gordon A., Henry Stommel, and Dean F. Bumpus, *Quantitative Ecology of the Plankton of the Western North Atlantic*, Bulletin of the Bingham Oceanographic Collection, Vol. XII, Yale University, New Haven, Connecticut, 1949.
9. Schaefer, Milner B. and Roger Revelle, "Marine Resources," Chapter 4 in Martin R. Huberty and Warren L. Flock (eds.), *Natural Resources*, New York, McGraw-Hill, 1959, pp. 73–109.
10. U.S. Bureau of the Budget, Executive Office of the President, *Standard Industrial Classification Manual*, U.S. Government Printing Office, Washington, D.C., 1957.

Combined Economic-Ecologic Analysis

4.1 Introduction

In Chapters 2 and 3 we have treated basic methodology for regional economic and natural resource analysis, respectively. In large part, the materials of these two chapters have been considered independently. We now arrive at the point where, in order to proceed further, we must indicate exactly how these two sets of materials are to be fused into a single unified framework.

To reiterate, our objective is to develop a more adequate methodology for evaluating various alternatives relating to the development of coastal areas, and of the environment in general. We have indicated that while there is much that is valid in the set of existing economic and regional science techniques, some of which are sketched in Chapter 2, each of these techniques is inadequate to identify costs and benefits from the standpoint of the functioning of the physical environment. Therefore, sound analysis must go beyond what any of these techniques currently is able to do in the narrow economic-regional science sense.

In Chapter 3, we developed some preliminary methodology for analysis of the functioning of ecosystems. While this methodology deals with *systematic* ecologic analysis, it is not very useful *per se* for the evaluation of development alternatives. As it stands, it does not translate ecologic magnitudes into dollars and cents, or any other common unit useful in welfare and planning analysis. Theoretically however, the methodology of Chapter 3 can be linked to that of Chapter 2, and thus to the common unit, the dollar.

Accordingly, to repeat, our objective in this chapter is to attempt to develop a methodology which fuses the two separate sets of materials of Chapters 2 and 3 into a single framework. By so doing, we will have also extended the analytic capabilities of the techniques of each of the first two chapters. Once this fused methodology is developed, however tentative and oversimplified it may be, we shall attempt to employ it in a case study in Chapter 5.

4.2 The General Approach

Our basic procedure for linking the economic and ecologic systems is an extension of what is generally characterized as linear systems by applied mathematicians. Economists and regional scientists frequently use certain linear systems models, such as input-output and linear programming. The basic procedure in one of the many possible developments of the approach may be set down as follows:

1. The investigator examines carefully all processes, whether economic or ecologic, in order to identify those processes which, either in whole or in large part, can be approximated in linear form.
2. He sets all such processes down in a matrix in accord with the input-output or the activity analysis (programming) format.
3. If some of these processes involve inputs which do not vary linearly with output,

he records these inputs outside the structural matrix, since the structural matrix is defined as embodying linear relations only.

4. He identifies those basic processes which are primarily non-linear and which cannot possibly be ignored.
5. He records the data for the non-linear representations of these basic processes in a form in which they can be operated upon.
6. Finally, he uses high-speed computers to carry through operations on the data in the linear part of the system while making various types of appropriate side computations and operations on the data of the non-linear part of the system.

Needless to say, many of the processes which are basic in the ecological system cannot at this time be approximated in linear form, although in sections 3.5 and 3.6 we attempt such approximation, mainly for illustrative purposes. Similarly, many basic elements of the economic system cannot be represented in linear form. Nonetheless, it is often useful to record data as if they represented processes which do obey linear rules. At least in this way we obtain a systematic description of relationships and magnitudes as they exist at a point in time. This description in itself often provides much insight. Also, to attempt a systematic description forces the analyst to develop a comprehensive classification system which is at least meaningful in terms of the existing theory and stock of knowledge. Such a classification system, in turn, by its requirement of consistency makes it possible to collect data much more productively and efficiently. Finally, it may be contended that even if many of the processes being investigated cannot be represented in linear form, or easily handled by side computations if they are non-linear, nonetheless by putting them in linear form we can make projections of the impact of changes which, when combined with good judgment, are at least as useful as projections made on the basis of good judgment alone.

Thus we proceed in this chapter on these premises:

1. The use of linear systems analysis, with side computations for nonlinearities, makes a useful linkage of the economic and ecologic systems possible, at least conceptually.
2. A description of processes in linear form, as of a given point in time, is useful in terms of the data it makes available as well as the consistent classification system it imposes.
3. A projection based on linear analysis, good judgment, and perhaps a few side computations for several key non-linear relations is, in many critical situations, as useful as a projection based on good judgment alone.

Because of limited resources for research, we will not carry through the analysis of the case study area on as extensive and complete a basis as just outlined. We shall adopt certain shortcuts, which other analysts who also have limited research funds, may choose to follow. However these shortcuts are tailored to our particular problem, and hence are not necessarily generally useful.

4.3 *The General Interrelations Table: Illustrations of Sector (Column) and Commodity (Row) Data*

The above general statements can be illustrated by data which might be contained for specific sectors and commodities in a general interrelations table, such as Table 4.3. First, however, the organization of the table must be described.

The first basic consideration in the construction of the table concerns the specification of regions. It is immediately apparent that the set of regions which may be appropriately developed for economic analysis may not be appropriate when such analysis is to be synthesized with ecologic analysis. This situation obtains when we construct a general interrelations table which has significance for the development problems of specific locations, such as the Plymouth Bay area. There, where recreational activities offer major potential, the Marine Area and the Land

TABLE 4.3

THE GENERAL INTERRELATIONS TABLE

ECOLOGIC – ECONOMIC ANALYSIS

LAND / ECONOMIC (rows) — PROCESS: LAND / ECONOMIC (columns)

CLASSIFI-CATION NUMBER	COMMODITY	UNIT	AGRICULTURE	MINING	.	.	.	2033 CANNED FRUITS AND VEGETABLES	.	2071 CANDY AND OTHER CONFECTIONARY PRODUCTS	.	3111 LEATHER TANNING AND FINISHING	.	.	.	SERVICES	.	.	GOVERNMENT
0122	FRUIT AND NUT TREE FARMS	DOLLARS						-.090423		-.025180									
0123	VEGETABLE FARMS	"						-.035098											
2011	MEAT PACKING PLANTS	"										-.135061							
2021	CREAMERY, BUTTER	"								-.000512									
2026	FLUID, MILK	"								-.017067									
2033	CANNED FRUITS AND VEGETABLES	"						+1.00000											
2037	FROZEN FRUITS AND VEGETABLES	"						-.032090											
2046	WET CORN MILLING	"								-.033293									
2061	CANE SUGAR (EXCEPT REFINING)	"								-.033293									
2062	CANE SUGAR REFINING	"								-.123477									
2071	CANDY AND OTHER CONFECTIONARY PRODUCTS	"								+1.00000									
2072	CHOCOLATE AND COCOA PRODUCTS	"								-.076803									
2087	FLAVORING EXTRACTS & SUGARS	"								-.068082									
2621	PAPER MILLS	"										-.000324							
2641	PAPER COATING & GLAZING	"								-.005689									
2651	FOLDING PAPERBOARD BOXES	"								-.039886									
2654	SANITARY FOOD CONTAINERS	"						-.058751											
2751	COMMERCIAL PRINTING (EXCEPT LITHOGRAPHY)	"						-.000364		-.034197									
2812	ALKALIES & CHLORINE	"										-.000275							
2815	DYES AND ORGANIC PIGMENTS	"										-.001946							
2816	INORGANIC PIGMENTS	"										-.001946							
2818	INDUSTRIAL ORGANIC CHEMISTRY	"						-.000241				-.012588							
2819	INDUSTRIAL INORGANIC CHEMISTRY	"										-.000722							
2842	SPECIALTY CLEANING PREPARATIONS	"										-.005189							
2843	SURFACE ACTIVE AGENTS	"										-.042151							
2861	GUM AND WOOD CHEMISTRY	"										-.105116							
2899	CHEMICALS AND CHEMICAL PREPARATIONS	"						-.003584											
2911-0	PETROLEUM REFINING	"						-.007256		-.009120		-.013460							
2911-1	PETROLEUM REFINING (FUEL)	GALLONS																	
3111	LEATHER TANNING & FINISHING	DOLLARS										+.877532							
3221	GLASS CONTAINERS	"						-.051705											
3274	LIME	"										-.001450							
3411	METAL CANS	"						-.026872											
3461	METAL STAMPINGS	"						-.000970											
3471	ELECTROPLATING & POLISHING	"										-.002595							
3732	BOATS (IN BOAT SEASON)	BOATS																	
39999	UNALLOCATED PRODUCED INPUTS	DOLLARS						-.000728		-.016646		-.002595							
4911	ELECTRICITY	"						-.006168		-.010582		-.014698							
4920	GAS	"								-.004449		-.000155							

ECOLOGIC (columns): ABIOTIC — CLIMATE, GEOLOGY, HYDROLOGY, SOILS; BIOTIC — PLANTS, ANIMALS

CLASSIFI-CATION NUMBER	PLX 21 PHOSPHATE PRODUCTION BY VOLCANIC ACTION (GEOLOGY)	PLX 24 EROSION OF PHOSPHATE ROCKS	P1LX 42 DISSOLVING OF PHOSPHATES IN STREAMS (HYDROLOGY)	P1LX 51 IRRIGATION OF SOILS BY STREAMS	P1MX 420 STREAM FLOW OF DISSOLVED PHOSPHATES TO OCEAN	PMX 410 TRANSPORT BY STREAMS OF ERODED SOILS CONTAINING PARTICULATE PHOSPHATE TO OCEAN	P1MX 6001 TRANSPORT BY STREAMS OF DEAD PLANT MATTER TO OCEAN	P1MX 7001 TRANSPORT BY STREAMS OF FECAL MATTER TO OCEAN	P1MX 7004 TRANSPORT BY STREAMS OF DEAD ANIMAL MATTER TO OCEAN	P1MX 7005 TRANSPORT BY STREAMS OF BONES AND TEETH TO OCEAN	P2LX 51 DISSOLVING OF PHOSPHATES IN SOILS (SOILS)	PLX 610 PHOTOSYNTHESIS (PLANT PRODUCTION) (PLANTS)	PLX 62 FOOD CONSUMPTION BY PARASITE PLANTS	PLX 6001 PLANT MORTALITY	PLX 710 FOOD CONSUMPTION BY HERBIVORES (ANIMALS)	PLX 721 FOOD CONSUMPTION BY PRIMARY CARNIVORES	PLX 722 FOOD CONSUMPTION BY SECONDARY CARNIVORES	PLX 73 FOOD CONSUMPTION BY PARASITE ANIMALS	PLX 74 FOOD CONSUMPTION BY SCAVENGERS	PLX 7001 EXCRETION	PLX 7004 ANIMAL MORTALITY	PLX 7005 FLESH REMOVAL BY CARNIVORES, SCAVENGERS, ETC.	PLX 7501 DECOMPOSITION BY DECOMPOSERS	P2LX 42 PHOSPHATE PRODUCTION BY TRANSFORMERS
0122																								
0123																								
2011																								
2021																								
2026																								
2033																								
2037																								
2046																								
2061																								
2062																								
2071																								
2072																								
2087																								
2621																								
2641																								
2651																								
2654																								
2751																								
2812																								
2815																								
2816																								
2818																								
2819																								
2842																								
2843																								
2861																								
2899																								
2911-0																								
2911-1																								
3111																								
3221																								
3274																								
3411																								
3461																								
3471																								
3732																								
39999																								
4911																								
4920																								

Code	Item	Unit																														
9300	MUNICIPAL TAX	"	-.008419	-.048204	-.005982																											
9888	PAYROLL	"	-.026972	-.285878	-.326719																											
98882	EMPLOYEE WELFARE PAYMENTS	"	-.001068	-.009984	-.017564																											
98884	UNEMPLOYMENT COMPENSATION AND SOCIAL SECURITY PAYMENTS	"	-.017773	-.005098	-.016888																											
9899	RESIDUAL	"	-.087533	-.151422	-.144836																											
	LABOR																															
LL 794-01	GENERAL MANAGER	MAN HRS																														
LL 794-02	OTHER ADMINISTRATIVE	"																														
LL 794-03	DOCK MASTER	"																														
LL 794-04	DOCK OPERATIONS PERSONNEL	"																														
LL 794-05	BOAT SALES MANAGER	"																														
LL 794-06	BOAT SALESMAN	"																														
LL 794-07	MARINE SUPPLIES SALES MANAGER	"																														
LL 794-08	MARINE SUPPLIES SALESMAN	"																														
LL 794-09	PARTY BOAT CREWS	"																														
LL 794-10	PACKAGED FOOD & BAIT PERSONNEL	"																														
LL 794-11	REPAIR SHOP PERSONNEL	"																														
ECOLOGIC — ABIOTIC — CLIMATE																																
GEOLOGY																																
LX 21	PHOSPHATE ROCKS: VOLCANIC APATITE						+	-																								
LX 22	" : GUANO DEPOSITS & FOSSIL BONES							-																								
LX 23	" : UPLIFTED SEDIMENTARY ROCKS							-																								
LX 24	PARTICULATE PHOSPHATE							+	-			-						-														
PHYSIOGRAPHY																																
LX 3101	LAND AREA FOR: PARKING	SQ. FT.																														
LX 3102	" : TOTAL INDOOR STORAGE	"																														
LX 3103	" : LOCAL INDOOR STORAGE	"																														
LX 3104	" : TOTAL REPAIRS	"																														
LX 3105	" : LOCAL REPAIRS	"																														
LX 3106	" : BOAT & MOTOR SHOWROOM	"																														
LX 3107	" : SALES & MARINE ACCESSORIES	"																														
LX 3108	" : REST ROOM & LOUNGE	"																														
LX 3109	" : GEAR STORAGE	"																														
LX 3110	" : ADMINISTRATIVE OFFICE	"																														
LX 3111	" : TRANSIENT & RENTAL OFFICE	"																														
LX 3112	" : BAIT & PACKAGED FOOD SALES	"																														
LX 3113	" : FUEL SALES	"																														
LX 3114	" : RAMPS	"																														
LX 3115	" : BATHHOUSE	"																														
LX 3116	" : BEACH AREA	"																														
HYDROLOGY																																
LX 42	DISSOLVED PHOSPHATE: IN STREAMS								+	-	-								-											+		
WPC 1000	WATER INTAKE - TOTAL	1000 GALLONS	-.019277	-.003180	-.019965																											
WPC 1001	FOR SANITARY USE	"	-.000446	-.001256	-.000408																											
WPC 1002	FOR PRODUCTION	"	-.015997	-.000630	-.019557																											
WPC 1003	FOR COOLING	"		-.000988																												
WPC 1004	FOR BOILER FEED	"		-.000306																												
WPC 1009	FOR OTHER, N.E.C.	"	-.002834																													
SOILS																																
LX 51	DISSOLVED PHOSPHATE: IN SOILS									+							+	-												+		
ECOLOGIC — BIOTIC — PLANTS																																
LX 610	GREEN PLANTS																	+	-	-	-											
LX 62	PARASITE PLANTS																		+	-	-											
LX 6001	PLANT PRODUCT: DEAD PLANT MATTER												-							+									-			
ANIMALS																																
LX 710	HERBIVORES																				+	-		-		-	-					
LX 721	PRIMARY CARNIVORES																					+	-	-		-	-	±				
LX 722	SECONDARY CARNIVORES																						+	-		-	-	±				
LX 73	PARASITE ANIMALS																							+		-	-					
LX 74	SCAVENGERS																								+	-	-	±				
LX 7001	ANIMAL PRODUCTS: FECES													-												+			-			
LX 7004	" : DEAD ANIMAL MATTER														-										-		+	-	-			
LX 7005	" : BONES & TEETH															-												+				
LX 75	DECOMPOSERS: DECOMPOSING BACTERIA																												±			
LX 7501	DECOMPOSED ORGANIC MATTER																												+	-		
LX 76	TRANSFORMERS: PHOSPHATIZING BACTERIA																													±		

LAND

Group	Classification number	Activity title
		AGRICULTURE
		MINING
		.
		.
		.
	2033	CANNED FRUITS AND VEGETABLES
		.
	2071	CANDY AND OTHER CONFECTIONARY PRODUCTS
		.
	3111	LEATHER TANNING AND FINISHING
		.
		.
		SERVICES
		.
		.
		GOVERNMENT
CLIMATE		
GEOLOGY	PLX 21	PHOSPHATE PRODUCTION BY VOLCANIC ACTION
	PLX 24	EROSION OF PHOSPHATE ROCKS
HYDROLOGY	PILX 42	DISSOLVING OF PHOSPHATES IN STREAMS
	PILX 51	IRRIGATION OF SOILS BY STREAMS
	PIMX 420	STREAM FLOW OF DISSOLVED PHOSPHATES TO OCEAN
	PMX 410	TRANSPORT BY STREAMS OF ERODED SOILS CONTAINING PARTICULATE PHOSPHATE TO OCEAN
	PIMX 6001	TRANSPORT BY STREAMS OF DEAD PLANT MATTER TO OCEAN
	PIMX 7001	TRANSPORT BY STREAMS OF FECAL MATTER TO OCEAN
	PIMX 7004	TRANSPORT BY STREAMS OF DEAD ANIMAL MATTER TO OCEAN
	PIMX 7005	TRANSPORT BY STREAMS OF BONES AND TEETH TO OCEANS
SOILS	P2LX 51	DISSOLVING OF PHOSPHATES IN SOILS
PLANTS	PLX 610	PHOTOSYNTHESIS (PLANT PRODUCTION)
	PLX 62	FOOD CONSUMPTION BY PARASITE PLANTS
	PLX 6001	PLANT MORTALITY
ANIMALS	PLX 710	FOOD CONSUMPTION BY HERBIVORES
	PLX 721	FOOD CONSUMPTION BY PRIMARY CARNIVORES
	PLX 722	FOOD CONSUMPTION BY SECONDARY CARNIVORES
	PLX 73	FOOD CONSUMPTION BY PARASITE ANIMALS
	PLX 74	FOOD CONSUMPTION BY SCAVENGERS
	PLX 7001	EXCRETION
	PLX 7004	ANIMAL MORTALITY
	PLX 7005	FLESH REMOVAL BY CARNIVORES, SCAVENGERS, ETC.
	PLX 7501	DECOMPOSITION BY DECOMPOSERS
	P2LX 42	PHOSPHATE PRODUCTION BY TRANSFORMERS

MARINE

Group	Classification number	Activity title	Units	2033	2071	3111	PMX 410	PIMX 420
ECONOMIC	M 794-0	RECREATION	1000 MAN DAYS					
ABIOTIC: CLIMATE	MX 11	LIGHT: INCIDENT SOLAR RADIATION AT THE OCEAN SURFACE	G.CAL/CM²/MIN					
GEOLOGY								
PHYSIOGRAPHY	MX 31	WATER AREA: BAY OR ESTUARY WATER AREA	ACRES					
	MX 32	" : INTERTIDAL & SUBTIDAL SHOAL WATER AREA	"					
	MX 3301	WATER SURFACE AREA: FOR DOCKED BOATS	SQ. FT.					
	MX 3302	WATER SURFACE AREA: FOR MOORED BOATS	"					
	MX 3303	WATER SURFACE AREA: FOR SWIMMING	"					
HYDROLOGY	MX 410	PARTICULATE PHOSPHATE: IN ESTUARINE WATERS					+	
	MX 411	" IN ESTUARINE WATERS @ 14 mg.P/M²	mg.P/M²/DAY					
	MX 420	DISSOLVED PHOSPHATE: IN OCEAN WATER	mg-at/M³					+
	MX 421	DISSOLVED PHOSPHATE: IN OCEAN WATER @19 mg.P/M²	mg.P/M²/DAY					
	MX 431	DISSOLVED ORGANIC PHOSPHORUS: @6 mg.P/M²	"					
	MX 44	WATER TRANSPARENCY: (t = 1/k)						
	WPC 1010	WATER DISCHARGE, TOTAL	1000 GALLONS	+.003279	+.002542	+.017816		
	WPC 1011	SANITARY USE	"	+.000446	+.001268	+.000376		
	WPC 1012	PRODUCTION	"		+.000566			
	WPC 1013	COOLING	"		+.000708			
	WPC 1019	OTHER, N.E.C.	"	+.002833		+.017440		
	WPC 1031	B.O.D., 5 DAY	1000 POUNDS	+.000118		+.000094		
	WPC 10311	SETTLEABLE 5 DAY B.O.D.	"			+.000038		
	WPC 1033	C.O.D.	"	+.000206		+.000228		
	WPC 1040	SOLIDS, TOTAL	"	+.000172		+.000361		
	WPC 1041	SOLIDS, SUSPENDED	"	+.000017		+.000107		
	WPC 1042	SOLIDS, SETTLEABLE	"	+.000155		+.000254		
	WPC 1051	ALKALINITY	"	+.000025		+.000046		
	WPC 1052	ACIDITY	"			+.000009		
	WPC 1091	CHROMIUM	"			+.000004		
	WPC 1092	CHLORIDE	"			+.000112		
		QUALITY CONSTRAINTS						
	MX 4501	COLIFORM INDEX [PER 100mL (MAX.)]						
	MX 4502	DISSOLVED OXYGEN [ppm (AVE.)]	PPM					
	MX 4503	pH (RANGE)						
	MX 4504	B.O.D. [ppm (MONTHLY AVE.)]	PPM					
	MX 4505	B.O.D. [ppm (MAX.)]	PPM					
	MX 4506	TURBIDITY [ppm (MAX.)]	PPM					
	MX 4507	COLOR (UNITS)	UNITS					

Group	Code	Commodity	Units	
ECOLOGIC	MX 4508	WATER TEMPERATURE (MAX.) COD	°C	
	MX 4509	WATER TEMPERATURE (MAX.) WINTER FLOUNDER	°C	
	MX 4510	WATER TEMPERATURE (RANGE) CLAMS	°C	
	MX 4511-1	SALINITY (RANGE) COD	°/oo	
	MX 4511-2	SALINITY (RANGE) WINTER FLOUNDER	°/oo	
	MX 4511-3	SALINITY (RANGE) CLAMS	°/oo	
SUBSTRATE	MX 51	MUDDY & SANDY BOTTOM - WATER AREA @ LOW TIDE	ACRES	
	MX 52	FIRM BOTTOM & SOLID MATERIAL - WATER AREA @ LOW TIDE	"	
	MX 53	PHOSPHATES IN SHALLOW MARINE SEDIMENTS		
BIOTIC / PLANTS	MX 610	MARINE GREEN PLANTS		
	MX 62	MARINE PARASITE PLANTS		
	MX 61-10	PLANKTON	POUNDS	
	MX 61-11	PHYTOPLANKTON	POUNDS	
	MX 61-12	PHYTOPLANKTON - EXISTING POPULATION STOCK	GRAMS CARBON PER M^2	
	MX 61-13	PHYTOPLANKTON (AS CONSUMED IN RESPIRATION)	"	
	MX 61-14	PHYTOPLANKTON PRODUCED BY PHOTOSYNTHESIS	GRAMS CARBON $/M^2/DAY$	
	MX 61-15	PHYTOPLANKTON (AS MAINTAINED AFTER RESPIRATION)	"	
	MX 612	ALGAE	POUNDS	
	MX 60	ALL MARINE PLANTS	"	
	MX 6001	PLANT PRODUCTS: DETRITUS (DEAD PLANTS)	"	+
	MX 6002	" DETRITUS (PARTICULATE FOOD FOR MUSSELS)	mg.P PER M^2/DAY	
ANIMALS	MX 710	HERBIVORES		
	MX 711	ZOOPLANKTON	POUNDS	
	MX 712	HERBIVOROUS INVERTEBRATES: ANNELIDA	"	
	MX 713	" : MOLLUSCA	"	
	MX 714	" : BLUE MUSSEL	"	
	MX 715	" MUSSEL POPULATION (MEASURED :BY PHOSPHORUS CONTENT)	mg.P PER $METER^2$	
	MX 716	" : SOFT-SHELLED CLAM	BUSHELS	
	MX 717	" : CRUSTACEA	POUNDS	
	MX 718	" : MISCELLANEOUS	"	
	MX 719	HERRING	"	
	MX 720	PRIMARY CARNIVORES		
	MX 721	CARNIVOROUS INVERTEBRATES: LARGE GASTROPODS	"	
	MX 722	SMALL FISH	"	
	MX 723	WINTER FLOUNDER	"	
	MX 724	SECONDARY CARNIVORES		
	MX 725	COD	POUNDS	
	MX 73	PARASITE ANIMALS		
	MX 74	SCAVENGERS		
	MX 7151	ANIMAL PRODUCTS: INGESTED PHOSPHORUS BY MUSSELS	mg.P PER M^2/DAY	
	MX 7001	" : FECES		+
	MX 7152	" : FECES BY MUSSEL POPULATION	"	
	MX 7153	" : PSEUDOFECES BY MUSSEL POPULATION	"	
	MX 7202	" : MARINE BIRD DROPPINGS		
	MX 7004	" : DEAD MARINE ANIMAL MATTER		+
	MX 7154	" : DEAD MUSSELS	"	
	MX 7155	" : MUSSEL GAMETES	"	
	MX 7005	" : BONES, SHELLS & TEETH		+
	MX 75	DECOMPOSERS: DECOMPOSING AGENTS AS BACTERIA, ETC.		
	MX 7501	DECOMPOSED ORGANIC MATTER		
	MX 76	TRANSFORMERS: PHOSPHATIZING AGENTS AS BACTERIA, CRABS, ETC.		

b: Data not available c: This is a minimum for winter flounder fishing.

ECONOMIC

MARINE

LAND

ECONOMIC

CLASSIFICATION NUMBER	ACTIVITY TITLE	UNITS	RE 7949-101 PLEASURE BOATING: OUTBOARD SEASONAL	RE 7949-102 " : OUTBOARD TRANSIENT	RE 7949-103 " : INBOARD SEASONAL	RE 7949-104 " : INBOARD TRANSIENT	RE 7949-105 " : ROWBOATING RENTAL	RE 7949-106 " : ROWBOATING TRANSIENT	RE 7949-107 " : PARTY BOAT	RE 7949-108 " : SAILING SEASONAL	RE 7949-109 " : SAILING TRANSIENT	RE 7949-201 SPORT FISHING: PIER, ETC.	RE 7949-202 " : OUTBOARD SEASONAL	RE 7949-203 " : OUTBOARD TRANSIENT	RE 7949-204 " : INBOARD SEASONAL	RE 7949-205 " : INBOARD TRANSIENT	RE 7949-207 " : ROWBOATING RENTAL	RE 7949-208 " : ROWBOATING TRANSIENT	RE 7949-209 " : PARTY BOAT	RE 7949-210 " : SURF	RE 7949-211 " : CLAMMING	SIC 7943 BEACH ACTIVITY; SWIMMING
0122	FRUIT AND NUT TREE FARMS	DOLLARS																				
0123	VEGETABLE FARMS	"																				
2011	MEAT PACKING PLANTS	"																				
2021	CREAMERY, BUTTER	"																				
2026	FLUID, MILK	"																				
2033	CANNED FRUITS AND VEGETABLES	"																				
2037	FROZEN FRUITS AND VEGETABLES	"																				
2046	WET CORN MILLING	"																				
2061	CANE SUGAR (EXCEPT REFINING)	"																				
2062	CANE SUGAR REFINING	"																				
2071	CANDY AND OTHER CONFECTIONARY PRODUCTS	"																				
2072	CHOCOLATE AND COCOA PRODUCTS	"																				
2087	FLAVORING EXTRACTS & SUGARS	"																				
2621	PAPER MILLS	"																				
2641	PAPER COATING & GLAZING	"																				
2651	FOLDING PAPERBOARD BOXES	"																				
2654	SANITARY FOOD CONTAINERS	"																				
2751	COMMERCIAL PRINTING (EXCEPT LITHOGRAPHY)	"																				
2812	ALKALIES & CHLORINE	"																				
2815	DYES AND ORGANIC PIGMENTS	"																				
2816	INORGANIC PIGMENTS	"																				
2818	INDUSTRIAL ORGANIC CHEMISTRY	"																				
2819	INDUSTRIAL INORGANIC CHEMISTRY	"																				
2842	SPECIALTY CLEANING PREPARATIONS	"																				
2843	SURFACE ACTIVE AGENTS	"																				
2861	GUM AND WOOD CHEMISTRY	"																				
2899	CHEMICALS AND CHEMICAL PREPARATIONS	"																				
2911-0	PETROLEUM REFINING	"																				
2911-1	PETROLEUM REFINING	GALLONS	-2900	-2900	-5000	-5000	-1100	-1250	-940	-666	-660		-2900	-2900	-5000	-5000	-1100	-1250	-940			
3111	LEATHER TANNING & FINISHING	DOLLARS																				
3221	GLASS CONTAINERS	"																				
3274	LIME	"																				
3411	METAL CANS	"																				
3461	METAL STAMPINGS	"																				
3471	ELECTROPLATING & POLISHING	"																				
3732	BOATS (IN BOAT SEASON)	BOATS	-6.17	-6.17	-4.63	-4.63	-6.17	-6.17	-0.28	-6.17	-6.17		-6.17	-6.17	-4.63	-4.63	-6.17	-6.17	-0.28			
[illegible]	UNALLOCATED PRODUCED INPUTS	DOLLARS																				

	9888	PAYROLL	"																				
	98882	EMPLOYEE WELFARE PAYMENTS	"																				
	98884	UNEMPLOYMENT COMPENSATION AND SOCIAL SECURITY PAYMENTS	"																				
	9899	RESIDUAL	"																				
		LABOR																					
	LB 794-01	GENERAL MANAGER	MAN HRS.	-20	-20	-20	-20	-20	-20	-20	-20	-20	-20	-20	-20	-20	-20	-20	-20	-20	-20		
	LB 794-02	OTHER ADMINISTRATIVE	"	-37	-37	-37	-37	-37	-37	-37	-37	-37	-37	-37	-37	-37	-37	-37	-37	-37	-37		
	LB 794-03	DOCK MASTER	"	-30		-30					-30			-30		-30							
	LB 794-04	DOCK OPERATIONS PERSONNEL	"	-110	-110	-110	-110	-110	-110		-110	-110		-110	-110	-110	-110	-110	-110				
	LB 794-05	BOAT SALES MANAGER	"	-24	-24	-24	-24		-24		-24	-24		-24	-24	-24	-24		-24				
	LB 794-06	BOAT SALESMAN	"	-24	-24	-24	-24		-24		-24	-24		-24	-24	-24	-24		-24				
	LB 794-07	MARINE SUPPLIES SALES MANAGER	"	-24	-24	-24	-24		-24		-24	-24		-24	-24	-24	-24		-24				
	LB 794-08	MARINE SUPPLIES SALESMAN	"	-8	-8	-8	-8		-8		-8	-8		-8	-8	-8	-8		-8				
	LB 794-09	PARTY BOAT CREWS	"							-714										-714			
	LB 794-10	PACKAGED FOOD & BAIT PERSONNEL	"	-10	-10	-10	-10	-10	-10	-10	-10	-10	-23	-23	-23	-23	-23	-23	-23	-23	-23	-10	
	LB 794-11	REPAIR SHOP PERSONNEL	"	-104		-157					-209			-105		-157							
ECOLOGIC — ABIOTIC — CLIMATE																							
GEOLOGY	LX 21	PHOSPHATE ROCKS: VOLCANIC APATITE																					
	LX 22	" : GUANO DEPOSITS & FOSSIL BONES																					
	LX 23	" : UPLIFTED SEDIMENTARY ROCKS																					
	LX 24	PARTICULATE PHOSPHATE																					
PHYSIOGRAPHY	LX 3101	LAND AREA FOR: PARKING	SQ. FT.	-3757	-5368	-3426	-4028	-2684	-5368	-1624	-3757	-5368	-870	-3757	-5368	-3426	-4028	-2684	-5368	-1624	-1740	-1740	-3045
	LX 3102	" : TOTAL INDOOR STORAGE	"	-229	-658	-771	-933		-658		-1064	-1242		-229	-658	-771	-933		-658				
	LX 3103	" : LOCAL INDOOR STORAGE	"	-165		-670					-950			-165		-670							
	CX 3104	" : TOTAL REPAIRS	"	-59	-23	-84	-34		-23		-111	-44		-59	-23	-84	-34		-23				
	CX 3105	" : LOCAL REPAIRS	"	-59		-84					-111			-59		-84							
	LX 3106	" : BOAT & MOTOR SHOWROOM	"	-31.8	-31.8	-31.8	-31.8		-31.8		-31.8	-31.8		-31.8	-31.8	-31.8	-31.8		-31.8				
	LX 3107	" : SALES & MARINE ACCESSORIES	"	-9	-9	-9	-9		-9		-9	-9		-9	-9	-9	-9		-9				
	LX 3108	" : REST ROOM & LOUNGE	"	-17.5	-17.5	-17.5	-17.5	-17.5	-17.5	-17.5	-17.5	-17.5	-17.5	-17.5	-17.5	-17.5	-17.5	-17.5	-17.5	-17.5	-17.5	-17.5	
	LX 3109	" : GEAR STORAGE	"	-9	-9	-9	-9	-9	-9	-9	-9	-9	-9	-9	-9	-9	-9	-9	-9	-9	-9	-9	
	LX 3110	" : ADMINISTRATIVE OFFICE	"	-4.4	-4.4	-4.4	-4.4	-4.4	-4.4	-4.4	-4.4	-4.4	-4.4	-4.4	-4.4	-4.4	-4.4	-4.4	-4.4	-4.4	-4.4	-4.4	
	LX 3111	" : TRANSIENT & RENTAL OFFICE	"		-7.86		-7.86	-7.86	-7.86	-7.86		-7.86			-7.86		-7.86	-7.86	-7.86	-7.86			
	LX 3112	" : BAIT & PACKAGED FOOD SALES	"	-3.85	-3.85	-3.85	-3.85	-3.85	-3.85	-3.85	-3.85	-3.85	-8.94	-8.94	-8.94	-8.94	-8.94	-8.94	-8.94	-8.94	-8.94	-3.85	
	LX 3113	" : FUEL SALES	"	-1.38	-1.38	-1.38	-1.38				-1.10	-1.10		-1.38	-1.38	-1.38	-1.38						
	LX 3114	" : RAMPS	"		-3628		-3628		-3628			-3628			-3628		-3628		-3628				
	LX 3115	" : BATHHOUSE	"																				-70
	LX 3116	" : BEACH AREA	"																				-3000
HYDROLOGY	LX 42	DISSOLVED PHOSPHATE: IN STREAMS																					
	WPC 1000	WATER INTAKE - TOTAL	1000 GALLONS																				
	WPC 1001	FOR SANITARY USE	"																				
	WPC 1002	FOR PRODUCTION	"																				
	WPC 1003	FOR COOLING	"																				
	WPC 1004	FOR BOILER FEED	"																				
	WPC 1009	FOR OTHER, N.E.C.	"																				
SOILS	LX 51	DISSOLVED PHOSPHATE: IN SOILS																					
BIOTIC — PLANTS	LX 610	GREEN PLANTS																					
	LX 62	PARASITE PLANTS																					
	LX 6001	PLANT PRODUCT: DEAD PLANT MATTER																					
ANIMALS	LX 710	HERBIVORES																					
	LX 721	PRIMARY CARNIVORES																					
	LX 722	SECONDARY CARNIVORES																					
	LX 73	PARASITE ANIMALS																					
	LX 74	SCAVENGERS																					
	LX 7001	ANIMAL PRODUCTS: FECES																					
	LX 7004	" : DEAD ANIMAL MATTER																					
	LX 7005	" : BONES & TEETH																					
	LX 75	DECOMPOSERS: DECOMPOSING BACTERIA																					
	LX 7501	DECOMPOSED ORGANIC MATTER																					
	LX 76	TRANSFORMERS: PHOSPHATIZING BACTERIA																					

ECONOMIC

MARINE

CLASSIFICATION NUMBER	ACTIVITY TITLE	UNITS	RE 7949-101 PLEASURE BOATING: OUTBOARD SEASONAL	RE 7949-102 " : OUTBOARD TRANSIENT	RE 7949-103 " : INBOARD SEASONAL	RE 7949-104 " : INBOARD TRANSIENT	RE 7949-105 " : ROWBOATING RENTAL	RE 7949-106 " : ROWBOATING TRANSIENT	RE 7949-107 " : PARTY BOAT	RE 7949-108 " : SAILING SEASONAL	RE 7949-109 " : SAILING TRANSIENT	RE 7949-201 SPORT FISHING: PIER, ETC.	RE 7949-202 " : OUTBOARD SEASONAL	RE 7949-203 " : OUTBOARD TRANSIENT	RE 7949-204 " : INBOARD SEASONAL	RE 7949-205 " : INBOARD TRANSIENT	RE 7949-207 " : ROWBOATING RENTAL	RE 7949-208 " : ROWBOATING TRANSIENT	RE 7949-209 " : PARTY BOAT	RE 7949-210 " : SURF	RE 7949-211 " : CLAMMING	SIC 7943 BEACH ACTIVITY: SWIMMING
ECONOMIC — MARINE																						
M 794-0	RECREATION	1000 MAN DAYS	+1	+1	+1	+1	+1	+1	+1	+1	+1	+1	+1	+1	+1	+1	+1	+1	+1	+1	+1	0
ABIOTIC — CLIMATE																						
MX 11	LIGHT : INCIDENT SOLAR RADIATION AT THE OCEAN SURFACE	G.CAL/CM^2/MIN																				
GEOLOGY																						
PHYSIOGRAPHY																						
MX 31	WATER AREA: BAY OR ESTUARY WATER AREA	ACRES																				
MX 32	" : INTERTIDAL & SUBTIDAL SHOAL WATER AREA	"																				
MX 3301	WATER SURFACE AREA: FOR DOCKED BOATS	SQ. FT.	-5152	-1717	-5156	-5880	-2468	-823	-507	-7287	-7836		-5152	-1717	-5156	-5880	-2468	-823	-507			
MX 3302	WATER SURFACE AREA: FOR MOORED BOATS	"			-2493					-2820	-3000				-2493							
MX 3303	WATER SURFACE AREA: FOR SWIMMING	"																				-3000
HYDROLOGY																						
MX 410	PARTICULATE PHOSPHATE: IN ESTUARINE WATERS																					
MX 411	: IN ESTUARINE WATERS @ 14mg.P/M^2	mg.P/M^2/DAY																				
MX 420	DISSOLVED PHOSPHATE: IN OCEAN WATER	mg.-at/M^3																				
MX 421	DISSOLVED PHOSPHATE: IN OCEAN WATER @ 19 mg.P/M^2	mg.P/M^2/DAY																				
MX 43	DISSOLVED ORGANIC PHOSPHORUS: @ 6 mg.P/M^2	"																				
MX 44	WATER TRANSPARENCY: $(t = \frac{1}{k})$																					
WPC 1031	WATER DISCHARGE, TOTAL	1000 GALLONS																				
WPC 1011	SANITARY USE	"																				
WPC 1012	PRODUCTION	"																				
WPC 1013	COOLING	"																				
WPC 1019	OTHER, N.E.C.	"																				
WPC 1031	B.O.D., 5 DAY	1000 POUNDS																				
WPC 10311	SETTLEABLE 5 DAY B.O.D.	"																				
WPC 1033	C.O.D.	"																				
WPC 1040	SOLIDS, TOTAL	"																				
WPC 1041	SOLIDS, SUSPENDED	"																				
WPC 1042	SOLIDS, SETTLEABLE	"																				
WPC 1051	ALKALINITY	"																				
WPC 1052	ACIDITY	"																				
WPC 1091	CHROMIUM	"																				
WPC 1092	CHLORIDE	"																				
	QUALITY CONSTRAINTS																					
MX 4501	COLIFORM INDEX [PER 100mL (MAX.)]		5000	5000	5000	5000	5000	5000	5000	5000	5000	-5000	-5000	-5000	-5000	-5000	-5000	-5000	-5000	-5000	b	2400
MX 4502	DISSOLVED OXYGEN [ppm (MIN.)]	PPM	4.0	4.0	4.0	4.0	4.0	4.0	4.0	4.0	4.0	2.5[c]	2.5[c]	2.5[c]	2.5[c]	2.5[c]	2.5[c]	2.5[c]	2.5[c]	2.5[c]	b	7.0
			6.0-8.5	6.0-8.5	6.0-8.5	6.0-8.5	6.0-8.5	6.0-8.5	6.0-8.5	6.0-8.5	6.0-8.5	6.7-8.6	6.7-8.6	6.7-8.6	6.7-8.6	6.7-8.6	6.7-8.6	6.7-8.6	6.7-8.6	6.7-8.6	b	6.5-8.5

Group	Code	Commodity	Unit																				
ECOLOGIC	MX 4504	B.O.D. [ppm (MONTHLY AVE.)]	PPM	3.0	3.0	3.0	3.0	3.0	3.0	3.0	3.0	3.0	b	b	b	b	b	b	b	b	b	b	b
	MX 4505	B.O.D. [ppm (MAX.)]	"	5.0	5.0	5.0	5.0	5.0	5.0	5.0	5.0	5.0	b	b	b	b	b	b	b	b	b	b	b
	MX 4506	TURBIDITY [ppm (MAX.)]	"	b	b	b	b	b	b	b	b	b	10^5	10^5	10^5	10^5	10^5	10^5	10^5	10^5	10^5	b	20
	MX 4507	COLOR (UNITS)	UNITS	b	b	b	b	b	b	b	b	b	b	b	b	b	b	b	b	b	b	b	30
	MX 4508	WATER TEMPERATURE (MAX.) COD	DEGREES CENTIGRADE											b	b	b	b	b	b	b			
	MX 4509	WATER TEMPERATURE (MAX.) WINTER FLOUNDER	"										25	25	25	25	25	25	25	25	25		
	MX 4510	WATER TEMPERATURE (RANGE) CLAMS	"																			10-20	
	MX 4511-1	SALINITY (RANGE) COD	o/oo											4-30	4-30	4-30	4-30	4-30	4-30	4-30			
	MX 4511-2	SALINITY (RANGE) WINTER FLOUNDER	o/oo										4-30	4-30	4-30	4-30	4-30	4-30	4-30	4-30	4-30		
	MX 4511-3	SALINITY (RANGE) CLAMS	o/oo																			9-25	
SUBSTRATE	MX 51	MUDDY & SANDY BOTTOM - WATER AREA @ LOW TIDE	ACRES																				
	MX 52	FIRM BOTTOM & SOLID MATERIAL - WATER AREA @ LOW TIDE	"																				
	MX 53	PHOSPHATES IN SHALLOW MARINE SEDIMENTS																					
PLANTS	MX 610	MARINE GREEN PLANTS																					
	MX 62	MARINE PARASITE PLANTS																					
	MX 61-10	PLANKTON	POUNDS																				
	MX 61-11	PHYTOPLANKTON	"																				
	MX 61-12	PHYTOPLANKTON - EXISTING POPULATION STOCK	GRAMS CARBON PER M^2																				
	MX 61-13	PHYTOPLANKTON MATTER	"																				
	MX 61-14	PHYTOPLANKTON PRODUCED BY PHOTOSYNTHESIS	GRAMS CARBON $/M^2$/DAY																				
	MX 61-15	PHYTOPLANKTON MATTER UTILIZED IN RESPIRATION	"																				
	MX 612	ALGAE	POUNDS																				
	MX 60	ALL MARINE PLANTS	"																				
	MX 6001	PLANT PRODUCTS: DETRITUS (DEAD PLANTS)	"																				
	MX 6002	" DETRITUS (PARTICULATE FOOD FOR MUSSELS)	mg.P PER M^2 DAY																				
ANIMALS	MX 710	HERBIVORES																					
	MX 711	ZOOPLANKTON	POUNDS																				
	MX 712	HERBIVOROUS INVERTIBRATES: ANNELIDA	"																				
	MX 713	" : MOLLUSCA	"																				
	MX 714	" : BLUE MUSSEL	"																				
	MX 715	" : MUSSEL POPULATION (MEASURED BY PHOSPHORUS CONTENT)	mg.P PER $METER^2$																				
	MX 716	" : SOFT-SHELLED CLAM	POUNDS																			-500	
	MX 717	" : CRUSTACEA	"																				
	MX 718	" : MISCELLANEOUS	"																				
	MX 719	HERRING	"																				
	MX 720	PRIMARY CARNIVORES																					
	MX 721	CARNIVOROUS INVERTIBRATES: LARGE GASTROPODS	"																				
	MX 722	SMALL FISH	"																				
	MX 723	WINTER FLOUNDER	"										-1400	-3600	-3600	-1400	-1400	-3600	-3600	-1400	-1400		
	MX 724	SECONDARY CARNIVORES																					
	MX 725	COD	POUNDS											-6700	-6700	-26800	-26800	-6700	-6700	-13400			
	MX 73	PARASITE ANIMALS																					
	MX 74	SCAVENGERS																					
	MX 7151	ANIMAL PRODUCTS: INGESTED PHOSPHORUS BY MUSSELS	mg.P PER M^2 DAY																				
	MX 700[illegible]	" : FECES																					
	MX 7152	" : FECES BY MUSSEL POPULATION	"																				
	MX 7153	" : PSEUDOFECES BY MUSSEL POPULATION	"																				
	MX 7202	" : MARINE BIRD DROPPINGS																					
	MX 7004	" : DEAD MARINE ANIMAL MATTER																					
	MX 7154	" : DEAD MUSSELS	"																				
	MX 7155	" : MUSSEL GAMETES	"																				
	MX 7005	" : BONES, SHELLS & TEETH																					
	MX 75	DECOMPOSERS: DECOMPOSING AGENTS AS BACTERIA, ETC.																					
	MX 7501	DECOMPOSED ORGANIC MATTER																					
BIOTIC	MX 76	TRANSFORMERS: • PHOSPHATIZING AGENTS AS BACTERIA, CRABS, ETC.																					

NOTE: for complete identification information in this column, please refer to corresponding Classification Number on pages 100 and 101.

ECOLOGIC

Category	Code	Process
CLIMATE		
GEOLOGY	PLX 23	GEOLOGIC UPLIFT OF MARINE SEDIMENTS
PHYSIOGRAPHY		
HYDROLOGY (ABIOTIC)	P2MX420	DISSOLVING OF PHOSPHATES IN OCEAN
SUBSTRATE	PMX 53	SETTLEMENT OF MATERIALS CONTAINING PHOSPHOROUS TO THE OCEAN SEDIMENTS
PLANTS	PMX 610	GREEN PLANT PRODUCTION BY PHOTOSYNTHESIS
	PMX 62	FOOD CONSUMPTION BY PARASITE PLANTS
	PMX 61-14	PHYTOPLANKTON PRODUCTION BY PHOTOSYNTHESIS
	P1MX 61-15	UTILIZATION OF PHYTOPLANKTON MATTER BY RESPIRATION @ 2°C
	P2MX 61-15	" @ 7°C
	P3MX 61-15	" @ 12°C
	P4MX 61-15	" @ 17°C
	PMX 61-11	PHYTOPLANKTON IN LBS. (DUMMY UNIT CONVERSION PROCESS)
	PMX 61-10	PLANKTON PRODUCTION
	PMX 612	ALGAE PRODUCTION
	PMX 60	ALL MARINE PLANT PRODUCTION
	P2MX 6001	MORTALITY OF MARINE PLANTS
ANIMALS (BIOTIC)	PMX 710	FOOD CONSUMPTION BY HERBIVORES
	PMX 711	FOOD CONSUMPTION BY ZOOPLANKTON
	PMX 712	HERBIVOROUS INVERTEBRATES: ANNELIDA PRODUCTION
	PMX 713	" : MOLLUSCA PRODUCTION
	PMX 714	" : BLUE MUSSEL PRODUCTION
	PMX 7151	" : INGESTION BY MUSSEL POPULATION
	PMX 716	" : SOFT-SHELLED CLAM PRODUCTION
	PMX 717	" : CRUSTACEA PRODUCTION
	PMX 718	" : MISCELLANEOUS PRODUCTION
	PMX 719	HERRING PRODUCTION
	PMX 720	FOOD CONSUMPTION BY PRIMARY CARNIVORES
	PMX 721	LARGE CARNIVOROUS INVERTEBRATES: GASTROPOD PRODUCTION
	PMX 722	SMALL FISH PRODUCTION
	PMX 723	WINTER FLOUNDER PRODUCTION
	PMX 724	FOOD CONSUMPTION BY SECONDARY CARNIVORES
	PMX 725	COD PRODUCTION
	PMX 73	FOOD CONSUMPTION BY ANIMAL PARASITES
	PMX 74	FOOD CONSUMPTION BY SCAVENGERS
	P2MX 7001	EXCRETION
	PMX 7152	FECES PRODUCTION BY MUSSEL POPULATION
	PMX 7153	PSEUDOFECES PRODUCTION BY MUSSEL POPULATION
	PMX 7202	EXCRETION BY MARINE BIRDS
	PLX 22	COLLECTION OF MARINE BIRD DROPPINGS
	P2MX 7004	MORTALITY OF MARINE ANIMALS
	PMX 7154	MORTALITY OF MUSSELS
	PMX 7155	GAMETE PRODUCTION BY MUSSEL REPRODUCTION
	P2MX 7005	REMOVAL OF FLESH BY CARNIVORES & SCAVENGERS
	PMX 7501	DECOMPOSITION BY DECOMPOSERS
	P3MX 420	DISSOLVED PHOSPHATE PRODUCTION BY TRANSFORMERS
	PMX 421	DISSOLVED PHOSPHATE PRODUCTION BY MUSSEL POPULATION
	PMX 431	DISSOLVED ORGANIC PHOSPHORUS PRODUCTION BY MUSSEL POPULATION

ECONOMIC — **LAND**

CLASSIFICATION NUMBER: 0122, 0123, 2011, 2021, 2026, 2033, 2037, 2046, 2061, 2062, 2071, 2072, 2087, 2621, 2641, 2651, 2654, 2751, 2812, 2815, 2816, 2818, 2819, 2842, 2843, 2861, 2899, 2911-0, 2911-1, 3111, 3221, 3274, 3411, 3461, 3471, 3732, 39999, 4911

4920
9300
9888
98882
98884
9899
LB 794-01
LB 794-02
LB 794-03
LB 794-04
LB 794-05
LB 794-06
LB 794-07
LB 794-08
LB 794-09
LB 794-10
LB 794-11
LX 21
LX 22
LX 23
LX 24
LX 3101
LX 3102
LX 3103
CX 3104
CX 3105
LX 3106
LX 3107
LX 3108
LX 3109
LX 3110
LX 3111
LX 3112
LX 3113
LX 3114
LX 3115
LX 3116
LX 42
WPC 1000
WPC 1001
WPC 1002
WPC 1003
WPC 1004
WPC 1009
LX 51
LX 610
LX 62
LX 6001
LX 710
LX 721
LX 722
LX 73
LX 74
LX 7001
LX 7004
LX 7005
LX 75
LX 7501
LX 76

CLIMATE
GEOLOGY
PHYSIOGRAPHY
HYDROLOGY
SOILS
PLANTS
ANIMALS

ABIOTIC
BIOTIC
ECOLOGIC

NOTE:
for complete identification information in this column, please refer to corresponding Classification Number on pages 102 and 103.

ECON-OMIC: MARINE — ABIOTIC: CLIMATE, GEOLOGY, PHYSIOGRAPHY, HYDROLOGY

ECOLOGIC: ABIOTIC — CLIMATE, GEOLOGY, PHYSIOGRAPHY, HYDROLOGY, SUBSTRATE; BIOTIC — PLANTS, ANIMALS

Group	Classification number	Process	M 794-0	MX 11	MX 31	MX 32	MX 3301	MX 3302	MX 3303	MX 410	MX 411	MX 420	MX 421	MX 43	MX 44	WPC 1031	WPC 1011	WPC 1012	WPC 1013	WPC 1019	WPC 1031	WPC 10311	WPC 1033	WPC 1040	WPC 1041	WPC 1042	WPC 1051	WPC 1052	WPC 1091	WPC 1092	MX 4501	MX 4502
GEOLOGY	PLX 23	GEOLOGIC UPLIFT OF MARINE SEDIMENTS																														
HYDROLOGY	P2MX420	DISSOLVING OF PHOSPHATES IN OCEAN								-		+																				
SUBSTRATE	PMX 53	SETTLEMENT OF MATERIALS CONTAINING PHOSPHOROUS TO THE OCEAN SEDIMENTS								-																						
PLANTS	PMX 610	GREEN PLANT PRODUCTION BY PHOTOSYNTHESIS										-																				
	PMX 62	FOOD CONSUMPTION BY PARASITE PLANTS																														
	PMX 61-14	PHYTOPLANKTON PRODUCTION BY PHOTOSYNTHESIS		-1.79								-.0589			-68.68																	
	P1MX 61-15	UTILIZATION OF PHYTOPLANKTON MATTER BY RESPIRATION @ 2°C																														
	P2MX 61-15	" @ 7°C																														
	P3MX 61-15	" @ 12°C																														
	P4MX 61-15	" @ 17°C																														
	PMX 61-11	PHYTOPLANKTON IN LBS. (DUMMY UNIT CONVERSION PROCESS)																														
	MX 61-10	PLANKTON																														
	MX 612	ALGAE				-8×10^{-6}																										
	MX 60	ALL MARINE PLANTS																														
	P2MX 6001	MORTALITY OF MARINE PLANTS																														
ANIMALS	PMX 710	FOOD CONSUMPTION BY HERBIVORES																														
	PMX 711	FOOD CONSUMPTION BY ZOOPLANKTON																														
	MX 712	HERBIVOROUS INVERTIBRATES: ANNELIDA																														
	MX 713	" : MOLLUSCA																														
	MX 714	" : BLUE MUSSEL																														
	PMX 7151	" : INGESTION BY MUSSEL POPULATION									-4.63		-0.07																			
	MX 716	" : SOFT-SHELLED CLAM																														
	MX 717	" : CRUSTACEA																														
	MX 718	" : MISCELLANEOUS																														
	MX 719	HERRING																														
	PMX 720	FOOD CONSUMPTION BY PRIMARY CARNIVORES																														
	MX 721	CARNIVOROUS LARGE INVERTIBRATES: GASTROPODS																														
	MX 722	SMALL FISH																														
	MX 723	WINTER FLOUNDER			-.04																											
	PMX 724	FOOD CONSUMPTION BY SECONDARY CARNIVORES																														
	MX 725	COD																														
	PMX 73	FOOD CONSUMPTION BY ANIMAL PARASITES																														
	PMX 74	FOOD CONSUMPTION BY SCAVENGERS																														
	P2MX 7002	EXCRETION																														
	PMX 7152	FECES PRODUCTION BY MUSSEL POPULATION																														
	PMX 7153	PSEUDOFECES PRODUCTION BY MUSSEL POPULATION																														
	PMX 7202	EXCRETION BY MARINE BIRDS																														
	PLX 22	COLLECTION OF MARINE BIRD DROPPINGS																														
	P2MX 7004	MORTALITY OF MARINE ANIMALS																														
	PMX 7154	MORTALITY OF MUSSELS																														
	PMX 7155	GAMETE PRODUCTION BY MUSSEL REPRODUCTION																														
	P2MX 7005	REMOVAL OF FLESH BY CARNIVORES & SCAVENGERS																														
	PMX 7501	DECOMPOSITION BY DECOMPOSERS																														
	P3MX 420	DISSOLVED PHOSPHATE PRODUCTION BY TRANSFORMERS										+																				
	PMX 421	DISSOLVED PHOSPHATE PRODUCTION BY MUSSEL POPULATION											+0.260																			
	PMX 431	DISSOLVED ORGANIC PHOSPHORUS PRODUCTION BY MUSSEL POPULATION												+0.023																		

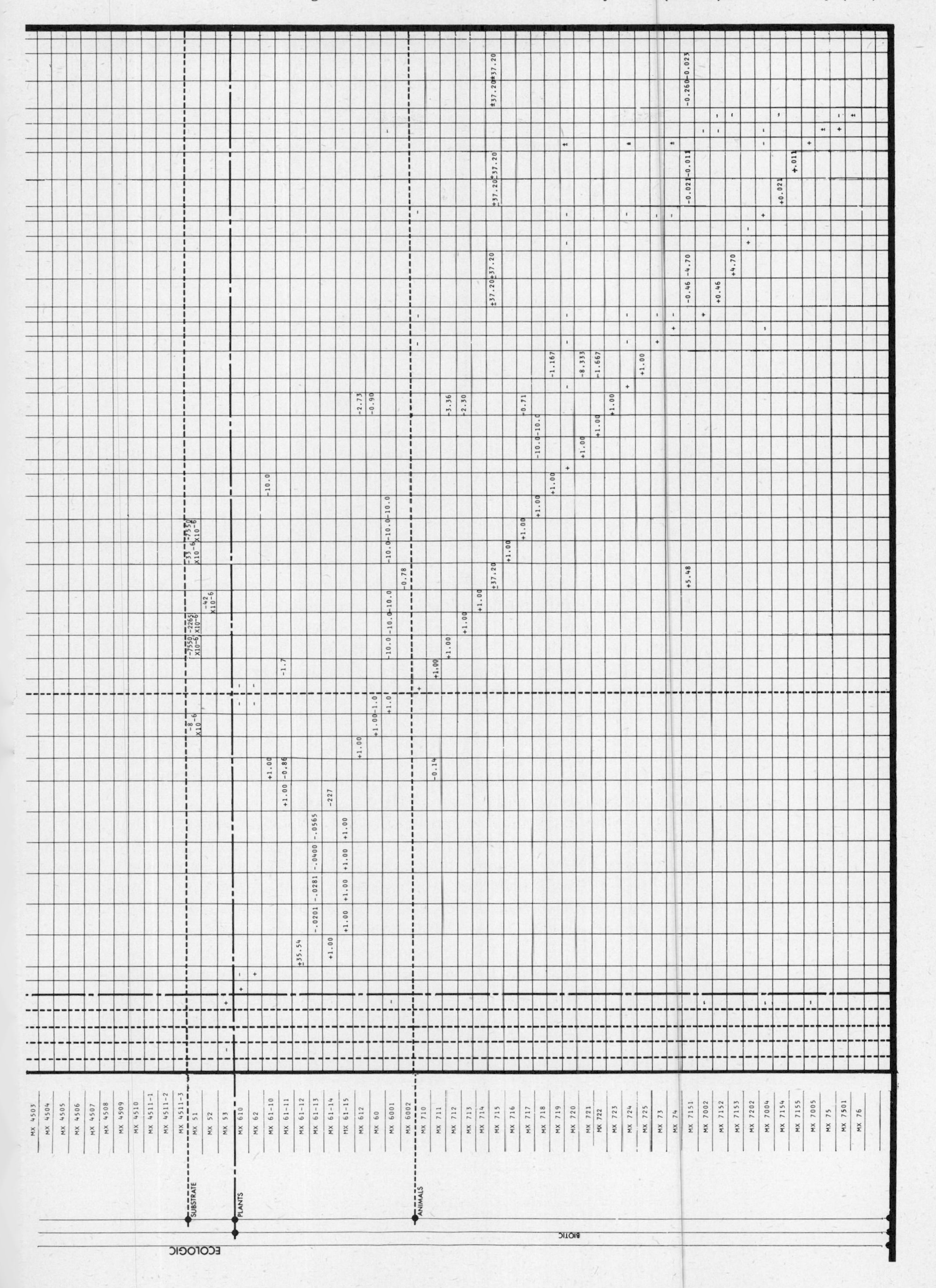
MX 4503
MX 4504
MX 4505
MX 4506
MX 4507
MX 4508
MX 4509
MX 4510
MX 4511-1
MX 4511-2
MX 4511-3
MX 51
MX 52
MX 53
MX 610
MX 62
MX 61-10
MX 61-11
MX 61-12
MX 61-13
MX 61-14
MX 61-15
MX 612
MX 60
MX 6001
MX 6002
MX 710
MX 711
MX 712
MX 713
MX 714
MX 715
MX 716
MX 717
MX 718
MX 719
MX 720
MX 721
MX 722
MX 723
MX 724
MX 725
MX 73
MX 74
MX 7151
MX 7002
MX 7152
MX 7153
MX 7202
MX 7004
MX 7154
MX 7155
MX 7005
MX 75
MX 7501
MX 76
SUBSTRATE
PLANTS
ANIMALS
BIOTIC
ECOLOGIC

Area exist as two critical areas which differ in their basic physical processes and structure. Thus we find it appropriate to designate these two as the two major regions, LAND and MARINE. Accordingly, the first major division of columns refers to LAND activities, and the second to MARINE activities; while the first major division of rows refers to commodities from LAND sources, and the second major division to commodities from MARINE sources. (Upon further analysis, we might find a set of three critical areas, LAND, MARINE, and INTERTIDAL, more meaningful.[1]

If we focus on just the two major regions, LAND and MARINE, there are four major sets of cells in the flow, or coefficient, table to be considered. For example, for the coefficient table A we have:

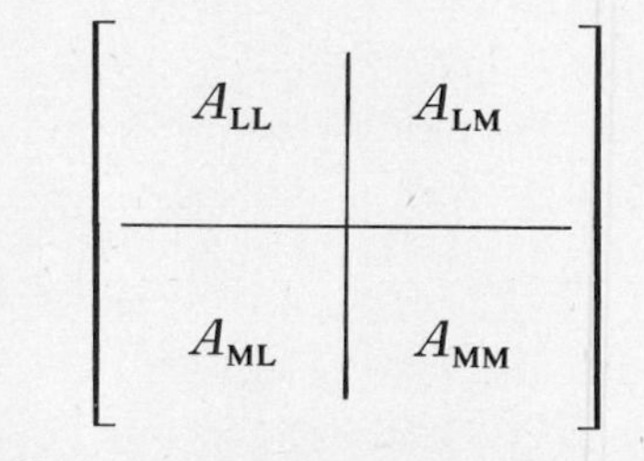

$$\left[\begin{array}{c|c} A_{LL} & A_{LM} \\ \hline A_{ML} & A_{MM} \end{array}\right]$$

where: A_{LL} covers the coefficients indicating the flows of commodities from LAND sources to meet the requirements of LAND activities.

A_{LM} covers coefficients indicating the flows of commodities from LAND sources to meet the requirements of MARINE activities.

A_{ML} covers the coefficients indicating the flows of commodities from MARINE sources to meet the requirements of LAND activities.

A_{MM} covers the coefficients indicating the flows of commodities from MARINE sources to meet the requirements of MARINE activities.

For each of the four major cells, both the activities and the commodities are divided into two classes. The activities in the first set are economic; those in the second set are ecologic. Thus, moving horizontally along the column headings, we first observe economic activities in the LAND region, then ecologic activities in the LAND region, then economic activities in the MARINE region, and then ecologic activities in the MARINE region. Going down the left-hand tab of the table, we first observe economic commodities from LAND sources, then ecologic commodities from LAND sources, then economic commodities from MARINE sources, and finally ecologic commodities from MARINE sources.

Against this background, we are in a position to look at Table 4.3 in some detail, with reference to actual coefficients. For the LAND region, we list at the head of the columns the diverse economic activities to be operated, beginning at the upper left with *Agricultural activities*, as is typical in input-output studies, and ending with *Service and Government activities*. At the left-hand tab, we list for the LAND region the corresponding commodities produced by these LAND activities. In the strict input-output format, there are as many rows as columns (one commodity being associated with one and only one activity, with each activity producing only one commodity). However, we wish to adapt the input-output table for programming use; hence, we may have more commodities than activities, or vice-versa, as we allow any commodity to be produced by more than one activity and any activity to produce more than one commodity. Accordingly, in Table 4.3 we do not have the same number of rows as columns.

Once the economic activities are listed, we proceed to list the ecologic activities. We begin with the abiotic processes, and in particular those associated with geologic

[1] As has already been indicated the best set of regions depends on the problem being investigated, among other factors. If, for example, development of heavy industry was also under investigation, a fourth environmental type of region, namely, AIR, would need to be introduced in order to evaluate potential air pollution magnitudes and costs. In general, our conceptual framework is sufficiently flexible to embrace all types of ecologic and economic-oriented regions.

processes. Among the first listed are: *Phosphate Production via Volcanic Action* and *Erosion of Phosphate Rock*. We proceed through other abiotic processes to plant biotic processes (such as *Food Consumption by Parasite Plants*) and end with the animal biotic activity: *Phosphate Release by Transformers*.

Observe next that a full set of economic and ecologic activities may also be listed in the column headings of the major division MARINE. In general it is possible to list the same economic and ecologic activities in both major divisions. If we were to do so, then many of the activities would be run at zero level, since technologically it is impossible to operate a marine-type activity (such as winter flounder production) on land, and vice versa (such as steel production on the water). Other activities, however, such as sport fishing for fresh water bass could take place on both land and water.

We have chosen not to list the same set of activities in both major divisions since the table, already too large to handle easily, would become unmanageable. Thus, among the economic activities in the MARINE region, we do not list manufacturing, but we do list a set of recreational activities which are MARINE-oriented. The first three are (1) *Pleasure Boating: Outboard Seasonal*; (2) *Pleasure Boating: Outboard Transient*; (3) *Pleasure Boating: Inboard Seasonal*; and the last one is *Swimming*. Then we list ecologic activities in the winter flounder and cod food chains discussed in Section 3.6.

We now turn to the list of commodities along the left-hand tab. As already indicated, we first list for the LAND region the economic commodities, which correspond to the economic activities which head the first set of columns. The first ones are *Products of Fruit and Nut Tree Farms*, and *Products of Vegetable Farms*. Once all the economic commodities are set down for the LAND region, we list the ecologic commodities. The first are *Phosphate Rock* and *Particulate Phosphate*. Next comes *Land for Parking*, and Land for a number of other purposes. (We consider Land an abiotic physiographic commodity.) Finally, *Decomposed Organic Matter* and *Transformers* (*Phosphatizing Bacteria*) are listed. The last commodity serves basically as a catalyst; both a plus and a minus sign appear in any cell in which that type of commodity is involved. For the MARINE region, the list begins with the economic commodities, such as *Boats* and *Recreation*, and ends with animal biotic ecologic commodities, such as *Decomposed Organic Matter*, and *Transformers* (*Phosphatizing Agents*).

We now wish to illustrate the specific linkage of the economic and ecologic systems by reference to actual coefficients which are recorded in Table 4.3. For our purposes, the coefficients which relate to the system comprising the economy of Salem (which is located on the Massachusetts coast) may be used. Accordingly, we record in Table 4.3 data for selected manufacturing sectors of the Salem economy. The collection and processing of the data for these manufacturing sectors are fully described elsewhere.[2]

Specifically, consider the manufacturing industry, S.I.C. 3111: *Leather Tanning and Finishing*. Historically, this industry has been important to the Salem economy, and it can be expected to maintain a primary position. The listing of the input-output coefficients for this industry starts at the upper left-hand corner of Table 4.3. The first coefficient is -0.135061. The coefficient indicates that approximately $13\frac{1}{2}$ cents of the products of S.I.C. 2011: *Meat Packing Plants*, are required per dollar of gross output in the leather tanning and finishing industry. The ninth coefficient is -0.042151; it indicates that just over 4 cents of the products of S.I.C. 2843: *Surface Active Agents*, are required per dollar of gross output in S.I.C. 3111. Each of the coefficients which is preceded by a minus ($-$) sign represents an input. In the same column and along the row labelled S.I.C. 3111: *Leather Tanning and Finishing*, the coefficient $+.877532$ is recorded. The plus sign

[2] See Isard, Bassett, Choguill *et al.* [2], Appendix D. Also see Isard, Langford, and Romanoff [3].

signifies a net output. Thus, for each dollar value of gross output in S.I.C. 3111, the value of net output is nearly 88 cents. Conversely, just over 12 cents of the products of S.I.C. 3111 are required per dollar value of gross output in that industry. Proceeding further down the column, we come to inputs of ecologic commodities from LAND sources. Here is listed the coefficient for *Total Water Intake*; namely, −0.019965.[3]

Still further down the column we come to the major division, MARINE. In the lower section of this major division, within the ecologic subsection, a number of non-zero entries are recorded. These represent the pollutants exported (or dumped) by the leather tanning and finishing industry. The coefficients listed have plus (+) signs indicating that the corresponding commodities are outputs of the industrial process and are fed (exported) to the MARINE region. Certain of these coefficients are measured in terms of 1,000 gallons per dollar of gross output, while others are measured by 1,000 pounds per dollar of gross output. For example, the coefficient +0.017816 refers to commodity WPC 1010: *Total Water Discharge.* It states that for each dollar of gross output from S.I.C. 3111: *Leather Tanning and Finishing*, 17.816 gallons of water are discharged from the plant. The coefficient for WPC 1040: *Solids*, *Total*, indicates that for each dollar value of output from S.I.C. 3111, 0.361 pound of solid pollutants is discharged.[4,5]

Similar illustrations are given for two other activities: S.I.C. 2033, *Canned Fruits, Vegetables, Preserves, Jams and Jellies*, and S.I.C. 2071, *Candy and Other Confectionery Products*. Both of the corresponding columns contain input-output coefficients derived for the Salem economy.

From the examples, it is apparent that each of the three industries have major linkages to the ecologic system. The leather tanning and finishing industry obtains a major commodity input from the ecologic system (water for production) and then exports, or forces upon the ecologic system, certain of its outputs (pollutants).

Recall that to reach this formulation, three distinct steps were taken. First, the traditional a_{ij} input-output or activity analysis coefficients were derived for an economy. Second, the framework under consideration was broadened to include ecologic activities and commodities for the entire region LAND. Thus the economic activity analysis table was expanded and subsections showing linkages between the LAND-based economic sectors and the LAND-based ecologic sectors (both abiotic and biotic) were added. The third step involved the addition of the major region MARINE, again with economic and ecologic subsections. Here it was necessary to specify the linkages not only between the subsections of the MARINE region, but also between the subsections of the LAND region and the subsections of the MARINE region.

Now, it can be seen that the pollutants from the leather tanning and finishing industry which are dumped on the ecologic system are of a critical nature. They affect not only the characteristics of the ecologic system, but also the capability of that system to provide adequate inputs for other economic activities. This latter point is particularly relevant when these other economic activities are based in the MARINE region, such as are sport fishing recreation (which requires a fish input) and swimming (which requires a water input).

[3] It is assumed that the Salem leather tanning and finishing industry obtains its water from the LAND region and dumps its waste water into the MARINE region. However, in other situations, an industry could obtain water from the MARINE region (a large lake) and could dispose of its pollutants in the LAND region (a stream fully contained in the LAND region.)

[4] An alternative way of noting the output of these pollutants would be to list them as ecologic commodities, and thus in the lower half of the commodity rows of the LAND region. This might be the more valid procedure, but it would necessitate specifying activities which transfer (transport) such pollutants to the MARINE region, where they become ecologic commodities of the MARINE region.

[5] A preliminary classification and coding system with regard to water use and water pollutant commodities is given in Table 4.3a. The development of this system is presented in Isard and Romanoff [4].

Table 4.3a Water Pollution Classification (WPC) Code

WPC Code	Water Related Item	Units
1000	Water Intake, Total[a]	1,000 gal./$
1001	Sanitary use	,,
1002	Production use	,,
1003	Cooling	,,
1004	Boiler feed	,,
1008	Irrigation	,,
1009	Other, n.e.c.	,,
1010	Water Discharge, Total	,,
1011	Sanitary use	,,
1012	Production	,,
1013	Cooling	,,
1019	Other, n.e.c.	,,
1020	Water consumed	,,
1031	Biochemical oxygen demand (BOD, 5-day)	1,000 lb./$
1032	Ultimate oxygen demand (UOD)	,,
1033	Chemical oxygen demand (COD)	,,
1040	Solids, total[b]	,,
1041	Suspended solids	,,
1042	Settleable solids	,,
1047	Turbidity	,,
1048	Color	,,[c]
1051	Alkalinity	,,
1052	Acidity	,,
1061	Oils and greases	,,
1062	Surfactants	,,
1070	Pathogenic (disease-causing) organisms	—[d]
1080	Temperature	—[d]
1090	Other pollutants	,,
1095	Toxic materials[e]	,,
1096	Radioactive waste	—[d]
1099	Not classified	,,

[a]Cost of water intake is given by S.I.C. code 4941: water supply.
[b]1040 = 1041 + 1042.
[c]In addition, color should be specified by kind by wave length.
[d]No one satisfactory measure was decided upon at this time, although thermal pollution may be specified most appropriately in terms of millions of Btu's per dollar output.
[e]Phenols, which fall in this category, may be identified by a five-digit code such as WPC 10951.

Consider again the water pollutants associated with the leather tanning and finishing industry. These pollutants are listed in the lower part of the table relating to the MARINE region, and have positive (+) signs. Consider also the inputs into the recreational activities, which inputs are listed along the same rows of the MARINE region. These recreational activities are specifically listed at the headings of the columns in the economic subsection of the major division relating to the MARINE region. It can be seen that for a given geographic area, if the leather tanning and finishing industry were operated at a high enough level, then given the biological oxygen demand (BOD) coefficients [indicated by + signs] in the *Leather Tanning and Finishing* column in the LAND region, the result would be a quality of water inconsistent with the dissolved oxygen input requirements of the swimming activity which are listed in the *Beach Activity: Swimming* column. In this case, the inconsistency, which the table helps identify, must be resolved, perhaps by a zero or low level of swimming activity, or reduced level of leather tanning and finishing, or by some treatment of the pollutants,[6] or by some combination of these.[7]

This illustration reveals the importance of having a single table, such as Table 4.3, which includes both economic and ecologic activities and commodities. The table not only has descriptive value but it also identifies potential inconsistencies and conflicts in planning and programming.

Proceeding further, we may note in Table 4.3 the specific input coefficients derived for the recreational swimming activity, where its unit level is defined as 1,000 man-days of recreational swimming. These coefficients include a land requirement of 3,045 square feet of parking area, 70 square feet of bathhouse area, and 3,000 square feet of beach area. Hence, not only are the implications of environmental quality levels revealed by this table, but so are the implications for spatial, land-use planning.

To this point, the illustrations from the table have centered around two kinds of economic activities: manufacturing (such as in the Salem area), and recreation at a proposed marine-oriented recreation facility. Each of these kinds of activities requires both economic and ecologic commodities. Likewise, each has linkages with both the LAND region and the MARINE region. But there are other kinds of critical linkages. For example, a feasible investment in a marine-oriented recreational complex may require the inclusion of more than a single recreational activity. Any single recreational activity may require inputs from the LAND region, such as land area for parking, and inputs from the MARINE region, such as fish for sport fishing. These inputs are indicated in the columns relating the recreational activities to the various commodity sectors of the MARINE and LAND regions. The supply of the fish inputs is obviously related to fish production activities—which represents another type of production activity; namely, an ecologic production activity. Such an activity is cod production, which is listed in the MARINE region. Its column indicates that in order to produce 1 pound of cod, 1.167 pounds of herring, 8.333 pounds of carnivorous invertebrates: large gastropods, and 1.667 pounds of small fish are required. These requirements in turn imply that other ecological production processes must be going on, such as small fish production, herring production, phytoplankton production (photosynthesis), and the like. In sum, a sound investment in an economic development on the LAND region may be critically linked to diverse sequences and chains of ecologic processes in the MARINE region.

Finally, to complete the set of illustrations, we examine a LAND-based ecologic production activity. Although we have not yet collected and processed the data for such LAND-based ecologic activities, we are able to suggest commodities which are outputs by plus signs and inputs by minus signs. For example, consider *Plant Production by Photosynthesis*. Two of the required inputs, *Dissolved Phosphate in Streams*, and *Dissolved Phosphate in Soil*, are indicated in Table 4.3. The output is *Green Plants*. Notice that by going across the commodity row, *Green Plants*, this

[6] Although treatment activities are not listed in the framework of the present table, they can be added. If a treatment activity were land-based, it would be introduced as a column under the economic subsection of the LAND region. One of the inputs into the treatment activity would be BOD, 5-day, a negative (−) sign being associated with it. The output would be water of the desired quality (dissolved oxygen content, etc.) denoted by a plus (+) sign. The output could then become the required input for the swimming activity, where the coefficient would be preceded by a minus (−) sign.

[7] We may trace out another path of interrelations. The solids discharged by the leather tanning and finishing industry decrease water transparency (increase the extinction coefficient). This tends to reduce the rate of phytoplankton production (see the column headed *Phytoplankton Production by Photosynthesis*). In turn, this may lead ultimately to reduction in fish production and have implications for sport fishing activity.

output in turn becomes an input into three other activities: *Food Consumption by Parasite Plants*, *Plant Mortality*, and *Food Consumption by Herbivores*. One of these activities, *Plant Mortality*, yields as an output *Dead Plant Matter*, which becomes an input into PMX 6001, *Transport by Streams of Dead Plant Matter to Ocean*. This activity, then, provides a basic link between ecologic processes in the LAND region and ecologic processes in the MARINE region.

With these diverse illustrations, it should be clear how an interrelations table, such as Table 4.3, is useful for systematic description, for comprehensive planning and programming, and for thorough study of the direct and indirect impacts of major developments.[8] Such a table has considerable general value. In any case, however, such as in the case study that follows, the investigator employs only those parts of the table which are useful for the particular problem being examined. The parts which are useful will of course vary from case study to case study.

Bibliography

1. Isard, Walter, "Some Notes on the Linkage of the Ecologic and Economic Systems," *Papers*, Regional Science Association, Vol. XXII, 1969.
2. ———, Kenneth E. Bassett, Charles L. Choguill, John G. Furtado, Ronald M. Izumita, John Kissin, Richard Seyfarth, Richard Tatlock, *Report on Ecologic-Economic Analysis for Regional Development: Some Initial Explorations with a Particular Reference to Recreational Resource Use and Environmental Planning*, Regional Science and Landscape Analysis Project, Department of Landscape Architecture—Research Office, Graduate School of Design, Harvard University, December 1968.
3. ———, Thomas W. Langford, Jr., and Eliahu Romanoff, *Philadelphia Region Input-Output Study: Working Papers Vol. I–IV and Coefficient Table*, Regional Science Research Institute, G.P.O. Box 8776, Philadelphia, Pennsylvania, 19107, 1968.
4. ———, and Eliahu Romanoff, *Water Use and Water Pollution Coefficients: Preliminary Report*, Technical Paper No. 6, Regional Science Research Institute, Cambridge, Massachusetts, 1967.

[8] For some other relevant discussion, see Isard [1].

The Case Study

5.1 General Description of Plymouth-Kingston Duxbury Bay: The Case Study Area

5.1.1 Introduction

The purpose of this section is to present the case study area. The selection of the Plymouth-Kingston-Duxbury Bay area for study was made for the following reasons. First, the area is close and accessible to the Boston area. Second, the area has a number of landscape elements and water-land relationships which combine to present a challenging ecological situation. Finally, the area provides an opportunity to expand upon the methodologies initially developed in the Salem area for the systematic exploration of linkages between socio-economic and ecologic systems, especially with regard to recreational complex development.

The location of Plymouth Bay and its relation to the Massachusetts coastal area is shown on Chart 5.1a. The location of the Nook Site, which will be examined in detail, and Kingston Bay, within the context of Plymouth Bay, are presented in Chart 5.1b.

As already mentioned, no mineral deposits of any significance occur in the Continental Shelf of this area. Also, the area lacks potential for commercial fishing and industrial development. Therefore, only the recreational possibilities for this area are examined in the case study.

In what follows we provide a brief description of characteristics of estuaries such as the one being studied. An understanding of these major estuarine characteristics and processes can aid regional planners in evaluating possible resource development and management decisions. Because these characteristics affect the development costs as well as the possible destruction or enhancement of ecologically valuable areas, they exert an important influence on the location of a recreational complex and its successful operation.

5.1.2 Characteristics of Case Study Area

In Chapter 3, the concept of an ecosystem was introduced and its two major components, abiotic and biotic, were described briefly. In this section, attention will be focused upon a particular type of ecosystem—an estuary—of which Plymouth-Kingston-Duxbury Bay is an example.

In general, estuaries are characterized by being semi-enclosed water bodies and thus are natural harbors; they are effective nutrient traps which are rich in food; they connect the sea and the inland rivers and thus can act as natural transportation centers; and frequently their high rates of flux and flush permit disposal of great quantities of waste. Specifically, an estuary may be defined as a "semi-enclosed coastal body of water which has a free connection with the open sea and within which sea water is measurably diluted with fresh water derived from land drainage".[1]

[1] Pritchard [22], p. 3.

Chart 5.1a Plymouth Bay Location Map

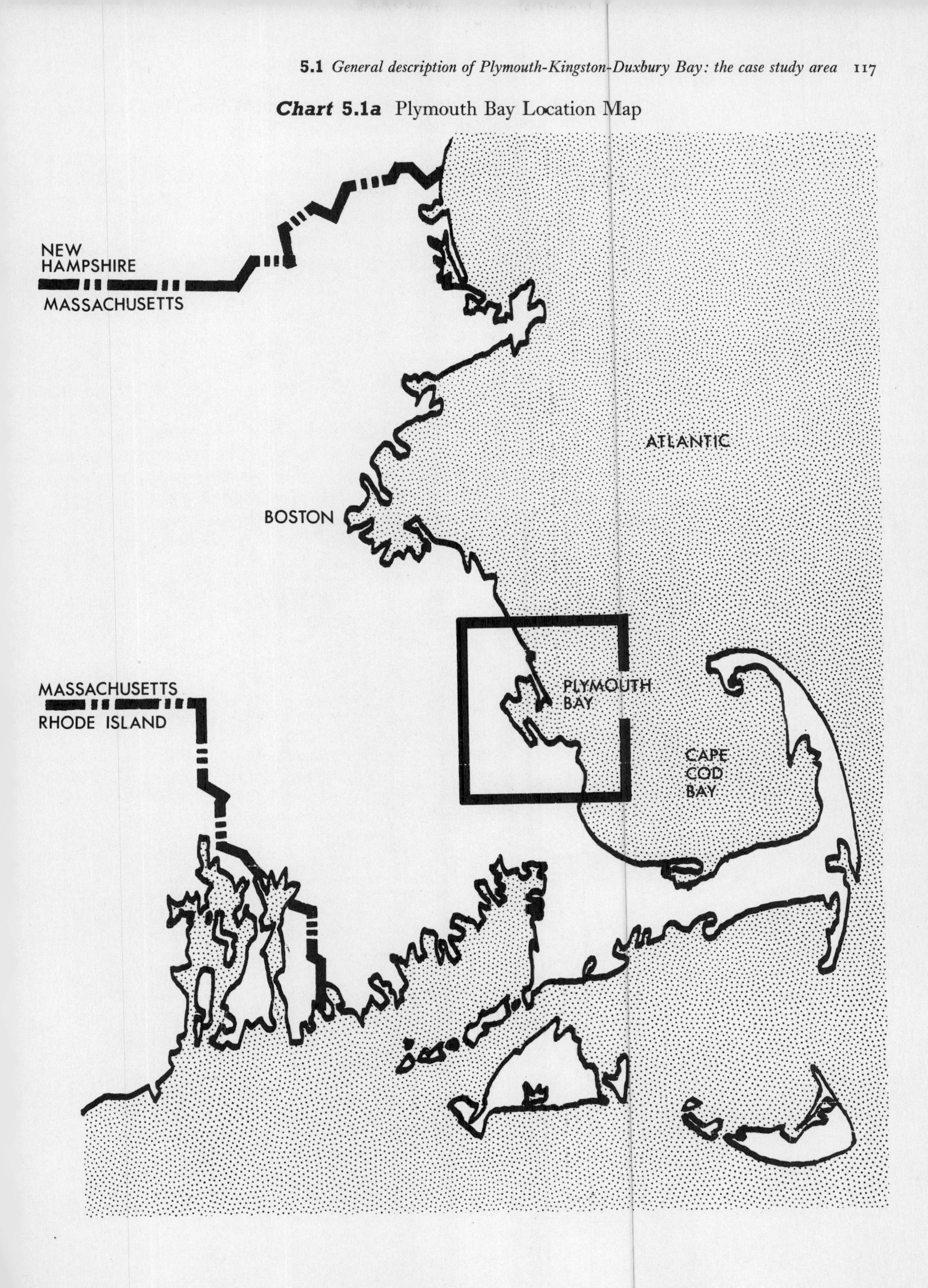

Chart* 5.1*b Kingston Bay and the Nook Site Within The Context of Plymouth Bay

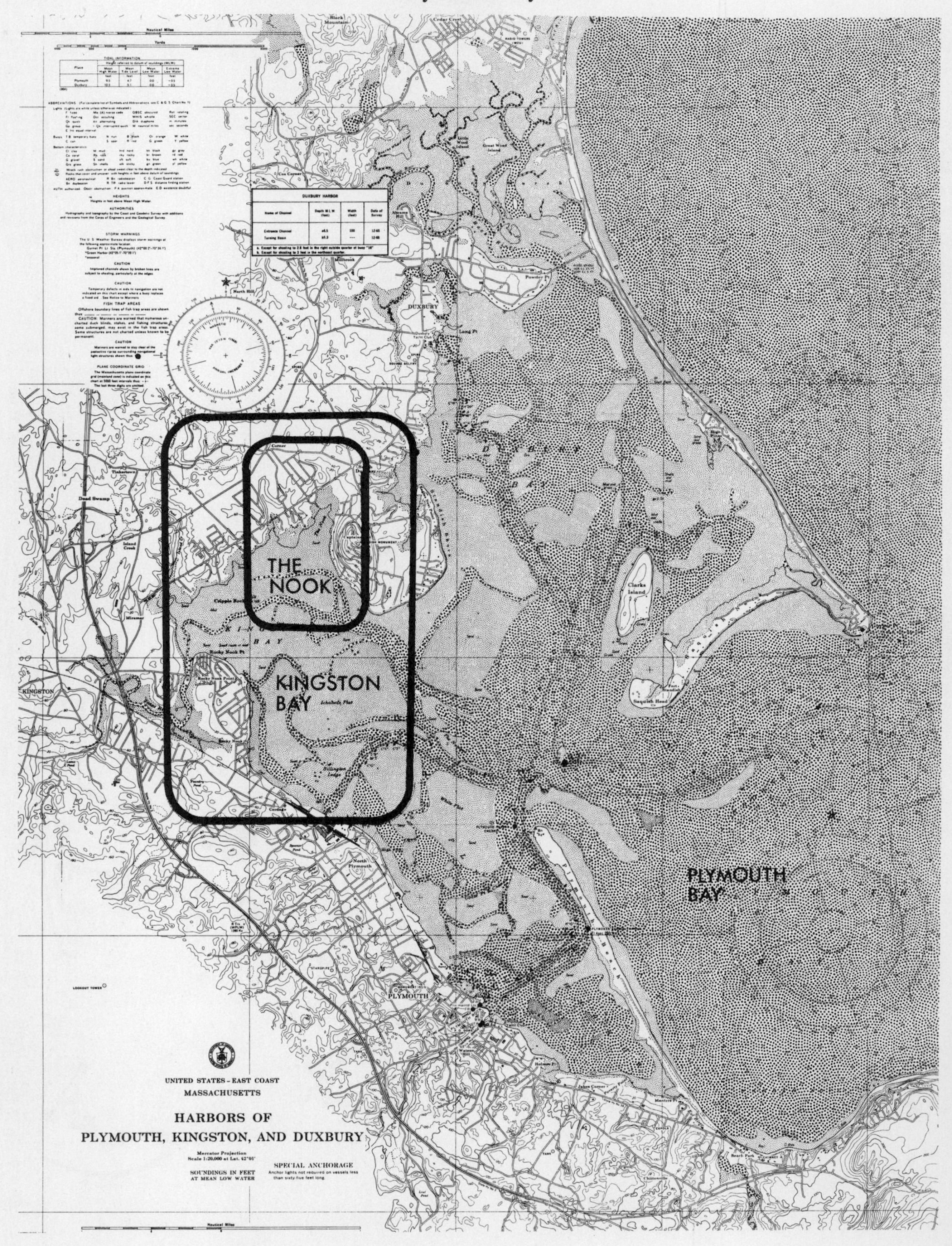

While no two estuaries are identical, the estuarine ecosystem is generally considered to be among the most naturally fertile areas in the world. The major mechanisms responsible for estuaries being so fertile are pointed out by Odum:[2]

> First, the mixing of waters of different salinities produces efficient vertical mixing that results in a sort of "nutrient trap." Thus, valuable nutrients are not swept out but move up and down and cycle rapidly between organisms, water and bottom sediments. Second, the back and forth tidal flow is a favorable factor since food, nutrients and oxygen are continually supplied and waste products removed automatically with the result that organisms need not waste their own energy in these processes. Other things being equal, a flowing system will be more productive than a standing system.
> A third reason why estuaries are productive [as stated by Odum] is their year-round crop production. The system tends to maintain a constant rate in a changing seasonal environment. Thus, not only do the mud algae function and produce at all seasons, but also the marsh grass and phytoplankton.[3]

It is important to consider the estuarine ecosystem as a highly complex interrelated system within which key elements interplay. With respect to the *Abiotic Component*, key elements include (a) physiographic factors such as geomorphological structure and substratum; and (b) environmental factors such as tides, currents, temperature, salinity, waves, winds, storms, turbidity, acidity, oxygen, and carbon dioxide. With respect to the *Biotic Component*, key elements include the principal species of plant and animal life present.[4]

5.1.3 Abiotic Component

(a) Physiography

From a geomorphological standpoint, Plymouth-Kingston-Duxbury Bay is a "Bar-built" estuary. This type of estuary is characterized by offshore barrier sand islands and sand spits built above sea level and extending between headlands in a chain, broken by one or more inlets, like Duxbury Beach, Saquish Neck, and Plymouth Beach. The area enclosed by the barrier beaches is generally elongated parallel to the coastline. Frequently, as in the case of Plymouth-Kingston-Duxbury Bay, more than one river flows into such an estuary though the total drainage area feeding it is not large. This type of estuary also tends to be rather shallow, with the wind acting as an important mixing mechanism.[5]

SUBSTRATUM

The estuarine substratum, where large numbers of marine organisms attach themselves, is a significant factor from the standpoint of providing a convenient classification. These organisms may be highly dependent on the nature and character of the substratum for shelter or burrowing and other processes. Also, the nature of the substratum material gives an indication of the relative slope (e.g., generally, the coarser the material, the steeper the slope) as well as ecological productivity and construction costs that may be encountered.

In general, the estuarine substratum varies less than that of an open shore. There may be rock and gravelly beaches, but the surfaces of the stones are covered with a film of silt. Clean sandy beaches are rarely found since the sand tends to trap particles of silt.[6] The most abundant estuarine substratum is mud of varying texture which tends to accumulate in comparatively sheltered areas where current velocity is low. Such areas are also frequently associated with a rich supply of organic material. Within Plymouth-Kingston-Duxbury Bay, rocks lie buried be-

[2] Odum [20], p. 13.
[3] *Ibid.*, p. 14.
[4] Emery and Stevenson [6], pp. 673–674.
[5] Pritchard [22], p. 5.
[6] Moore [16], p. 204.

neath a layer of sand, gravel, and clay of drift formation which is up to 200 feet thick in places. No ledge is evident in the bay except in the Kingston Bay area where it can be seen scattered throughout the bay at low tide.[7] A muddy-sandy substratum predominates throughout the bay except in areas near river mouths such as Jones River and Island Creek (in Kingston Bay) where mud accumulates. Sheltered areas containing shallow water also induce the growth of grasses such as eel grass which constrict water movement, accumulate fine silt, and hasten the formation of a muddy substratum. This situation is particularly evident in Duxbury Bay and to a lesser degree in Kingston Bay.

(b) Environmental Factors

TIDES

The tide is one of the most important ecological factors in an estuary since it is the agent which effects the exchange of water and determines the area which is alternately covered by water and exposed to the air.[8] Tides, through their mechanical mixing action, directly affect certain environmental factors such as the temperature and salinity of the water in an estuary. They also govern, through their cyclical process, the severity of estuarine bottom factors such as desiccation (drying out), insulation (heating), and exposure to extreme temperatures. Generally, the less extreme environmental conditions of an estuary are found near the tidal entrance where there may be an almost continuous resupply of sea water. The extreme environmental conditions generally occur near the head of the estuary where the supply of sea water is discontinuous. The geographical position of the transition point between saline and fresh water conditions is near the entrance of an estuary having a small tidal range and large runoff, and near the head of an estuary having a large tidal range and small runoff.[9] Plymouth-Kingston-Duxbury Bay is of the latter type.

Within Plymouth-Kingston-Duxbury Bay tides are semi-diurnal with a mean range of 9.6 feet and a spring range of 11.1 feet. Tide ranges in this area are generally directly proportional to tides at Boston and are modified by local topography and hydrography.[10] Exceptional high tides (12 feet) occur three to four times per year, usually twice in April or May and twice in October.[11] Through the semi-diurnal tide action, extensive intertidal flats are exposed twice during each 24-hour period. At low tides, the water surface area of the inner bay is decreased by more than 50 percent (from 9,000 acres to 4,000 acres).

These tides also cause a relatively large change in water volume. At mean high tide Plymouth-Kingston-Duxbury Bay contains over 3⅓ billion gallons, and approximately 6 hours later it contains only 1¼ billion gallons. This change results in strong channel currents which cause a high flushing rate throughout the bay. The concentration of pollutants which enter the bay at various points (primarily from Kingston and Plymouth) is greatly reduced by this flushing action. Also, the small amount of fresh water runoff from the several streams emptying into the area is quickly flushed into the ocean.[12]

This large tidal flow has several consequences. First, only certain organisms which can withstand such a drastic environmental change can exist on the exposed flats. Organisms able to live in this type of environment, such as the ribbed mussel (which has an important role in the phosphorus cycle), thus play a particularly important role within the estuarine ecosystem. Other organisms such as finfish must move into deeper subtidal areas or out of the bay completely during low water periods and therefore certain recreational activities such as sport-fishing are affected.

[7] Massachusetts, Commonweath of [13], p. 6.
[8] Emery and Stevenson [6], p. 679.
[9] *Ibid.*, p. 680.
[10] U.S., 86th Congress [29], p. 20.
[11] Interview March 7, 1968, with Mr. Manuel Oliver, Shellfish Officer of the Town of Duxbury.
[12] Massachusetts, Commonwealth of [13], p. 9.

Also, the resulting costs of providing a recreational complex in such an estuarine environment may be high in terms of both construction (e.g., dredging, bulkheading, etc.) and damage to the ecosystem. In general, the larger the tidal range, the higher construction costs may be.

CURRENTS

The chief cause of currents in estuaries is the tides. Varying relationships of tidal height and current velocity exist depending on the degree of bay enclosure. In general, ebb tide current velocities and duration will be slightly higher because of the addition of fresh water outflow. Also, the narrower the entrance of an estuary, the higher the current velocities, *ceteris paribus*; and the more inhibited the development of animal populations as compared with areas farther out in the bay.[13]

In general, tidal currents are of benefit in supplying food, oxygen, and nutrients to immobile organisms such as shellfish. However, tidal currents may also induce shifting of soft sediments, which in turn will smother organisms such as shellfish. This situation is prevalent in certain portions of Plymouth-Kingston-Duxbury Bay. Current velocities reach approximately 1.2 knots in the channel between Gurnet Point and Duxbury Pier.[14]

TEMPERATURE

Temperature is universally important and is often a limiting factor. Temperature rhythms, along with tidal and light rhythms, significantly control the seasonal and daily activities of organisms. Temperature is also responsible for the zonation and stratification which occurs in the marine environment. In general, the upper limits of temperature are more critical than the lower limits. This situation obtains despite the fact that many organisms appear to function more efficiently toward the upper limits of their tolerance ranges.[15]

The layer of water overlying the tidal flats of Plymouth-Kingston-Duxbury Bay, as in many estuaries, is relatively shallow. Because of this, estuarine water temperatures follow atmospheric temperatures more closely than do open seawater temperatures. Shallow waters are much colder in winter and much warmer in summer than the open sea. The diurnal variation is also greater, especially where the water has flowed over previously warmed exposed mud flats.[16]

During the summer water temperatures within Plymouth-Kingston-Duxbury Bay reach 70°F as compared to 55°F in the open sea. As just indicated, this difference arises primarily because of the sun heating the mudflats.[17] At the entrance to estuaries, water is nearly the same temperature as the open sea, while greater departures are exhibited at progressively greater distances from the estuary entrance.

SALINITY

Like temperature, salinity also represents a significant limiting factor.

Ecologically significant aspects of salinity in an estuary are its daily and seasonal range, and its rate of change through the tidal cycle. In many estuaries, a daily change of salinity may have a cumulative effect upon an organism, thus restricting it to higher salinities in nature than it may withstand under experimental conditions.[18]

Salinity in Plymouth-Kingston-Duxbury Bay is fairly high with an average of 34‰,[19] compared to the average salinity in the ocean which is 35‰. This rela-

[13] Emery and Stevenson [6], pp. 682–683. [14] U.S. Department of Commerce [31], p. 206.
[15] Odum [19], p. 105. [16] Emery and Stevenson [6], p. 684.
[17] Interview (October 23, 1967) with Mr. Frank Grice, Research Director, Division of Marine Fisheries, Mass. Department of Natural Resources, Boston, Mass.
[18] Emery and Stevenson [6], p. 685.
[19] Average of salinity records taken by the William F. Clapp Laboratories, Duxbury, Mass. Records were taken near the laboratories from August, 1966, to September, 1967.

tively high salinity in the Bay results from the low fresh-water inflow and the high flushing action by the tides. Because of the low fresh-water inflow, marine organisms tolerant of high salinity may be found in the upper as well as lower portions of the bay.

A significant phenomenon associated with estuaries, and one which influences salinity, is the tendency of the inward-flowing seawater and the outward-flowing fresh water to flow to their respective right sides in the northern hemisphere.[20] This factor is significant from the standpoint of locating marina complexes because of the higher maintenance costs associated with conditions such as increased corrosion and marina borer action in areas of higher salinity. This factor also affects the distribution and type of animal and plant species in such areas.

WAVES

Because of the short fetch and relatively shallow bottom of estuaries, ordinary wind waves in estuaries are smaller than in the open sea. However, because Plymouth-Kingston-Duxbury Bay is relatively large, waves can reach a considerable height during high tides. Along the coast in which the case study area is located, no wave observations have been made. However, wave characteristics for this area were derived by hindcast methods from a station in deep water off Nauset Beach, Cape Cod, about 70 miles east-south-east of Plymouth-Kingston-Duxbury Bay. The predominant direction of wave approach was found to be from the east-northeast direction. Duxbury Beach protects the inner area of Plymouth-Kingston-Duxbury Bay from major ocean waves which generate over long fetches from directions north to east. Although the inner bay is exposed to wave action from the southeast quadrant, the problem is less severe because the fetch is limited by the Cape Cod peninsula.[21]

WINDS

Records of winds observed by the U.S. Weather Bureau at Boston for the 7-year period, October, 1949, to September 1956, indicate that prevailing summer winds blow from westerly directions or offshore. The most common onshore winds are from the east and southeast, but east to northeast winds, which occur for shorter durations, have higher average velocities.[22] Winds may combine with other natural conditions such as waves either to augment or to moderate their individual damaging effects. Plymouth-Kingston-Duxbury Bay is particularly vulnerable to winds from the south-east. This is due to the position of the Bay entrance and the relatively long fetch where winds may coincide with wave directions and thus augment each other's effects.

STORMS

The shore of Massachusetts is vulnerable to storms from the north and east with typical wind velocities of 35–70 miles per hour or more. This problem is associated primarily with the "northeaster" coastal storms and not with hurricanes. Northeasters are more frequent than hurricanes and can occur at any time of the year, although they are more numerous in the winter. These storms are often accompanied by rain or snow and above-normal tides, which cause serious tidal flooding with levels of 3 feet higher than a spring tide. They tend to last longer than hurricanes, sometimes for as long as 3 days, with prolonged damaging effects.[23]

TURBIDITY

Suspended materials in water will often limit light penetration and thus decrease the depth of the photosynthetic zone and the associated production of phytoplankton and algae. Within estuaries, turbidity varies widely throughout the year

[20] Emery and Stevenson [6], p. 685.
[21] U.S., 86th Congress [29], p. 19.
[22] *Ibid.*
[23] U.S., 89th Congress [28], pp. 7, 14, and 40.

and reaches a maximum during floods of the rainy season. However, during all seasons, turbidity gradually decreases (i.e., transparency increases) as the distance from a river mouth increases.[24]

In addition to stream load, tidal channels are an important source of the sediment which makes water turbid. Consequently, water over a tidal flat is likely to be most turbid just before high tide. In deep water, turbidity is highest at or before low tide and lowest at high tide.[25] Due to the extensive tidal channels in Plymouth-Kingston-Duxbury Bay, more turbidity arises from sediment than from stream load.

OXYGEN, CARBON DIOXIDE, ACIDITY

Oxygen, carbon dioxide, and acidity are all critical to the functioning of the estuarine ecosystem. Dissolved oxygen is necessary for most forms of marine life. Carbon dioxide, which is produced in animal and plant respiration, is required for photosynthesis. It is also important in connection with the deposition and solution of calcium carbonate for shell and skeleton formation, and is related to the pH (acidity) factor. The pH factor is significant for respiration and photosynthesis processes.[26]

Generally, the interaction of these three factors within an estuary is as follows. During the night, both plants and animals increase the carbon dioxide content of the water by respiration. During the day, the plants convert this carbon dioxide back into oxygen. Therefore, the oxygen content of estuarine water reaches a minimum at night and a maximum during the day. The carbon dioxide content varies in an exact opposite manner. Generally, as the carbon dioxide content increases, carbonic acid increases with a subsequent decrease in pH. Thus, plant metabolism tends to lower pH at night and increase it during the day. The shallower the water, the greater the diurnal variation in pH. This variation ranges from 0.05 pH units in the open sea to 1.5 units in pools a few centimeters deep.[27]

Carbon dioxide and acidity are generally not limiting factors. Oxygen, however, can become a limiting factor. Temperature and dissolved salts greatly affect the ability of water to hold oxygen, the solubility of oxygen being increased by low temperatures and decreased by high salinities.[28]

5.1.4 Biotic Component

From a biological standpoint, the relative instability of environmental factors in estuaries is of key significance. Estuaries are regions of transition and sharp gradients, and in order to survive in such an environment an organism must be able to adapt to a wider range of fluctuations than an organism living in either the sea or fresh water. Although the variation of environmental factors in an estuary may be great, it is nevertheless a permanent feature; and organisms which have become adapted to such wide fluctuations have found in estuaries an environment which may actually be comparatively stable in the context of geological time. For example, at one end of the spectrum are organisms which tolerate no alteration of their environmental conditions, while at the other end are organisms which can tolerate extreme cyclic variations in temperature, salinity, tidal ranges, and so on.[29]

Because of the variability of environmental factors, the distribution of estuarine organisms cannot be based on any single factor, since the limits of distribution may be controlled by any one or more of several factors. The bottom communities of an estuary are especially important since they must survive extreme hydrographic changes, sometimes during the period of one tide. Therefore, extraordinary exces-

[24] Emery and Stevenson [6], p. 690. [25] *Ibid.* [26] Moore [16], pp. 83–90.
[27] Emery and Stevenson [6], pp. 687–689. [28] Odum [19], p. 124.
[29] Emery and Stevenson [6], p. 695.

sive variations in temperature, salinity, or turbidity may eliminate entire populations in an estuary.[30] (The range of tolerances for certain specific species such as winter flounder, cod, soft-shelled clam, and blue mussel are indicated in Appendix B.)

One of the most characteristic aspects of the junction of land and sea in the temperate latitudes is the tidal marsh. Within the total estuarine ecosystem the role of the tidal marsh is important and helps account for the fertility of estuaries. Odum points out that such fertility results from the interaction of three different production units.[31] These production units and the associated marsh zonation are shown in Chart 5.1c. Although this example refers to a situation in Georgia, a similar situation exists within the Plymouth-Kingston-Duxbury Bay.

***Chart* 5.1c** Marsh Zonation

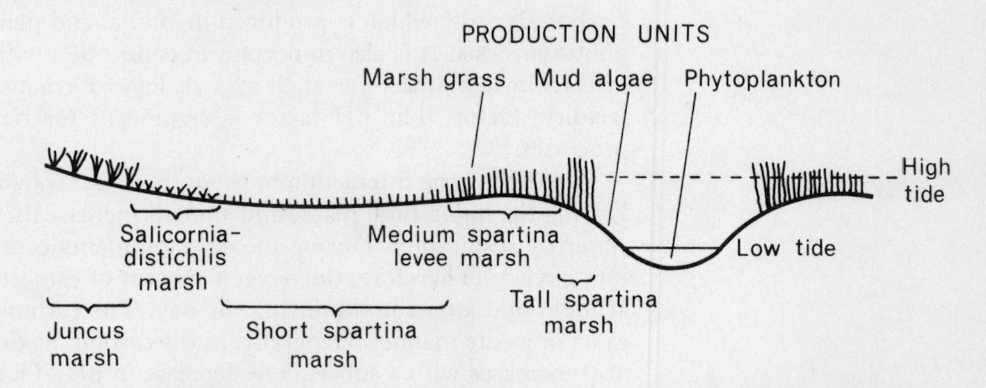

The three distinct production units in the order of their importance as food producers for the whole ecosystem are pointed up by Odum as follows:

A. *Spartina* (*Cord Grass*) *Marshes*. This production unit occupies a significant part of the whole estuarine ecosystem and provides shelter and food for a variety of wildlife. A small part of the marsh grass is consumed on the stalk by insects and other terrestrial herbivores, but most of it is consumed by the marine organisms in the form of detritus. The major types of cord grass evident are *spartina alterniflora*, which forms a narrow border along the intertidal flats, and *spartina patens*, which occupies an extensive area behind spartina alterniflora. Within Plymouth-Kingston-Duxbury Bay there are approximately 1,800 acres of this type of production unit.[32]

B. *Benthic or "Mud algae"*. This production unit involving organisms occurs throughout the intertidal sediments. Although these intertidal mud areas may appear rather barren, they are in fact quite productive. The processes within these areas are illustrative of the "inverse size-metabolism" law, which states that small organisms often have a higher rate of living and production per gram of standing crop than large organisms.[33] Within Plymouth-Kingston-Duxbury Bay this production unit is quite extensive and covers approximately 5,000 acres.

C. *Phytoplankton in the Water*. This production unit is particularly important in the open sea and has been discussed in detail in Section 3.6. In shallow water systems such as estuaries, where much of the bottom is alternately exposed and covered by tides, fertility depends more on the rich organic composition of the bottom than on phytoplankton. However, the phytoplankton production unit may vary considerably with the seasons and large "blooms" of dinoflagellates may develop within estuaries.

From the standpoint of management of tidal marshes and the three production units, Odum offers the following guiding principles. In the first zone to the far left of the diagram, drainage and cultivation of land or semi-aquatic crops can be considered. In the middle of the diagram, diking, drainage, and large-scale modifications

[30] Caspers [5], pp. 6–8.
[31] Odum [20], pp. 13–14.
[32] Massachusetts, Commonwealth of [12], p. 72.
[33] Odum [20], p. 14.

should be undertaken with caution. Toward the right of the diagram where spartina grasses, mud algae, and phytoplankton are abundant, utilization should be made of existing productivity. The intertidal portion of the estuary should be considered in terms of "marine farming" rather than land farming.[34]

5.1.5 Summary

Estuaries are among the most fertile types of ecosystems. The high productivity of the estuarine ecosystem, as well as the increasing demand to develop such areas, makes analysis of this ecosystem particularly important for regional resource planners. It is essential that the entire estuarine system, including streams, marshes, tidal flats, channels, and bays, be considered as one ecosystem or productive unit, wherein changes in one subsystem or subarea of this system can have pronounced effects on other subsystems and subareas of the system as well as on the total ecosystem.

A recreational complex development which is planned within an estuarine ecosystem must consider the major factors and processes characteristic of these systems. Within Plymouth-Kingston-Duxbury Bay certain factors are particularly relevant. With respect to the abiotic component, the most significant factor is the tide. The relatively large volume of water which is flushed in and out of the Bay daily, as well as the small input of fresh water, sets the framework (e.g. the relatively high salinity and the exposure of extensive tidal flats) within which other environmental factors work. This large water movement affects the location and type of man-made structures (e.g., breakwaters, bulkheads, etc.) and their maintenance costs. Such structures in turn affect the ecological balance by changing water patterns which can shift sediments with subsequent effects on marine organisms, especially those species of a burrowing nature such as clams. To a certain extent, the relative absence of such burrowing organisms in Plymouth-Kingston-Duxbury Bay may be due to the natural shifting of intertidal flats which in turn has a detrimental effect on marine organisms.

With respect to the biotic component, the two major production units of particular importance in Plymouth-Kingston-Duxbury Bay are the Spartina Marsh unit and the mud algae unit. The extensiveness of the intertidal flats makes the mud algae unit especially important.

5.2 *The Marina Site Selection Process: A Comparison of Key Economic and Ecologic Costs*

5.2.1 Introduction

In the preceding section, the basic estuarine characteristics of the Plymouth-Kingston-Duxbury Bay were presented. In this section, we wish to narrow down our analysis to a specific area within the Bay, and to identify a site for a hypothetical recreational complex. This site is to be selected from among several alternatives. In traditional location analysis, this selection is normally made on the basis of least cost when revenue potentials are judged to be the same for all alternatives. Thus, the costs incurred at various sites are derived and compared and the least-cost site is selected.

In the current analysis, however, it is recognized that not all costs incurred are strictly economic. The establishment and construction of a recreational complex can be expected to have some effect upon the natural environment. The proposed recreational complex consists of a marina and its associated facilities. So, various channels and basins will be necessary. The dredging of these channels and basins

[34] *Ibid.*, p. 15.

Chart 5.2a Alternative Sites for Recreational Complex

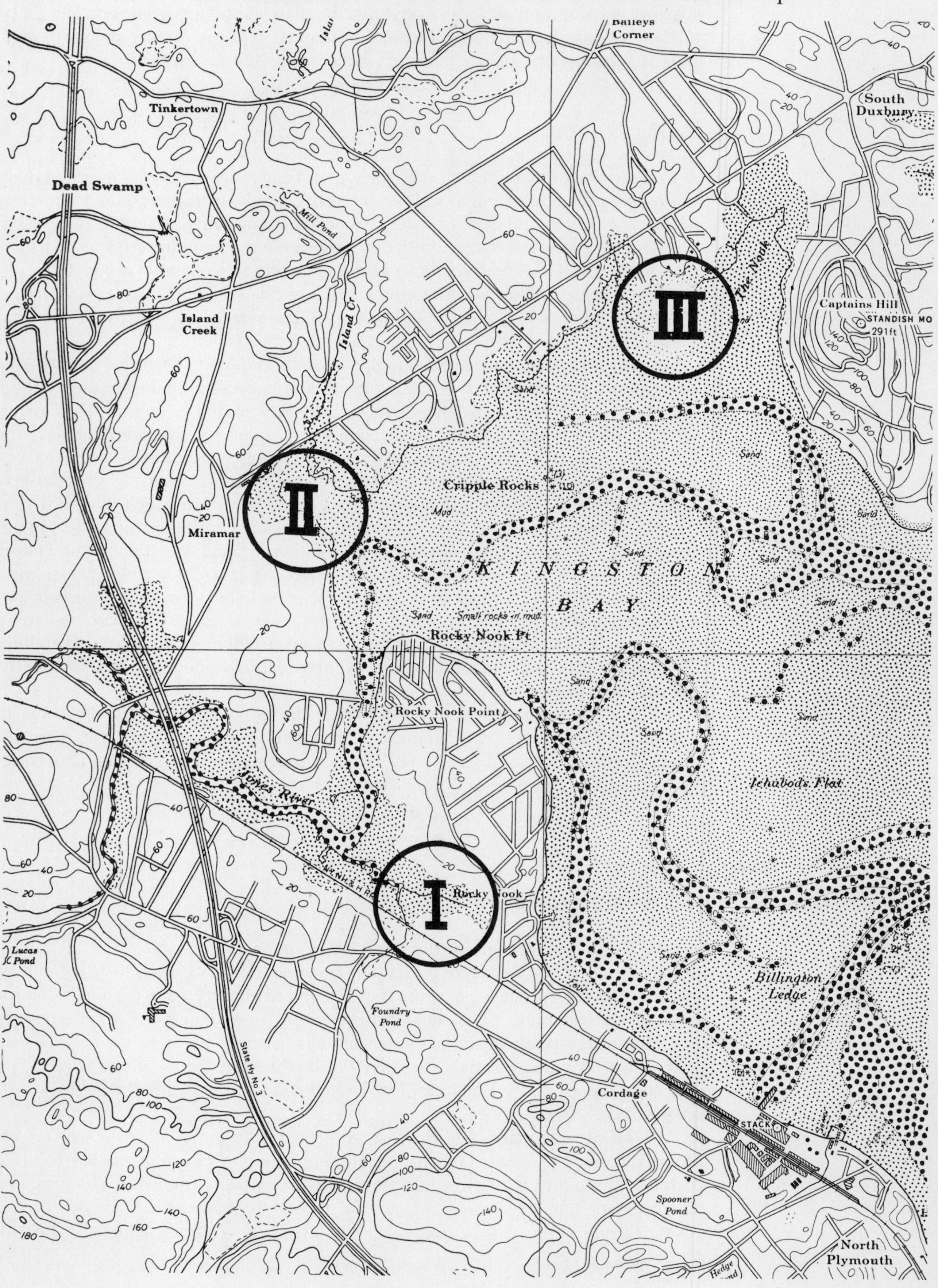

may have a profound effect upon the surrounding environment. It can be expected that new types of pollution might be introduced. They too have an effect upon the natural surroundings. Thus the problem of this analysis becomes the following: given the alternative sites available for marina development, select that site at which the combined economic and ecologic costs are minimized for a given assumed market.

The three sites to be considered in this analysis are located in Kingston Bay, Massachusetts. Two of the sites are on the northern shore, lying southwest of Duxbury. The third is in a protected area of the south shore, just to the north of Plymouth. These three sites are shown on Chart 5.2a. (Also, on this chart we indicate with large dots the area under water at low tide.)

The southern site is on the Jones River, and is designated Case I. Case II is located at the mouth of Island Creek. Case III is the most easterly of the sites, closest to the Atlantic Ocean. It is located in an area known as The Nook. In order to choose among these locations, it is necessary to develop a methodology which will discriminate among various economic costs and the ecological damage incurred at each site.

In the following section, 5.2.2, we conduct comparative economic cost analysis for the several sites. Initial capital costs and the associated maintenance costs are judged to be the relevant economic variables for the site-selection procedure. Once the economic costs are derived, we pursue in Section 5.2.3 comparative ecological cost analysis. For each site the ecological costs primarily depend on where the dredged material for the basins and channels, or the dredging spoil, is disposed. As the three sites are in relatively rich biological areas, it can be seen that if the spoil is dumped near the channel and basin areas, the ecological damage will be major. The damage can be reduced by moving the spoil out of the Bay for disposal, but this involves additional economic cost. Finally, in Section 5.2.4 we analyze differences among the sites in both economic and ecological costs to suggest the overall least-cost location.

5.2.2 Comparative Economic Cost Analysis

For each of the three sites under consideration, a 395-boat marina is hypothesized. The investments needed for each marina vary from site to site, as each location has its own peculiarities. In this analysis, interest centers on identifying those elements which are different among the sites. By isolating these variable elements, the net cost differentials among the various sites can be analyzed. For example, if an item costs $100 at one location and only $25 at another location, the latter would hold an advantage of $75. This positive differential would be the relevant element for analysis in a comparative cost study.

It appears reasonable to assume, at this early stage of the analysis, that the direct operating costs (exclusive of maintenance) would be invariant among the sites. Hence, as previously stated, initial capital costs and the associated maintenance costs are judged to be the relevant economic costs to be considered.

The capital costs which must be taken into account are those involving moorings, shore protection, the turning basin, the access channel, docks and piers, breakwaters, boat-handling equipment, ramps, site improvements, planning, land, sewage disposal systems, and access roads. At this stage of the research, a number of these capital items do not require analysis. Those items which do not contribute to cost differentials need not be considered until we reach that section of this book dealing with total capital and operating costs and expected revenues. At this point only those capital costs which vary from site to site need to be derived. Since the marina at each site is of the same size and roughly of the same configuration, it is expected that moorings, docks and piers, boat-handling equipment, ramps, site improvements, and planning will cost the same at each of the three sites. With this assumption, we need to focus only on those capital costs dealing with the access channels, basins, shore protection, land, access roads, sewage disposal equipment, and breakwaters.

ACCESS CHANNELS

The first item to be considered in this analysis deals with the construction of access channels. In order to derive the total capital costs of dredging the necessary channels to each site, it is necessary first to estimate the total quantities of material to be removed, or spoil, from each site. An estimate is then made of the appropriate cost for removing a cubic yard of spoil. Total number of cubic yards removed multiplied by cost per cubic yard yields the total dredging cost for each site.

To estimate the amount of materials to be dredged, it is convenient to divide the necessary channel into two segments, one to be designated the harbor access channel, the other, the secondary service channel. In this case, the harbor access channel follows the path of the Jones River from its mouth to where it enters Plymouth Harbor proper. The secondary service channels will be designated to run from the harbor access channel to each marina site. The courses of the harbor access and secondary access channels are shown for the Jones River, Island Creek, and Nook sites by the solid black stretches on charts 5.2b, 5.2c, and 5.2d, respectively.

The length of each of these channels can be determined from the appropriate U.S. Coast and Geodetic Survey Charts.[35] The harbor access channel length at the seaward end begins where the channel depths on the charts do not show an 8-foot depth at mean low tide. These lengths of channel are shown in Table 5.2a. It can be

Table 5.2a Required Channel Length by Type of Channel

Site	Secondary Access Channel	Harbor Access Channel
I. Jones River	750 feet	7,800 feet
II. Island Creek	1,050 feet	4,500 feet
III. The Nook	1,800 feet	none required

seen that the longest harbor access channel is needed for Case I, the Jones River site. This is to be expected as this site is farthest from the main Plymouth Harbor. The longest secondary access channel is needed at The Nook, Case III. However, at The Nook, the secondary access channel in effect serves as the harbor access channel.

Once the lengths of each channel are determined, as in Table 5.2a, it is necessary to compute the necessary widths of channels. In *Cost and Revenue Notes*[36] the width of required channels is shown to be dependent on the proportion of sailing boats in the fleet. As these boats are assumed to comprise a minimal proportion of the total fleet, a harbor access channel width of 100 feet is assumed adequate for all three cases. With regard to the secondary service channel, the appropriate formula suggests that the required width be taken to be roughly four times the width of the largest boat.[37] Assuming that the largest boat, such as a party boat, may have a width of 20 feet, this suggests that the width of the secondary service channel should be 80 feet. This width is used for each of the three secondary service channels.

With the width and length of each type of channel at each site determined, only the necessary dredging depths need to be specified in order to obtain dredging volumes.

In order to estimate the necessary depths, the following formula is employed[38]

$$DD = D + ELT + G + S$$

[35] U.S. Department of Commerce [30]. [36] See Tatlock [24], Section 1.3. [37] *Ibid.*
[38] *Ibid.*

where DD = dredged depth, expressed in feet below mean low tide
D = draft of deepest boat in feet
ELT = extreme low tide, expressed in feet below mean low tide
G = grounding margin in feet, and
S = siltation margin in feet

It is first assumed that the secondary service channel and the harbor access channel will be of the same depth for each site. This assumption follows because it is expected that the composition of the boating fleet will be the same at each site; thus the draft of the deepest boat will be the same at each site. From the U.S. Coast and Geodetic Survey Chart #245, extreme low tide on extreme low water is placed at 3.5 feet. Also, the draft of the deepest boat is assumed to be 43 inches, or approximately 3.5 feet.[39] Finally, an adequate grounding margin of 0.5 feet and siltation margin of 0.5 feet are assumed. Thus the formula suggests a dredged depth of:

$$DD = 3.5 + 3.5 + 0.5 + 0.5 = 8 \text{ feet}$$

for both the secondary service channel and the harbor access channel for each site. The necessary amount of dredging operations can be calculated from the extreme low water depths recorded on the Chart just cited. Table 5.2b provides the relevant data obtained from these calculations.

Table 5.2b Required Dredging for Channels

Site	Secondary Service Channel	Harbor Access Channel
I. Jones River	750 ft. to be dredged 8 ft.	3,900 ft. to be dredged 4 ft. 3,900 ft. to be dredged 6 ft.
II. Island Creek	1,050 ft. to be dredged 8 ft.	3,600 ft. to be dredged 4 ft. 900 ft. to be dredged 6 ft.
III. The Nook	1,350 ft. to be dredged 8 ft. 450 ft. to be dredged 2 ft.	no dredging required

Taking into account the width of the channels, their length, and the dredged depth, we obtain the approximate volumes of required dredged material. They are recorded in Table 5.2c.

Table 5.2c Cubic Yards of Dredged Material by Site and Type of Channel

Site	Secondary Service Channel	Harbor Access Channel
I. Jones River	18,000	145,000
II. Island Creek	25,000	73,000
III. The Nook	35,000	0

We now derive the costs of channel dredging for each site. It is expected that a barge-mounted clamshell dredge would be employed, as it would be most efficient and do no more damage to the ecological surroundings than other dredging equipment. From a table listing recent dredging projects, the unit cost of dredging can be estimated.[40] This table shows that, generally speaking, the larger the project, the lower the cost per cubic yard. Economies of scale are to be expected. As the Jones River site requires the greatest amount of dredging for channels, the site is expected to have the lowest cost per cubic yard. It is estimated that the cost of the Jones River project would be approximately \$1.25 per cubic yard, assuming that the

[39] On the basis of materials summarized in *ibid.*

[40] *Ibid.*

dredging spoil is dumped on the mudflats beside the channel. The corresponding Island Creek cost would be about $1.35 per cubic yard; and that of The Nook, about $1.45 per cubic yard.

The analysis is to be carried one step further. Dumping the spoil on the nearby mudflats would cause a great deal of ecological damage. The approximate value of this damage will be derived in the section of this book dealing with ecological damage. To avoid such damage the spoil can be entirely removed from Plymouth Bay; and here we may derive the added cost of such removal. If the spoil is removed from the Bay by barge and dumped at a designated spoil-dumping area offshore, it is expected that the unit costs for the Jones River site would rise to $2.50 per cubic yard. For the Island Creek site, the cost would rise to $2.25 per cubic yard, and for The Nook, to $2.00 per cubic yard. From these costs, it can be seen that the differences among the three sites in removal cost (because of different distances from the offshore dumping area) outweigh the differences among these sites in unit dredging costs stemming from scale economies. The unit cost at The Nook is the lowest of the three.

For the two alternative methods of disposing of spoil for each of the three sites, Table 5.2d gives the estimates of total channel dredging costs. Table 5.2d shows that due to the relative shortness of the channels required, The Nook would involve a lower total dredging cost than either of the other two sites. This advantage holds regardless of whether the spoil is dumped nearby or is totally removed.

BASINS

The second economic cost differential arises in the construction of basins. The size of the basin is dependent upon the size of boats hypothesized to use the facility. It is expected that the basin will be the same for each site. However, cost differentials arise when the problem of removing the dredging spoil from the area is considered.

Table 5.2d Total Channel Dredging Costs for Three Marina Sites

Site	Total Cost, Spoil Dumped in Mudflats	Total Cost, Spoil Removed
I. Jones River	$204,000	$408,000
II. Island Creek	132,000	221,000
III. The Nook	51,000	70,000

In the marinas under consideration, it is expected that 50 percent of the fleet will be 10–20 feet long, 30 percent 20–30 feet long, and the remaining 20 percent over 30 feet. Each of the 10–20 foot boats requires approximately 835 square feet of water space. With approximately 150 boats of this size expected, the total water area required by such boats is 125,250 square feet, or about 2.9 acres. Each of the 20–30 foot boats requires about 970 square feet; in total, they require about 2.0 acres of water area. Each of the larger boats requires about 1,505 square feet of water area.[41] In total, their requirements are 2.1 acres of water area. Additionally, water area is needed for rental boats, party boats, and moored boats; their water area requirements are estimated at 2 acres. All water area requirements total about 9 acres for the development of any one of the three sites.

The depth of the basin has already been determined for the various access channels. This depth, 8 feet, would also be required for the turning basin. Thus, with a water surface area of 9 acres (with 43,560 square feet per acre) and a required depth of $2\frac{2}{3}$ yards (8 feet) of dredging, as is indicated to be necessary by

[41] See Tatlock [24], Table 1 in General Introduction.

the U.S. Coast and Geodetic Survey Chart #245, 116,000 cubic yards of material must be dredged for the development of any one of the sites.

In the case of the basins the required dredging can be done by a land-based dragline. On the basis of a listing of costs of recent dredging projects, it is estimated that for each site, with the spoil dumped nearby, the unit cost would be about $1.25 per cubic yard.[42, 43] If the spoil is removed from the harbor entirely, the cost structure would be similar to that for channel dredging. Thus the cost of dredging and removing spoil from The Nook would be about $1.80–$2.00 per cubic yard; from Island Creek, $2.15–$2.25 per cubic yard; and from the Jones River site, $2.50.[44]

Table 5.2e Total Basin-Dredging Costs for Three Marina Sites

Site	Total Cost, Spoil Dumped Nearby	Total Cost, Spoil Removed
I. Jones River	$145,000	$290,000
II. Island Creek	145,000	261,000
III. The Nook	145,000	232,000

Table 5.2e presents the total basin-dredging cost for each site, both when spoil is dumped nearby, and when spoil is removed from the harbor.[45] Again, The Nook

[42] *Ibid.*, Section 1.3.

[43] The sophisticated analyst recognizes that when undertaking a comparative cost analysis for planning purposes, it is usually necessary to adjust and restructure his set of assumptions and refine his calculations after the results of a first computation are obtained. For these results often suggest a more realistic set of assumptions and point up one or more new relationships which should have been incorporated into the analysis.

Moreover, even after the results of a second, improved computation are obtained, still better assumptions and still more desirable refinements may be suggested. And so on, for successive computations.

After our first computations were completed we did find that it would have been desirable to have employed somewhat different assumptions regarding physical design, scale economies, and the like, and to have conducted the analysis at a number of places in somewhat different ways. In reworking the analysis a number of improvements were made. However, there were a number of further refinements and restructuring of assumptions which we felt were not necessary to support the general recommendations which we make at the end of this study; we would insist on these refinements for any final recommendation on specifics of a recreational complex.

One refinement that might be made in our cost analysis pertains to scale economies in dredging operations in the basin. From Table 5.2c and the data just presented in the text, it is seen that the total volume of basin and channel dredging to be carried out at the Jones River site exceeds that at the Island Creek site, which in turn exceeds that at The Nook. Therefore, the rate of basin-dredging operations should be somewhat higher for Island Creek than for Jones River and somewhat higher for The Nook than for Island Creek. However, we did not choose to effect this refinement. Accordingly, the total cost for the situation in which spoil is dumped nearby is the same for all three sites, as indicated in the middle column on Table 5.2e.

Later, in calculating total cost for the situation in which the dredged spoil is removed, we did, in a somewhat inconsistent fashion, allow for scale economies. We did carry over the assumption that for basin dredging the Jones River site, as in channel dredging, would offer lower unit costs than the Island Creek, and still lower costs than The Nook. The inconsistency between our several assumptions regarding basin-dredging costs should be removed in any final analysis leading to a specific recommendation. However, we chose not to remove this inconsistency here since to do so would not alter the nature of our general conclusion and at the same time would entail much additional computation and reworking of the data.

[44] For both The Nook and Island Creek sites, the lower cost would be relevant if the basin dredging and spoil-removal operations were to realize the same scale economies achievable with respect to the Jones River site. The higher cost is relevant for both The Nook and Island Creek site if they achieve in basin dredging no greater scale economies than they do in channel dredging. Actually, because their dredging and spoil-removal operations for both channel and basin are sizeable, but still not as large as required at Jones River, a figure somewhere in the center of the range for each site would be the most relevant for that site.

[45] Since The Nook will be later shown to be the most advantageous of the three sites, our use of the conservative figure of $2.00 per cubic yard for the Nook tends to understate its advantage relative to Jones River. We also use the conservative figure of $2.25 for Island Creek.

has a cost advantage over the other two sites, if the spoil is removed from the harbor. If the spoil is dumped nearby, the costs for each site are approximated to be the same.

SHORE PROTECTION

In order to protect the shoreline from the potential damage which could result from increased use of the three marina sites, some type of shore protection is required. A number of materials can be used for protection purposes. In the present instance, the shore protection is visualized as consisting of timber and pile to the low-water line, with stone block on plastic filter cloth on the slope.[46] This particular arrangement appears advantageous for the present sites because it involves little loss of water area and it is less expensive than 100 percent use of wooden timber and pile bulkhead.

In order to estimate the unit costs of the required installation, it is necessary first to estimate the height of the bulkhead above the dredged depth, and then the distance below the dredged depth. The bulkhead height above the dredged depth is determined by use of the following formula.[47]

$$\text{Shore protection bulkhead height above } (DD) = EHT + DD + OM$$

where EHT = the extreme high tide to be expected
DD = dredged depth, expressed in feet below mean low tide
OM = overtopping margin, expressed in feet above the extreme high tide elevation

Because each marina is located in an area with hard-surfaced ground, OM is assigned a value of 1 foot. U.S. Coast and Geodetic Survey Chart #245 suggests that the mean tidal range is approximately 9.6 feet. The dredged depth, or DD, was determined previously to be 8 feet for each basin. Hence the formula yields:

$$\begin{aligned}\text{Shore protection bulkhead height above } (DD) &= 12.6 + 8 + 1 \\ &= 21.6 \text{ feet}\end{aligned}$$

In order to determine that portion of the bulkhead below the dredged depth, the following formula is used.[48]

$$\text{Shore protection bulkhead below } (DD) = \frac{EHT + DD + OM}{2}$$

where EHT, DD, and OM are as previously defined.

This particular formula is chosen for once the organic material at each site is dredged, it is expected that a sand and gravel fill will be placed on the bottom. The values for the variables in this formula have been previously determined. Hence

$$\begin{aligned}\text{Shore protection bulkhead below } (DD) &= \frac{12.6 + 8 + 1}{2} \\ &= \frac{21.6}{2} \\ &= 10.8 \text{ feet}\end{aligned}$$

Thus the total shore protection bulkhead height is 21.6 feet plus 10.8 feet, or 32.4 feet. This height should be appropriate for the breakwaters required at the Jones River site and the Island Creek site. As the basins at the two sites are of equal size, it is expected that 1,325 feet of such shore protection bulkhead would be required.

At The Nook, further shore protection is required. In addition to the shore protection about the turning basin, i.e., 1,325 feet of 32.4-foot bulkhead, there should be another 1,565 feet of 8-foot protection on the south and west edge of The Nook's landfill.

[46] This alternative is designated as Type VII in Tatlock [24] Section 1.2. [47] *Ibid.*
[48] *Ibid.*

From the *Cost and Revenue Notes*[49] the cost per linear foot of a 20-foot standard bulkhead may be set at $91. For our situation, however, a 32.4 foot bulkhead is required. Thus, the cost may be set at about $120 per foot of such bulkhead.[50] For the 8-foot bulkhead required at The Nook, the cost may be set at about $44 per foot. Accordingly, in Table 5.2f, we present the total expected shore protection costs for each site.

Table 5.2f Total Costs of Shore Protection for Three Marina Sites

Site	Total Length of Bulkhead	Total Height	Cost per Foot		Total Cost
I. Jones River	1,325 ft.	32.4 ft.	$120		$159,000
II. Island Creek	1,325 ft.	32.4 ft.	120		159,000
III. The Nook	1,325 ft.	32.4 ft.	120	$159,000	
	1,565 ft.	8 ft.	44	68,860	
					227,860

From Table 5.2f, it can be seen that the Jones River site and the Island Creek site each possess a net advantage of $68,860.

LAND COSTS

The amount of land required for a marina depends on two factors: the range of services offered and the water surface area encompassed by the marina. For minimum-service marinas, the ratio of land area to water surface area is roughly 1 to 1. Marinas with a moderate range of services require 1.3 acres of land per acre of water surface. In the marina hypothesized in this study, a fairly complete range of services is visualized. Hence, it is expected that about 1.5 acres of land will be required per acre of water surface.[51] With the basin areas determined to be 9 acres, this ratio implies that at each site about 13.5 acres of land are required. The variable of interest at this stage, then, becomes the price per acre of the land. This price varies from site to site.

The assessed valuation per acre of land at each site is readily obtained. On the assumption that the market value of land is 1.7 times the assessed value, the expected cost per acre of land and total cost of land are recorded for each site in Table 5.2g. Thus, with regard to land costs, The Nook holds a net advantage of $6,885 over the Island Creek site, and $2,295 over the Jones River site.

Table 5.2g Land Costs for Three Marina Sites

Site	Assessed Valuation per Acre	Market Valuation of Land	Acres Required	Total Cost of Land
I. Jones River	$1,000	$1,700	13.5	$22,950
II. Island Creek	1,200	2,040	13.5	27,540
III. The Nook	900	1,530	13.5	20,655

ACCESS ROADS

For two of the marina sites under consideration, existing access roads appear to be adequate. An additional road approximately one-quarter of a mile long is necessary to provide access to the Jones River site. We estimate from a study of Massachusetts highway needs that one-fourth mile of rural highway with two 12-foot lanes, and a capacity of 100 to 400 vehicles per hour, would cost about $20,650.

[49] *Ibid.* [50] *Ibid.* [51] *Ibid.*

SEWAGE DISPOSAL SYSTEMS

At each marina some facility must be provided to dispose of sewage. It is expected that the cost of collecting sewage from boats at each site would be the same. However, the Jones River site has the advantage of being located close to the Plymouth City sewage disposal system. In this case, only collection pipes would be necessary. At Island Creek and The Nook, a self-contained sewage system would be required. It is estimated that approximately 5,000 gallons of sewage would be discharged at each marina per day. The plants at Island Creek and The Nook would cost approximately \$2.25 per gallon of daily capacity.[52] Hence, at these two sites, the necessary sewage treatment plants would each cost about \$11,250. At the Jones River site, approximately 400 feet of collection pipe would be required. At \$5.00 per foot, this pipe would cost about \$2,000. Table 5.2h summarizes the sewage disposal facility cost at each site.

Table 5.2h Costs of Sewage Disposal Facility for Three Marina sites

Site	Collection Pipe	Sewage Disposal System	Total Cost
I. Jones River	\$2,000	\$ 0	\$ 2,000
II. Island Creek	0	11,250	11,250
III. The Nook	0	11,250	11,250

From Table 5.2h, it is apparent that the Jones River site holds a net advantage of \$9,250 over each of the other sites.

BREAKWATERS

An analysis of historical climatological data reveals that winds in the region generally originate from the northeast and east. As the Jones River site is located inland on the west side of the shore, the land on its eastward side forms a natural breakwater; hence a breakwater at this site is unnecessary. On the other hand, at the Island Creek and The Nook sites there are open expanses of water to the east and south. Unimpeded wave action could seriously damage docks and piers. Damage to the docked boats could also be expected. Hence, investment in a breakwater is desirable at these two sites as it would be expected to lower their future repair and maintenance costs.

In order to derive the physical dimensions of the necessary breakwaters, the expected wave heights must first be determined. Wave height can be determined by use of the following standard formula.[53]

$$h = 1.5\sqrt{D}$$

where h = height of wave in feet, and

D = the distance in nautical miles over which the wind acts

In the cases of Island Creek and The Nook, the distances (D) are roughly the same, as determined from the U.S. Coast and Geodetic Survey Chart #245. This distance is determined to be 4.8 miles; hence the maximum expected wave height is 3.3 feet. This figure indicates how high the breakwater must be built above high tide in order to achieve the necessary protection.

The second element of height is determined by the tidal range in the area where construction is to take place. At low tide, each area is dry. At high tide, there is 2 feet of water. Thus the tidal range in each calculation is taken to be 2 feet. When added to the previously determined height of 3.3 feet, it is found that the breakwater must be at least 5.3 feet high.

It is desirable to add 10 percent of the previously determined height to compensate for settling. For ease of calculation, the total required height is then rounded to 6 feet.

[52] Estimates are from Robert Snow Means Company [23], p. 15.
[53] Tatlock [24], Section 1.5.

We next calculate the length of the required breakwaters. With the location of the turning basins determined for both Island Creek and The Nook, this calculation can be made directly from the map of the area. Thus it is determined that the breakwater required at the Island Creek site should be 525 feet long, while the breakwater at The Nook should be 600 feet long.

The top width of the breakwater is determined by its height.[54] For breakwaters up to 20 feet high, a 6 foot top width is required. The recommended base is determined from the formula:

$$\text{Base width} = 4(\text{Total height}) + \text{Top width}$$

In the present case, for each site, this formula gives:

$$\begin{aligned}\text{Base width} &= 4(6 \text{ feet}) + 6 \text{ feet} \\ &= 30 \text{ feet}\end{aligned}$$

The unit costs relevant for breakwater construction are developed in terms of dollars per ton of material required. From geometry, one can calculate the cubic feet of material needed for each linear foot of the trapezoidal breakwater. One multiplies the height of the breakwater, which is 6 feet, by the arithmetic average of the width of the top of the breakwater and the width of the bottom of the breakwater, which is 18 feet, to obtain the desired result—namely, 108 cubic feet of material per linear foot of breakwater. As the material used is expected to be stone, this volume can be reduced because of space between stones when stone is put in place.[55]

On the average, this space accounts for 40 percent of the volume when large boulders are used. Thus the volume of stone required per linear foot of breakwater is about 65 cubic feet. Stone weighs about 165 pounds per cubic foot; thus each linear foot of breakwater requires 10,725 pounds, or about 5.4 tons, of stone. Multiplying the total weight per foot of breakwater, 5.4 tons, by the length of breakwater, yields the total weight of stone required for the job. At the Island Creek site, it was determined that 525 feet of breakwater were required. Hence this project requires 2,835 tons of stone. The 600-foot breakwater at The Nook requires 3,240 tons.

Stone for the breakwater costs on the average $8 per ton for the New England area.[56] Thus the breakwater at the Island Creek site would cost about $22,680, while the breakwater at The Nook would cost $25,920. Breakwater costs at each site are summarized in Table 5.2i.

Table 5.2i Breakwater Costs for Three Marina Sites

Site	Length	Stone Required	Total Cost
I. Jones River	0	0	$ 0
II. Island Creek	525 ft.	2,835 tons	22,680
III. The Nook	600 ft.	3,250 tons	25,920

CONCLUSIONS FROM ECONOMIC COMPARATIVE COST ANALYSIS

At this stage, each capital item has been evaluated at each site.[57] One is now

[54] *Ibid.* [55] *Ibid.* [56] *Ibid.*

[57] Subsequent refinements in analysis have suggested that at The Nook a different design would involve 765 feet less of 8-foot high bulkhead and 200 feet more of breakwater. Such would entail capital cost savings of approximately $24,000. See Section 5.11.1 below. We have not, however, introduced such refinement for The Nook site into the computations which follow. To do so would require that for the *comparative* cost analysis which follows we should consider similar refinements for the other two sites—which consideration was beyond the resources of our study.

interested in comparing the capital cost of an item at one site with the capital cost of that item at each other site, emphasizing the differences in these costs. In calculating the cost differentials relevant for any particular capital item, the dollar figure for this item assigned to the least cost location is set at zero. The cost differentials for the same item which are assigned to the other sites are obtained by subtracting the cost of this capital item at the lowest cost location from the cost of this item at the other sites. However, as there are two possible ways of disposing of the spoil at each of the three sites, five rather than two comparisons are relevant, and an adjustment of the procedure is necessary, as will be demonstrated.

To illustrate, consider the first capital item concerning the access channels. Recall that the construction of access channels was basically a dredging process. The dredging spoil could either be dumped at the edge of the channel, or removed from the Bay entirely. The latter process was shown to be more expensive. In Table 5.2d, the total dredging costs were presented. If the spoil were to be dumped nearby, the cost at the Jones River site would be $204,000, the cost at Island Creek, $132,000, and the cost at The Nook, $51,000. If the spoil were totally removed, the cost of access channels would rise. Under this alternative, the capital cost at the Jones River site would be $408,000, the cost at Island Creek would be $221,000, and the cost at The Nook would be $70,000. Of these six cost items regarding access channels, it can be seen that the cheapest alternative is The Nook with the spoil dumped nearby. Associated with this alternative for The Nook (costing $51,000) is a cost differential equal to zero. The remaining cost differentials are obtained by subtracting $51,000 from the cost at the other two sites, under the two dredging spoil disposal alternatives, and from the cost at The Nook with the spoil totally removed. Hence the differential at Island Creek with the spoil dumped nearby is $132,000 minus $51,000 = $81,000. This net figure indicates that the alternative would cost $81,000 more than the lowest cost alternative which is provided by The Nook, with spoil dumped nearby. Cost differentials are derived in similar manner for the other alternatives.

By this procedure we also compute the relevant cost differentials for each other capital cost item for each alternative. These are presented in Table 5.2j. The Total row of this table sums these cost differentials. When the differentials are summed, the lowest total is for the alternative: location at The Nook, with the spoil dumped nearby. Its total for the cost differentials recorded in the table is $104,030. Assigning a zero overall cost differential to this alternative and subtracting the figure of $104,030 from every other alternative leads to a comparison of each site and dredge spoil alternative. Thus it costs $106,000 more to remove the spoil from The Nook than to dump nearby. Likewise, it costs $15,785 more to provide all capital facilities at Island Creek with spoil dumped nearby. And so forth.

It is also of relevance to note that under each spoil-disposal alternative the data of Table 5.2j reveal that The Nook as a location holds a cost advantage.

At this point, one economic item has yet to be considered. This item relates to maintenance of the dredged channels and basins. It is felt that redredging would be necessary every 10 years at the Jones River site. At the Island Creek and The Nook sites, redredging would be required every 15 years. With expected unit costs of redredging being approximately proportional to original dredging costs, the derived cost differentials would be reinforced. Thus the advantage of The Nook is somewhat understated.

In the following section, ecological costs will be brought into the analysis. In this manner, it will be determined if, in total, removal of the dredging spoil from the Bay is justified.

5.2.3 Comparative Ecological Cost Analysis

In Section 5.2.2 of this analysis, it was determined that the marina capital

Table 5.2j Capital Cost Differentials for Three Marina Sites

Capital Item	Case I. Jones River		Case II. Island Creek		Case III. The Nook	
	Dredging Spoil Removed	Spoil Nearby	Dredging Spoil Removed	Spoil Nearby	Dredging Spoil Removed	Spoil Nearby
Access channels	+ $357,000	+ $153,000	+ $170,000	+ $ 81,000	+ $ 19,000	$ 0
Turning basins	+ 145,000	0	+ 116,000	0	+ 87,000	0
Shore protection	0	0	0	0	+ 68,860	+ 68,860
Land	+ 2,295	+ 2,295	+ 6,885	+ 6,885	0	0
Access roads	+ 20,650	+ 20,650	0	0	0	0
Sewage disposal system	0	0	+ 9,250	+ 9,250	+ 9,250	+ 9,250
Breakwater	0	0	+ 22,680	+ 22,680	+ 25,920	+ 25,920
Total	+ $524,945	+ $175,945	+ $324,815	+ $119,815	+ $210,030	+ $104,030
Overall cost differential relative to the alternative: Location at The Nook, spoil dumped nearby	+ $420,915	+ $ 71,915	+ $220,785	+ $ 15,785	+ $106,000	0

requirements at The Nook were less than at the other sites. This is true regardless of whether the comparisons are made from among the set of costs relevant for removal of dredging spoil, or for dumping the spoil nearby.

In evaluating the ecological costs at each site, it is found that they are primarily dependent on the destination of the dredging spoil from the access channels and the basins. In the economic analysis, separate computations were made for alternative destinations of spoil. In every case, it was more expensive to remove the spoil to a designated offshore dumping area than to dump the spoil on the mudflats beside the channel. This additional cost basically comprised barging costs.

However, one can pose the hypothesis that if the spoil were dumped on the mudflats, where the level of biological activity is high, and if this biological life were destroyed, then perhaps the total cost (both economic and ecologic) would be higher than if the spoil were dumped offshore.

The Kingston Bay area maintains a relatively large number of ecological activities. It would, of course, be possible to identify and attempt an approximate determination of the value of each of them. However, in the present analysis, only a few pertinent activities are isolated and their value approximated.

Most of the mudflat area of the Bay is covered by various types of marine grass. Two of these grasses are chosen for examination. Both are members of the spartina grass family, or cord grass. Spartina grass forms a major part of the vegetation in New England brackish coastal marshes and is an important food source (organic detritus) for finfish and shellfish. In addition, it serves as a habitat for other wild life. If the spoil from dredging the channel is dumped on any of these species of grass, it is assumed that the resulting destruction of that species is permanent. Each species requires a specific tidal range. Hence, in every case it is assumed that no species will reestablish itself. As only minor changes may result in the tidal range, this assumption may prove to be too strong.[58]

The Kingston Bay area is also dotted with beds of shellfish which could be harmed and perhaps destroyed by dredging activity. Two types of shellfish have been selected for examination: soft-shelled clams and blue mussels.

Finally, the westward portions of the Bay are rich in sea worms. These worms are used by fishermen for bait. Dredging activity through areas inhabited by sea worms could have some detrimental effect on the local economy.

The required dredging and biological activity areas of the three sites are shown in Charts 5.2b, 5.2c, 5.2d. In Chart 5.2b, relating to the marina development at the Jones River site (Case I), the dotted areas reveal natural channels. The offshore solid black areas indicate the channels that must be dredged. The dark hachures on either side of the channel indicate areas where the spoil would be dumped if that disposal alternative were chosen. The lighter hachures beyond the dump areas indicate that some spoil would be washed into these areas by tides and other currents. Other features on the map will be explained later. These remarks are also relevant for Chart 5.2c relating to the Island Creek site, and for Chart 5.2d relating to The Nook site.

SPARTINA GRASS

As previously stated, spartina grass serves as a source of organic detritus. This organic detritus in turn becomes a food input for shellfish and finfish. If, in the course of a dredging operation, the spartina grass were eliminated from the area dredged, not only would the habitat of wildlife be destroyed, but so would the intermediate organic detritus link in one or more food chains. Here we may focus upon the link between spartina grass and shellfish.

The two most abundant and important species of spartina grass in the Kingston Bay area are *spartina alterniflora* and *spartina patens*. The spartina alterniflora is a

[58] For details on the critical range of various vegetational units, see Emery and Stevenson [6], p. 725, Figure 28.

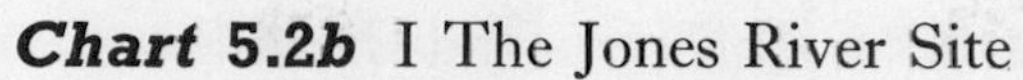

Chart 5.2b I The Jones River Site

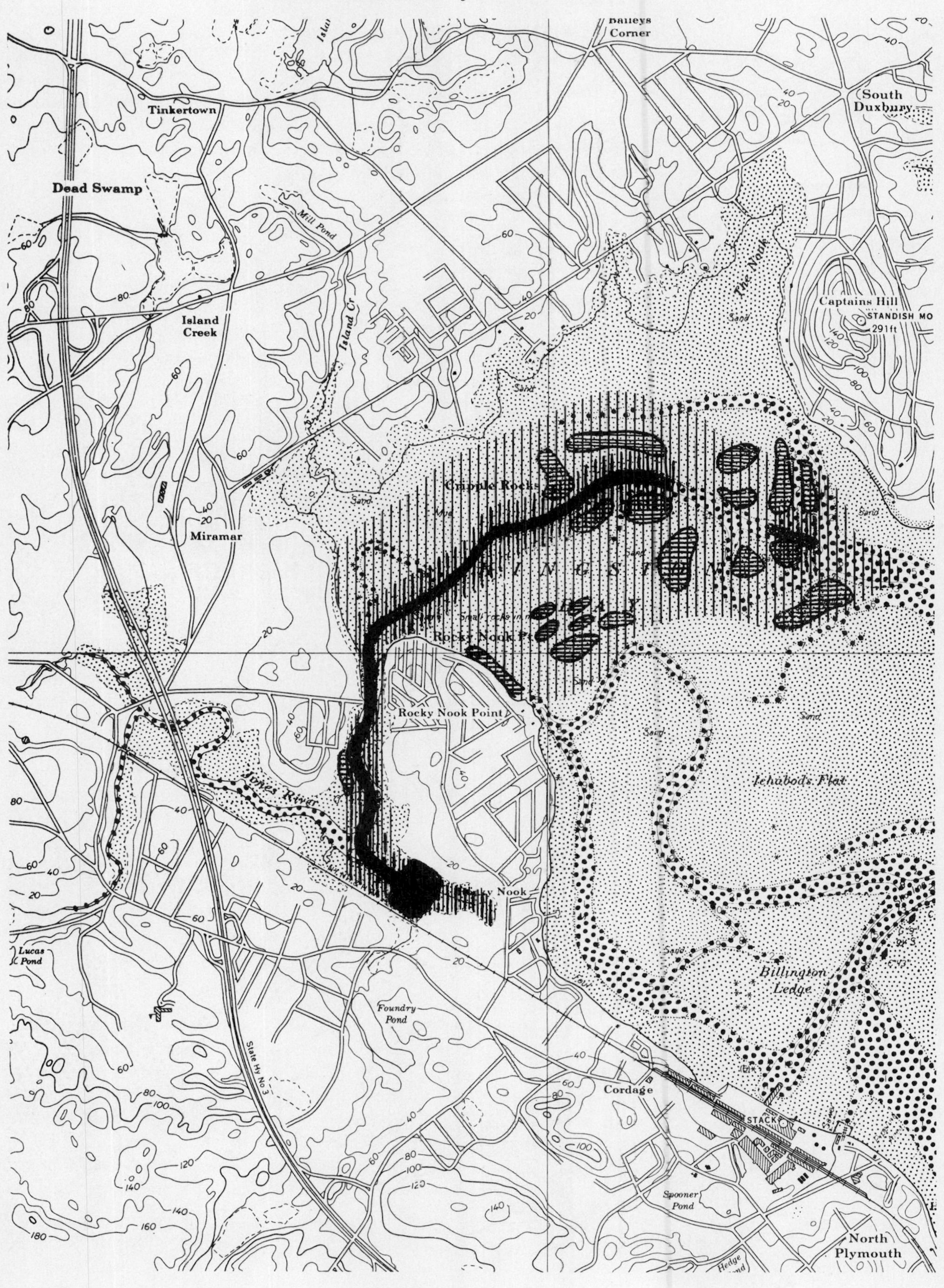

Chart 5.2c II The Island Creek Site

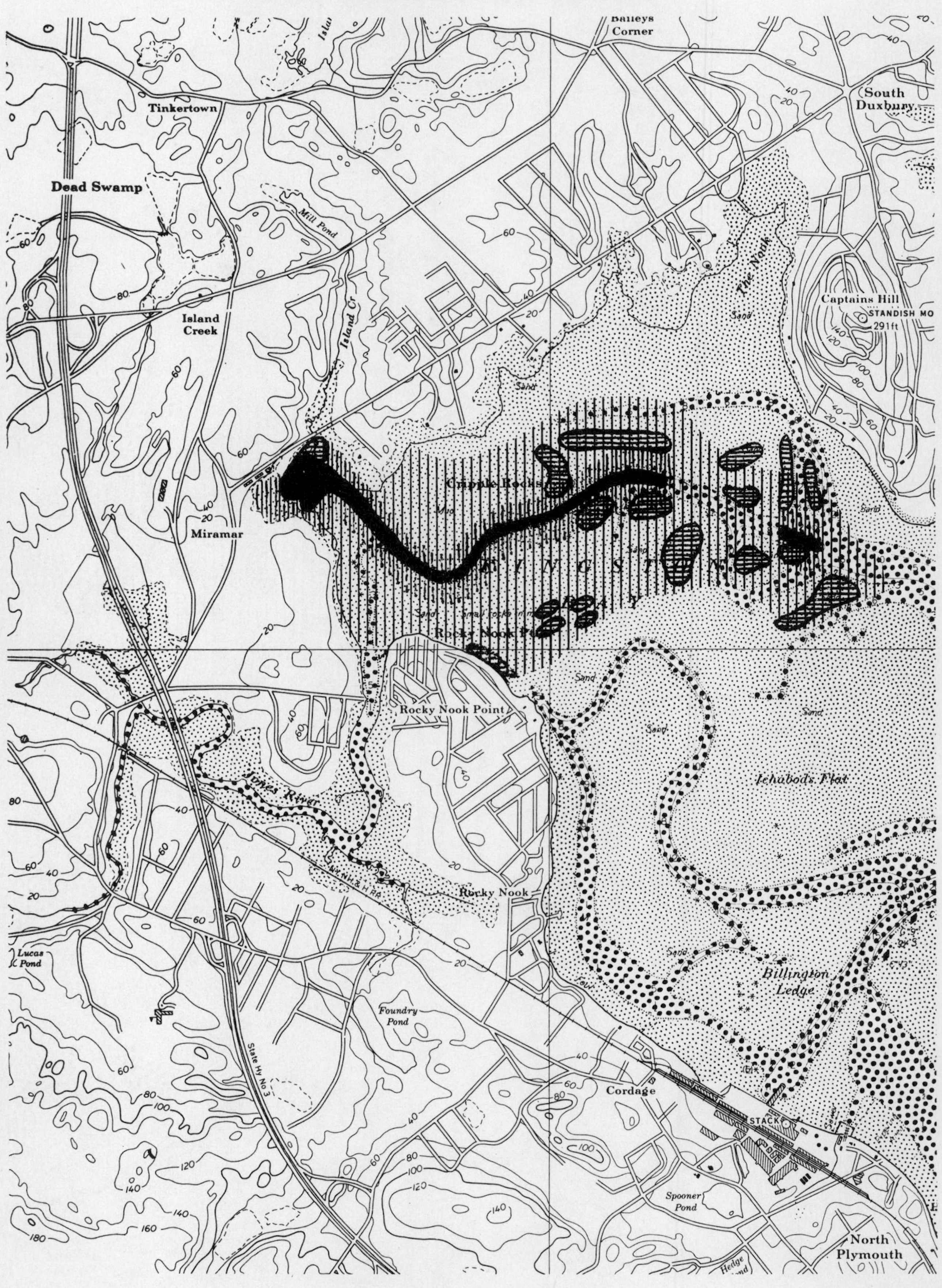

***Chart* 5.2d** III The Nook Site

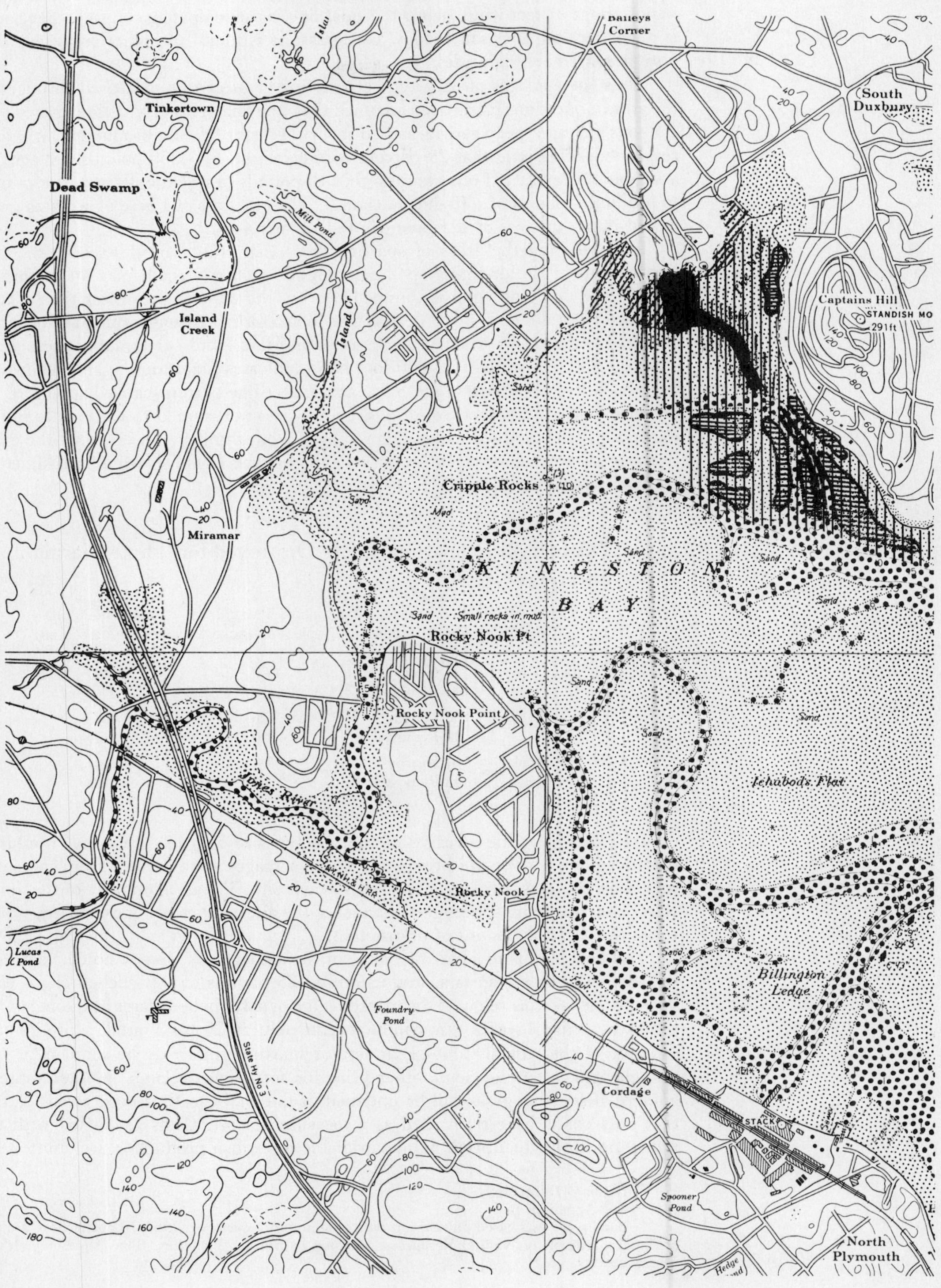

medium-tall, tidewater and saltmarsh plant. It is found throughout the area, in bands about 25 feet wide, below the tidal line. Spartina patens, on the other hand, is a smaller and finer saltmeadow cordgrass. It is found in higher areas, exposed only to extremely high tides.

Thus the acreages of each type of spartina grass can be measured throughout the area in question. It has been assumed that spartina grass production approaches 2.5 tons per acre per year, measured in dry weight. Of this production, it seems reasonable to assume that 25 percent of the weight, or 1,250 pounds per acre, is available to clams.[59] If one assumes that 10 pounds of organic detritus is required to produce 1 pound of soft-shelled clams,[60] then the loss of 1 acre of spartina grass would imply the loss of 125 pounds of clams per year.

In calculating the areas of spartina grass that would be destroyed, the two destinations of the dredging spoil relevant for each site again play an important role. If the dredging spoil is dumped nearby, the damage is greater than if it is removed from the Bay. Total destruction in the former case is assumed to occur in the dredging area for basins and channels and in a band surrounding these areas which is 200 feet wide. This 200-foot band indicates the dumping area, shown in dark hachures on Charts 5.2b, 5.2c, and 5.2d. (The current-carried spoil settling on areas beyond 200 feet from the dredging area is assumed to cause only minor damage.) If the dredged material is removed from the Bay entirely, only the grass in the areas actually dredged for basins and channels (100 feet wide) is assumed to be destroyed.

Table 5.2k Spartina Grass Destroyed for Three Marina Locations

Site	Spoil Disposal	Spartina Alterniflora Destroyed (acres)	Spartina Patens Destroyed (acres)
I. Jones River	a. Nearby	14.0	26.0
	b. Removed	6.0	11.0
II. Island Creek	a. Nearby	5.0	21.0
	b. Removed	4.0	16.0
III. The Nook	a. Nearby	4.0	16.0
	b. Removed	3.0	7.0

In Table 5.2k, the acreages of the two types of spartina grass that would be destroyed at each site are presented. These acreages were derived from measurements on the grass areas as observed at each site. The development of the Jones River site, involving the longest channel of the alternatives being examined, would cause the greatest amount of destruction.

The next step is to assess the value of the damage. As already noted, each acre of spartina grass supports a production of 125 pounds of soft-shelled clams each year. If one takes as relevant the market value of soft-shelled clams as quoted at the time when this research was conducted, namely $0.20 per pound, a preliminary estimate of the annual value of an acre of spartina grass may be set at $25.[61] If one chooses to employ some other price for soft-shelled clams, another value of an acre of spartina grass will be obtained. Table 5.2l can thus be derived. Notice that only clams have been used as a measure of cost. Costs associated with the reduction in the quantity of inputs available for finfish production are omitted.

[59] Niering [18], p. 169.
[60] See Appendix B.
[61] This price was based on relevant data obtained in November, 1967, from the Boston office of the Department of Natural Resources, Division of Marine Fisheries, The Commonwealth of Massachusetts.

Table 5.21 Preliminary Estimate of Annual Spartina Grass Damage (via clams)

Site	Spoil Disposal	Value of Spartina Alterniflora Destroyed	Value of Spartina Patens Destroyed	Total
I. Jones River	a. Nearby	$350	$650	$1,000
	b. Removed	150	275	425
II. Island Creek	a. Nearby	125	525	650
	b. Removed	100	400	500
III. The Nook	a. Nearby	100	400	500
	b. Removed	75	175	250

SOFT-SHELLED CLAMS

The next ecological cost to be determined is that related to damage to soft-shelled clam production. To do so, we first indicate by horizontal hachures on Charts 5.2b, 5.2c, and 5.2d the location of the shellfish beds. These locations were determined from interviews with shellfish officers in Kingston and Duxbury, as well as from aerial photographs. Hence, these beds, particularly those of the blue mussels, were able to be demarcated with a high degree of precision. They are primarily to the east of the Island Creek site.

In the case of soft-shelled clams, it was necessary to determine those areas where both total destruction and only partial damage would occur. If the dredging spoil were dumped nearby, it was assumed that total destruction would occur to shellfish beds in the dredging areas and in a band 200 feet wide on either side of them. As tides and other currents can be expected to wash the dredging spoil into wider areas, such as the areas designated by the lighter vertical hachures on Charts 5.2b, 5.2c, and 5.2d, it also was necessary to estimate destruction of shellfish beds in these wider areas. Such destruction was assumed to be 50 percent.

Under these assumptions we were able to estimate the total acreages of destruction and damage to soft-shelled clam beds. The figures are presented in Table 5.2m.

Table 5.2m Soft-Shelled Clam Acreages Destroyed and Damaged

	With Spoil Dumped in Bay		**With Spoil Removed**
Site	100 percent damage (acres)	50 percent damage (acres)	100 percent damage (acres)
I. Jones River	0	2.0	0
II. Island Creek	0.5	2.0	0
III. The Nook	1.0	9.5	1.0

With the acreages of destruction determined, it is then necessary to derive the potential annual output per acre of soft-shelled clam beds. Assuming a normal annual production of 500 bushels per acre,[62] with one bushel of clams weighing 60 pounds, production of 30,000 pounds per acre per year is anticipated. At a market price of $.20 per pound, the value of production is approximately $6,000 per acre per year. Value of production per acre per year times number of acres destroyed yields the preliminary estimate of the annual value of damage to soft-shelled clams. These preliminary figures are presented in Table 5.2n.[63] From

[62] See Appendix B.

[63] Notice that we assume here (and later in blue mussel and sea worm analysis), that labor (and other resource) costs (except for spartina grass) are zero either because labor would otherwise be unemployed or because there are other gains (for example, recreational benefits) which offset these costs.

Table 5.2n Preliminary Estimates of Annual Value of Damage to Soft-Shelled Clams

Site	With Spoil Dumped Nearby			With Spoil removed
	100 percent Damage	50 percent Damage	Total Damage	100 percent Damage
I. Jones River	$ 0	$6,000	$6,000	$ 0
II. Island Creek	3,000	6,000	9,000	0
III. The Nook	6,000	28,500	34,500	6,000

Table 5.2n, it can be seen that the greatest damage, if the spoil is dumped nearby, is at The Nook site, with damage of $34,500. This heavy damage would be created by the dredging of the access channel for that site since the channel would pass through rich clam beds in its way. If the spoil is removed, the damage to clams at The Nook site drops to $6,000.

It should be observed at this point that double counting has occurred. The annual value of organic detritus as food inputs to clams and the annual value of clams for market sale have both been used. Hence, both Tables 5.2l and 5.2n have been designated as preliminary. In order to remove this double counting, one might propose that the estimated damage in terms of value of spartina grass destroyed be omitted. However, in order to point up the importance of this grass as an intermediate link in the food chain, a certain amount of the final value of clam production is attributed to it. Thus, in Table 5.2o, the value of clam production is distri-

Table 5.2o Revised Estimates of Annual Damage to Spartina Grass and Soft-Shelled Clams

Site	Spoil Disposal	Value of Spartina Alterniflora Destroyed	Value of Spartina Patens Destroyed	Value of Soft-Shelled Clams Destroyed
I. Jones River	a. Nearby	$300	$558	$ 5,142
	b. Removed	150	275	0
II. Island Creek	a. Nearby	117	486	8,397
	b. Removed	100	400	0
III. The Nook	a. Nearby	99	394	34,007
	b. Removed	72	168	5,760

buted across spartina alterniflora, spartina patens, and clam production, on a percentage basis. Although our procedure must be arbitrary at this time (when our knowledge of the process linkages within the ecosystem is so limited), it does eliminate the double counting, and yet attributes some contribution to each category.[64]

BLUE MUSSELS

Since blue mussels lie on the surface, their locale is readily determined by aerial photographs. Thus, the number of acres of mussel beds that would be destroyed

[64] Specifically, for each alternative we calculated the total of (1) the value of soft-shelled clams destroyed as given in Table 5.2n and (2) the value of spartina grass damage as given in Table 5.2l. We then determined the percentage by which this total had to be reduced in order to yield the estimate of value of damage to soft-shelled clams alone. We next applied this percentage reduction factor to the value of spartina alterniflora destroyed (as given in Table 5.2l), to the value of spartina patens destroyed (as given in Table 5.2l), and to the value of damage to soft-shelled clams (as given in Table 5.2n) to obtain the data in Table 5.2o. For example, the value of spartina grass damage by the Jones River development with spoil dumped nearby is $1,000. The value of damage to soft-shelled clams by the Jones River development with spoil dumped nearby is $6,000. The sum is $7,000. To decrease the sum, namely $7,000, to the value of damage to soft-shelled clams alone (namely, $6,000) requires a reduction factor of 1/7. Therefore, this reduction factor is applied to the relevant data in Tables 5.2l and 5.2n to obtain the data in the first row of Table 5.2o.

can be readily determined. As in the case of the clams, areas of 100 percent and 50 percent damage are determined. Where the spoil is dumped nearby, the mussel beds in the dredging area and a 200-foot surrounding band are assumed to be totally destroyed. It is assumed also that fifty percent destruction occurs when these beds are in areas where currents distribute the dredging spoil. Estimated acreages of destruction are shown in Table 5.2p.

Table 5.2p Acreages of Blue Mussels Destruction

Site	With Spoil Dumped in Bay		With Spoil Removed
	100 percent Damage (acres)	50 percent Damage (acres)	100 percent Damage (acres)
I. Jones River	0	78.0	0
II. Island Creek	0	71.0	0
III. The Nook	2.0	33.0	2.0

The manner of determining the annual value of production of blue mussels is similar to the one used to determine the annual value of production of soft-shelled clams. Assuming a production of 400 bushels of blue mussels per acre per year and a weight of 60 pounds of mussels per bushel, one derives a per acre yield of 24,000 pounds per year. If one considers as a relevant measure the market price of $.07 per pound, the value of blue mussels per acre of production is about $1,700 per year.[65] From the acreage data of Table 5.2p, the value of blue-mussel destruction from the development of each site can then be calculated. This value is presented in Table 5.2q.

Table 5.2q Annual Value of Blue-Mussel Damage

Site	With Spoil Dumped in Bay			With Spoil Removed
	100 percent Damage	50 percent Damage	Total Damage	100 percent Damage
I. Jones River	$ 0	$66,300	$66,300	$ 0
II. Island Creek	0	60,350	60,350	0
III. The Nook	3,400	28,050	31,450	3,400

Clearly, if one views the market price of blue mussels as a poor indicator of the worth of blue mussels in terms of its critical position in the ecosystem, then the figures in Table 5.2q must be replaced by others which would be calculable from a specific substitute measure proposed as relevant.

SEA WORMS

The last ecological cost to be determined in this study deals with sea worms. These worms are sold to fishermen for bait. They are found where there are slightly polluted waters, such as at the mouths of the Jones River and Island Creek. It has been estimated that in these areas, the annual production of sea worms approaches 6,000 per acre.[66] When sold for $.04 per worm, this implies an annual value of production approaching $240 per acre.

In attempting to determine the destruction of sea worms, it was assumed that only those directly in the basin and channel dredging areas would be destroyed. Furthermore, it was determined that in the area of The Nook, none were present. Thus sea-worm destruction would occur only at Island Creek and Jones River. In Table 5.2r, the acreages of sea worms destroyed are presented.

[65] These data are based on interviews with staff of the Boston office, Division of Marine Fisheries, Commonwealth of Massachusetts.

[66] Estimated by Tony Cazale, Shellfish Officer, Kingston, Mass.

Table 5.2r Acreages of Sea Worms Destroyed by Dredging

Site	With Spoil Dumped in Bay	With Spoil Removed
I. Jones River	12.0	12.0
II. Island Creek	16.0	16.0
III. The Nook	0	0

With $240 as the annual value per acre of sea-worm production, the value of sea worms which would be destroyed at each site is presented in Table 5.2s.

Table 5.2s Annual Value of Sea-Worm Destruction

Site	With Spoil Dumped in Bay	With Spoil Removed
I. Jones River	$2,880	$2,880
II. Island Creek	3,840	3,840
III. The Nook	0	0

Conclusions from Comparative Ecological Cost Analysis

At this stage, a limited number of ecological costs have been derived. Again the differential costs at each site are determined. Such a process parallels that described in detail with regard to economic cost differentials. Again, for any given item, a cost differential of zero is assigned to the development alternative with which the lowest cost is associated. All other alternatives are assigned a cost differential equal to the amount by which their cost exceeds that of the lowest cost alternative. Thus in Table 5.2t for the first item—namely, ecological cost from damage to spartina alterniflora, the best alternative is The Nook location with dredging spoil removed. This alternative is assigned a zero cost differential. Another alternative, whose cost from damage to spartina alterniflora is $28 greater, is the Island Creek location with dredging spoil removed. This alternative is then assigned a cost differential of $28. In similar manner, the cost differentials are determined for each other alternative, and they are recorded in the first row of Table 5.2t.

For each other ecological cost item which we have examined, the relevant cost differentials are determined. They are all presented in Table 5.2t. From this table it can be seen that the lowest ecological costs for the five items of Table 5.2t would be incurred if the marina were located at the Jones River site with dredging spoil removed. From the standpoint of capital cost, however, it will be recalled that this was the most expensive of the six alternatives. Hence, further analysis is required.

5.2.4 Combined Analysis of Ecologic and Economic Cost Differentials

Recall that Table 5.2j estimates capital cost differentials. Table 5.2t estimates annual ecological cost differentials. Now we wish to bring the two sets of cost differentials together in a combined analysis. But first these cost differentials must be made comparable. To do so, we convert the capital cost differentials to an annual basis. We accordingly assume a depreciation period for the economic capital items. This depreciation period would yield an approximation of the annual charges on capital. Two depreciation periods, 10 years and 20 years, are used with the implicit assumption that all capital items depreciate by the same annual amount. Obviously, refinements could be made on this assumption, but such refinement is not essential at this time.

Table 5.2t Ecological Cost Differentials of the Three Marina Sites

	Case I: Jones River		Case II: Island Creek		Case III: The Nook	
Ecological Item	Dredging Spoil Removed	Spoil Nearby	Dredging Spoil Removed	Spoil Nearby	Dredging Spoil Removed	Spoil Nearby
Spartina alterniflora	+ $ 78	+ $ 228	+ $ 28	+ $ 45	$ 0	+ $ 27
Spartina patens	+ 107	+ 390	+ 232	+ 318	0	+ 226
Soft-shelled clams	0	+ 5,142	0	+ 8,397	+ 5,760	+ 34,007
Blue mussels	0	+ 66,300	0	+ 60,350	+ 3,400	+ 31,450
Sea worms	+ 2,880	+ 2,880	+ 3,840	+ 3,840	0	0
Total	+ $3,065	+ $74,940	+ $4,100	+ $72,950	+ $9,160	+ $65,710
Overall cost differential relative to the alternative: location at Jones River with dredging spoil removed	0	+ $71,875	+ $1,035	+ $69,885	+ $6,095	+ $62,645

Table 5.2u Comparison of Annual Economic and Ecological Cost Differentials and Their Totals at Three Marina Sites

	Case I: Jones River		Case II: Island Creek		Case III: The Nook	
	Spoil Removed	Spoil Dumped Nearby	Spoil Removed	Spoil Dumped Nearby	Spoil Removed	Spoil Dumped Nearby
Annual ecological cost differentials	$ 0	$71,875	$ 1,035	$69,885	$ 6,095	$62,645
Annual capital cost differentials, 10-year depreciation period	42,092+	7,192+	22,079+	1,579+	10,600+	0
Annual capital cost differentials, 20-year depreciation period	21,046+	3,596+	11,039+	789+	5,300+	0
Total annual cost differentials, 10-year depreciation period	42,092+	79,067+	23,114+	71,464+	16,695+	62,645
Total annual cost differentials, 20-year depreciation period	$21,046+	$75,471+	$12,074+	$70,674+	$11,395+	$62,645

We now construct a new table, Table 5.2u. Its first row is the overall cost differential (ecological) row of Table 5.2t. Its second and third rows are the overall cost differential (capital) row of Table 5.2j when multiplied by 10 percent and 5 percent depreciation rates, respectively. The fourth and fifth rows of Table 5.2u are the sum of the first and second rows, and the first and third rows, respectively.

From the last two rows of Table 5.2u it can be seen that when all costs are taken into account, a marina at The Nook with the spoil completely removed from The Bay involves least cost and damage. This conclusion holds regardless of whether a 10-year depreciation period or the 20-year period is used. In the 10-year depreciation period, the combined annual cost and annual damage of removing the spoil is \$62,645 minus \$16,695, or \$45,950 less than the cost if the spoil were not removed. The Island Creek site is the second least costly, if the spoil is removed. Still, the combined annual cost and annual damage is \$23,114 minus \$16,695, or \$6,419 more than at The Nook. If a 20-year depreciation period is taken, The Nook has an annual advantage of only \$679 over the Island Creek Site, when spoil is removed.

However, one vital question is left unanswered: Who should bear the annual interest and other charges on the investment, especially the additional investment incurred for spoil removal? Should it be the marina operator who is making this change in the environment? Or should it be the clam industry, which in order to maintain its livelihood might insist that the spoil be removed? Should it be the state, federal, or local government interested in environmental development and control? This question is clearly in the realm of political decision-making and beyond the scope of comparative cost analysis. Moreover, some additional annual cost is involved in the interest charge (whether explicit or implicit when a pure public investment is effected) to be made on capital investments. We have indicated this cost by adding a + to annual capital cost differentials. While we have no firm basis for estimating the additional cost, except to state that the relevant interest might range from 0 to 10 percent, this additional cost increases the superiority of The Nook site over the Island Creek site when spoil is removed, and does not affect the clear superiority of The Nook site with spoil removed over other alternatives.

For the purposes of this study, the alternative involving the location of a marina at The Nook with the spoil removed will be selected for detailed analysis. In the next portion of this study, a complete determination of capital and operating costs, as well as potential revenues, will be presented for this alternative.

5.3 *Estimating Demand for a New Marina at a Plymouth Bay Site*

5.3.1 Total Demand

A vital step in planning any new facility involves estimating the demand for whatever services might be produced. It is almost axiomatic among major manufacturing establishments that market research should be conducted before the installation of any new capacity to produce some established or new commodity. Similarly, it is important to estimate the probable demand for the services of a recreational facility whenever such a facility is basic to a regional plan. In this case study, it was determined that some set of marine-oriented activities should be considered. The immediate question which follows is: At what scales should these activities operate? This question obviously relates to the willingness of the public to consume the services that might be provided. Thus, the problem of determining scales involves a still more basic question: What is the demand or size of the market for such a development?

As indicated in Section 2.4, these are the types of questions to which the gravity (spatial interaction) model can be applied. A preliminary decision was made to consider the construction of a marina complex in the Plymouth, Massachusetts, area. To determine the probable market for such a complex, an estimation procedure is needed which takes into account the distribution of population, family incomes, people's desire to participate in boating-type activities, competing facilities and their capacities, the distances between the proposed marina and the market population, and the distances between the proposed marina and its competitors. The gravity model can be used in a way which takes these variables into consideration and estimates the number of participants that might be expected. Furthermore, through certain side calculations, some idea of reasonable scales for the development can be derived.

Recall that the gravity model discussed in Section 2.4 was labeled a trip distribution model. It seemed best suited to answering questions regarding trip terminations. Thus, the first step is to estimate the number of trips that could be expected to be made from all areas which might provide consumers of the services of the proposed marina complex.

Given the location of the proposed marina, it appears reasonable to assume that nearly all the consumers might be expected to come from Massachusetts and Rhode Island. It does, however, appear unlikely that they will come from all areas of Massachusetts. For example, Berkshire County, in the extreme western part of Massachusetts, appears unlikely to furnish any significant number because it is too distant. Dukes and Nantucket Counties also seem unlikely sources because these two counties are actually offshore islands and can easily satisfy the boating recreational demands of their inhabitants.

Some participants might be expected to come from states located further away, such as Connecticut and New Hampshire, as well as vacationers from other areas. However, it is expected that their numbers would be minor.

In trying to estimate the number of trips that would be made from any geographical area, it was necessary to use indirect information sources since direct data were not available. There does exist, however, information on outboard motor sales by county[67] and on the number of boating days each year per person as a function of family income for the Northeastern United States.[68] By using the latter data, together with counts of the number of families in each income class residing in each county,[69] it was possible to estimate how many man-days of recreational activity boating would be demanded by the inhabitants of each county in a year. This estimate was then compared with the number of outboard motor sales for each county. It was found that outboard motor sales were roughly proportional to the man-days of demand for recreational activity boating which were predicted by considering family income only. This finding was independent of distance from the coast. While this relationship involved only Massachusetts counties, nevertheless it was felt that the family income distribution data constituted an adequate basis for a distribution model of trips associated with the man-days of demand for recreational boating generated in both Massachusetts and Rhode Island.

Our procedure can be illustrated by examining the data for Norfolk County, Massachusetts. The distribution of family income was obtained from census data. This distribution is shown in Table 5.3a.

Given the income distribution for Norfolk County, the next task was to transform the income groupings used by the census to those used by the National Recreation Survey. This step involved aggregating some classes and disaggregating others. For example, given the census data, derivation of a new class, $8,000–$9,999, involves adding the $8,000–$8,999 to the old class, $9,000–$9,999. However, to derive a new class $4,500–$5,999, certain assumptions must be made. In this new class we obviously place all the families in the old class, $5,000–$5,999.

[67] Boating Industry Association [4].
[68] Outdoor Recreation Resources Review Commission [21], p. 125.
[69] U.S. Bureau of the Census [26], Table 86, pp. 23, 256–257; and [27], Table 86, pp. 41, 103.

Table 5.3a Family Income Distribution in Norfolk County, Massachusetts, 1960

Family Income Class	Number of Families in Class
Less than $1,000	1,998
$1,000–$1,999	2,989
$2,000–$2,999	4,318
$3,000–$3,999	6,703
$4,000–$4,999	10,656
$5,000–$5,999	16,085
$6,000–$6,999	15,374
$7,000–$7,999	14,642
$8,000–$8,999	11,467
$9,000–$9,999	8,894
$10,000–$14,999	21,225
$15,000–$24,999	8,559
More than $25,000	4,049

Source: U.S. Bureau of the Census [26], Table 86, pp. 23, 257.

But what proportion of the old class, $4,000–$4,999, should be included? To determine this proportion, it was assumed that the numbers in the income classes on either side of the $4,000–$4,999 class would serve as valid indicators. Thus, with 6,703 families in the $3,000–$3,999 class, and 16,085 families in the $5,000–$5,999 class, the proportion was determined and total number of families in the $4,500–$5,999 income class was derived.[70] In a similar manner, the other transformations of the income classes were made. The number of families by income class is listed in column 2 of Table 5.3b.

Table 5.3b Derivation of Man-Days of Demand for Recreational Boating Generated in Norfolk County, Massachusetts, June–August

Family Incomes (1)	Number of Families (2)	Population per Family (3)	Persons per Income Classification (4)	Man-Days per Person June–August (5)	Total Man-Days, June–August (6)
Less than $1,500	2,954	3.3	9,748	0.36	3,509
$1,500–$2,999	6,351	3.3	20,958	0.96	20,120
$3,000–$4,499	9,793	3.3	32,317	0.95	30,701
$4,500–$5,999	23,651	3.3	78,048	0.88	68,682
$6,000–$7,999	30,016	3.3	99,053	1.02	101,034
$8,000–$9,999	20,361	3.3	67,191	2.02	135,726
$10,000–$14,999	21,225	3.3	70,043	2.61	182,812
More than $15,000	12,608	3.3	41,606	7.58	315,373
Total					857,957

With the numbers by family income classes thus derived, it was necessary to transform the numbers of families to the number of persons. Assuming 3.3 persons per family,[71] multiplication yields the number of individuals in each family income class. In Table 5.3b, column 2 is multiplied by column 3 to obtain column 4.

[70] That is, it is estimated that $\frac{16{,}085,}{6{,}703+16{,}085}$, or 71 percent of the 10,650 families in the $4,000–$4,999 class, had incomes from $4,500–$4,999. This yielded an estimate of 7,566 families. When these families were added to the 16,085 families in the $5,000–$5,999 class, this gave a total of 23,651 families within the class $4,500–$5,999.

[71] Limited research resources and time did not permit us to consider variation in number of persons per family among income classes. In our particular demand analysis, it was judged that such refinement would not have a significant effect on the estimated magnitudes.

In column 5, the man-days of effective demand for recreational boating per person by income class are given. These man-days are average participation rates for persons in the Northeastern United States and refer to participation during the June through August period. As this is the period of peak demand for boating activities, it was judged to be appropriate for use in estimating scales for activities of the proposed marina. It is evident that participation increases with higher family incomes. Whereas persons from family income classes of less than $1,500 participate, on the average, 0.36 days per season in boating activities, persons with family incomes greater than $15,000 participate on the average, 7.58 days per season.

In Table 5.3b, multiplying column 4, persons by income class, by column 5, man-days in June-August per person by income class, yields column 6, the total man-days generated during July-August by income class. The sum (857,957) of column 6 is the total man-days in the June-August period for Norfolk County.

The same steps were employed to derive the man-days of demand for recreational boating from the other counties in both Massachusetts and Rhode Island that were considered. The man-days for each county are shown in Table 5.3c.

Table 5.3c Man-Days of Demand for Recreational Boating by Selected Massachusetts and Rhode Island Counties June–August Season

County	Man-Days
Barnstable Co., Mass.	86,333
Bristol Co., Mass	452,935
Essex Co., Mass.	773,885
Franklin Co., Mass.	61,232
Hampden Co., Mass.	544,739
Hampshire Co., Mass.	112,376
Middlesex Co., Mass.	1,870,126
Norfolk Co., Mass.	857,957
Plymouth Co., Mass.	316,517
Suffolk Co., Mass.	903,850
Worcester Co., Mass.	714,923
Bristol Co., R.I.	52,859
Kent Co., R.I.	142,656
Newport Co., R.I.	74,379
Providence Co., R.I.	679,050
Washington Co., R.I.	63,680

With this computation of man-days to be expected by each of sixteen counties of origin, the next step is to distribute these days among various sites at which boating can be provided (supplied). That is, the next step is to distribute the trips originating in any county in order to satisfy demand for recreational boating among alternative destinations. In theoretical terms, the destinations could be considered to be every marine recreational facility (existing and potential) along the coast of New England. In operational terms, this total would be too broad for the purpose at hand. Therefore, the coastal area was divided into twenty coastal zones of destination. Additionally, it was realized that some boating recreation could take place at inland locations. Therefore, seven inland zones of destination were included, giving twenty-seven destinations in all.

In order to distribute the man-days of demand among points of supply, or zones of destination of trips, some measure of the relative attractiveness of the facilities in each zone was required. It was felt that the attractiveness of a zone for recreational boating could probably best be measured by some estimate of the amount of recreational boating facilities available in the zone. Therefore, the quantities of dock space, mooring facilities, and the boat storage area in each zone were derived from published materials.[72]

To distribute man-days of demand, it was first necessary to establish the "distances" between the counties of origin and the zones of destination. As both the counties of origins and zones of destination cover considerable areas, it was necessary to choose a central location for each. Grid lines were drawn on a map of southern New England. The origin of this system of coordinates was established at the western end of Long Island Sound. By establishing it west of the most westerly area included and south of the most southerly, we were able to avoid assigning negative coordinates to some areas, and thus were able to avoid complicated coding for a computer program. Once each location was assigned its pair of positive coordinates, the straight-line distance between any two pairs of coordinates was readily computed.

Consider the 857,957 man-days of demand that originate in Norfolk County. The distance from Norfolk County to each of the twenty-seven zones of destination of trips to satisfy the demand has now been specified. The relative attractiveness of each zone of destination to the boaters residing in Norfolk County is assumed to be proportional to the amount of boating facilities available in that zone of destination divided by the distance between that zone and Norfolk County. Accordingly, this ratio is calculated for each zone of destination. The 857,957 man-days of demand from Norfolk County are distributed among the twenty-seven alternative destinations according to these ratios. Thus, the ratio relating Norfolk County with any given zone of destination, when divided by the sum of the ratios relating Norfolk County with all twenty-seven zones of destination, yields the proportion of Norfolk County man-days of demand which are met in that given zone.

It can be seen that the denominator of this fraction will be the same for all calculations based on any given county of origin. Thus, only the numerator of the fraction changes as the various destinations are considered.

As it is known that 857,957 man-days originate in Norfolk County, then given the proportion of these man-days which relate to each zone of destination, it is only necessary to multiply through to obtain the actual number of man-days of demand from Norfolk County which are satisfied by each zone of destination. For any given zone this number also represents the man-days of recreational activity boating supplied by the facilities at that zone.

On this basis, if there is no new marina in Plymouth Bay, 28,040 man-days of demand for recreational boating by residents of Norfolk County are met in the Plymouth area. As previously noted, these man-days are scattered over a three-month period from June to August. If a 400-boat marina were added to the facilities already existing in the Plymouth area, then 44,233 man-days of demand by Norfolk County residents would be met in the Plymouth area. Therefore, the marina would be attracting 16,193 man-days of demand by residents of Norfolk County.

Similar computations can be made for each county of origin. In total, 213,136 man-days of demand are met in the Plymouth area if the proposed 400-boat marina is not built, and 336,887 if it is. Therefore, the addition of the marina would add 123,751 to the man-days of demand met in the Plymouth area over the three-month period, an average of about 1,300 per day. This figure suggests that there would be about 3.3 man-days per day attracted per boat in the proposed 400-boat marina. This statistic suggests that the new marina could probably be operated close to full capacity. We assume that these 123,751 man-days of demand are attracted to the Plymouth area from other competing areas because the addition of the new marina makes the Plymouth area relatively more attractive than it was before the marina

[72] These data for coastal areas were extracted from *Boating Almanac* [2] and [3]. For inland areas, data on available facilities were estimated from various sources, including Foster [8] and [9]; [14] and other unpublished data made available by Professor Foster.

is established. The same method used to determine the effect of the new marina upon the Plymouth area can be used to estimate the effects on competing areas. For instance, the effect on the coastal zone immediately to the north of Plymouth is to reduce the number of man-days of demand met there from 259,614 to 254,759. Similarly, the effect on the coastal area immediately to the south is to reduce the man-days satisfied there from 369,199 to 362,466. These declines may seem small, and indeed as the additional demand met in the Plymouth area would be at the expense of all other areas, no single area is likely to be markedly affected. Furthermore, the slight adverse effects on other areas from the introduction of a marina in any single area able to attract a large number of trips is likely to be offset at least partially by normal population growth in the larger region. We have not had the time and resources to account for such effects in our total analysis.

We pointed out in Section 2.4 that the correct exponent to be placed on the distance variable in calculating relative attractiveness has been a matter of some discussion among regional scientists. In the above formulation, an exponent of unity was assumed—i.e., the attractiveness was assumed to be inversely proportional to distance. Other values of the exponent could be employed, such as 2. If an exponent of 2 were used, the number of man-days of demand met in the Plymouth area, without the marina would be 183,847; but with the marina it would be 276,915. Thus, the addition of the marina would lead to an increase of 93,068 man-days met in the area. The effect of the marina, for various exponents on the distance variable, is given in Table 5.3d.

Table 5.3d Estimates of Man-Days of Demand for Recreational Boating Met in the Plymouth Area, for Selected Exponents on the Distance Variable

Exponent Value	Man-Days Without Marina	Man-Days With Marina	Increase in Man-Days Due to Marina
0.00	200,962	318,263	117,301
0.25	201,830	319,614	117,784
0.50	204,522	323,798	119,276
0.75	209,355	331,257	121,902
1.00	213,136	336,887	123,751
1.25	211,018	332,864	121,846
1.50	202,542	317,814	115,272
1.75	191,817	296,968	105,151
2.00	183,847	276,915	93,068
2.25	182,303	262,956	80,653
2.50	187,880	256,884	69,004
2.75	198,599	257,039	58,440
3.00	211,855	260,845	48,990
3.25	225,679	266,364	40,685
3.50	238,913	272,457	33,544
3.75	250,975	278,501	27,526
4.00	261,629	284,161	22,532
4.25	270,833	289,257	18,424
4.50	278,662	293,724	15,062
4.75	285,242	297,562	12,320
5.00	290,732	300,811	10,079

Table 5.3d shows that the number of man-days of demand met in the Plymouth area is relatively insensitive to the exponent on distance as long as that exponent is less than 2. For greater values of the exponent, the number of additional man-days attracted to the Plymouth Bay area declines rapidly. As recreational trips may be considered relatively insensitive to distance, it seems reasonable to expect that about 100,000 additional man-days of demand will be attracted to the Plymouth area as a result of the proposed marina.

5.3.2 Supply and Demand Estimates by Type of Recreational Activity

We now proceed to the next step and disaggregate total demand into demand for particular types of recreational boating activities, while at the same time deriving corresponding estimates of supply. The costs and qualities of the particular types of recreational boating activities which can be furnished influence the composition of total demand. In a real sense, demand and supply, as well as price, are simultaneously determined in the market. And in fact, our disaggregation of total demand will be based on the composition of the diverse types of recreational boating activities that might be reasonably supplied by a marina capable of meeting a 100,000 man-day demand—reasonably in terms of the demand and supply for recreational boating activities at other localities possessing marinas, both in New England and elsewhere. Our disaggregation is further checked with the information accumulated in pilot studies of the Fort Lee Cove site and the Industrial Point site of Salem, Massachusetts.

Granted that a Plymouth Bay marina of about 400-boat capacity is feasible from the demand point-of-view, a number of disaggregation schemes are possible. It has been decided that the boats should first be disaggregated on the basis of their use of the marina facilities. Thus, we begin with a breakdown in terms of (1) boats which will be docked at the marina throughout the entire season, (2) boats which will be left at the marina throughout the season but berthed on land when not in use, (3) boats which will be left at the marina throughout the season but moored offshore, and (4) boats which will be hauled to and from the marina for use and launched from ramps. This last category comprises the "transient fleet." In addition, there will be boats owned by the marina and rented to participants.

Consider first those boats which make use of the marina docking facilities. The boats which can be expected to make use of the proposed docking facility can be classified either by length (10–20 feet, 20–30 feet, or 30–40 feet) or by type of boat (seasonal outboard, seasonal inboard, or seasonal sailing).[73] If both groupings are used simultaneously, a cross-classification of the boats can be derived as in Table 5.3e.

Table 5.3e Classification of Boats Seasonally Docked at the Proposed Marina, by Size and Type of Boat

	Number of Boats by Length			
	10–20 Feet	20–30 Feet	30–40 Feet	**Total**
Number of Boats by Type				
Seasonal outboard	100	18	0	118
Seasonal inboard	0	45	50	95
Seasonal sailing	50	27	10	87
Total	150	90	60	300

Table 5.3e indicates that no small inboards are expected. Likewise, no large outboards are expected. Most sailing vessels will probably be fairly small. In all, 300 docked boats are anticipated.

The same type of cross-classification system can be used for seasonal boats which are berthed on land. Because of the problems of launching and landing these boats, they will, for the most part, be shorter in length. The relevant cross-classification is shown in Table 5.3f.

[73] "Seasonal" refers to the fact that these boats are left at the marina for the entire season, in contrast to "transients" which are not.

Table 5.3f Classification of Seasonal Boats Berthed on Land at the Proposed Marina, by Size and Type of Boat

	Number of Boats by Length		
	10–20 Feet	20–25 Feet	**Total**
Number of Boats by Type			
Seasonal outboard	30	20	50
Seasonal inboard	0	12	12
Seasonal sailing	10	8	18
Total	40	40	80

It is anticipated that larger seasonal boats will make use of the mooring facilities provided by the marina. The larger boats are assumed to be entirely seasonal inboards and seasonal sailing craft. The relevant cross-classification by length and type of boat is shown in Table 5.3g.

Table 5.3g Classification of Seasonal Boats Moored Offshore at the Proposed Marina, by Size and Type of Boat

	Number of Boats by Length		
	20–30 Feet	30–40 Feet	**Total**
Number of Boats by Type			
Seasonal outboard	0	0	0
Seasonal inboard	5	3	8
Seasonal sailing	5	2	7
Total	10	5	15

From the foregoing tables, it can be seen that 300 docked boats, 80 dry-land berthed boats, and 15 moored boats are expected, so 395 boats are expected to make seasonal use of the marina facilities.

At this stage, an over-simplification has been made in the tables. It has been assumed that all boats using docking, dry-land berthing, and mooring facilities are seasonal boats. Some of these facilities will be reserved for transient use and will not be used by seasonal boats. Such use occurs when boats are left at the facility overnight, or perhaps for a week at a time. Accordingly, we assume that such transient use is equivalent to the use of the facilities by 10 seasonal outboards, 5 seasonal inboards, and 5 seasonal sailing vessels. These equivalents are already included in tables 5.3e, 5.3f, and 5.3g. Accordingly, we list in column 1 of Table 5.3h, the number of boats by type, seasonal and transient. To ease subsequent computations, we have changed the numbers of outboard seasonal from 158 to 160 and sailing seasonals from 107 to 105.

The next step in the disaggregation of total demand is to determine whether boats would be used strictly for pleasure boating, or whether they might be used for sport fishing. This step is necessary, as will be seen later, because the inputs into these two types of recreational activities differ.

For our area, we consider it reasonable to assume that approximately 33 percent of all pleasure boating time will involve sport fishing. It is, therefore, posited that one-third of all inboards and outboards are used for fishing purposes, while two-thirds are used for pleasure boating. Although any single boat might be used for both activities, the employment of this time division is equivalent to dividing all boats into one of two categories: sport fishing and pleasure boating. This dichotomy

Table 5.3h Numbers of Boats and Man-Days Provided by Boat Type in Docking, Mooring, and Dry-Land Berthing Operations

Type of Boat	Total (1)	Boats for Fishing (2)	Boats for Pleasure (3)	Man-Days per Season per Boat (4)	Total Man-Days per Season by Boat Type (5)
Outboard seasonal	160	50	110	162	25,920
Outboard transient	10	4	6	162	1,620
Inboard seasonal	110	40	70	216	23,760
Inboard transient	5	2	3	216	1,080
Sailing seasonal	105	0	105	162	17,010
Sailing transient	5	0	5	162	810
Total	395				70,200

is performed in Table 5.3h. Columns 2 and 3 allocate the column 1 totals to boats for fishing and boats for pleasure, respectively. Sailboats are assumed to be strictly for pleasure.

In column 4 of Table 5.3h we list the man-days per season per boat which are provided (supplied). These man-days were computed by assuming that outboards and sailing boats would, on the average, carry 3 persons, while inboards would, on the average, carry 4. All boats would be used, on the average, $4\frac{1}{2}$ days per week throughout the season, consisting of 12 weeks. Thus, for seasonal outboard boats, 3 persons per boat times $4\frac{1}{2}$ days per week times 12 weeks = 162 man-days per season.

Finally, to derive the number of man-days of recreation provided by each category of boat which are recorded in column 5, the number of boats (in column 1) is multiplied by the relevant man-days figure (in column 4).

Table 5.3h shows that the docking, dry-land berthing, and mooring activities involving 395 boats will generate approximately 70,200 recreational man-days of activity. We now turn to the second major group of boating facilities available at the marina—namely, those associated with rental boat operations.

We have hypothesized that a marina of this size and at this location would maintain a rental fleet consisting of 12 rowboats without engines, 12 rowboats with engines, 12 outboards 10–20 feet long, and 12 sailboats. If it is assumed that all rental boats carry 3 persons on the average and are used $4\frac{1}{2}$ days per week for a season of 12 weeks, the man-days provided can be computed. This computation is shown in Table 5.3i. For example, each rental rowboat will provide 162 man-days of recreational activity in the course of the season so that twelve such rowboats will

Table 5.3i Rental Boat Operations: Numbers of Boats and Man-Days Provided, by Boat Type

Type of Boat	Number of Boats	Persons per Boat	Days Usage per Week	Weeks Usage per Year	Man-Days per Boat	Man-Days per Type of Boat
Rowboats, without engines	12	3	4.5	12	162	1,944
Rowboats, with engines	12	3	4.5	12	162	1,944
Outboards, 10–20 feet	12	3	4.5	12	162	1,944
Sailboats	12	3	4.5	12	162	1,944
Total	48					7,776

provide 1,944 man-days of recreation. The entire rental fleet, consisting of 48 boats, will provide 7,776 man-days.

We now turn to another major area of operation of the proposed marina—namely, its ramp operations. Ramps are provided for launching and landing *transient* boats which would make use of the marina facilities. Approximately 35 boats per day can be launched from a single ramp, while 70 boats per day can be handled by a double ramp. The larger ramp is expected to be more reasonable from the estimates of demand that have been presented. It is assumed that this ramp facility is operated at capacity 63 days per year (approximately 4½ days per week for a 14-week season). The ramp capacity, 70 boats per day, multiplied by 63 days of ramp use per year, yields 4,410 boat days per year. Because the ramps are used primarily by outboard boats, which are assumed to carry an average of 3 persons, then 13,230 man-days of transient recreational boating would be associated with the services provided over the course of the season by the ramp operations.

Finally, we assume that party boats provide 7,000 man-days of recreational activity. (Each of two party boats make 140 trips per 20-week season, carrying on the average 25 persons per trip). Of the 7,000 man-days, 6,300 involve fishing activity, and 700 are for pleasure only. Additionally, it is estimated that 2,000 man-days of surf, pier, and jetty fishing will be both generated and provided within and in the vicinity of the marina.

Table 5.3j Summary of Man-Days of Recreational Activities Provided by Proposed Marina

Operation	Man-Days
Docking, mooring, and dry-land berthing operations	70,200
Rental operations	7,776
Transient operations	13,230
Party boats	7,000
Surf, pier, and jetty fishing	2,000
Total	100,206

We may now total in Table 5.3j the man-days of the diverse recreational activities provided by the marina.

Recall from Table 5.3h that the calculations for the man-days provided by the docking, dry-land berthing, and mooring operations yield a figure of 70,200. Rental operations, as computed in Table 5.3i, supply an additional 7,776 man-days. Associated with the ramp operations are 13,230 man-days. Finally, party boat and surf, pier, and jetty fishing provide 7,000 and 2,000 man-days respectively. All together, it can be seen that a total of 100,206 man-days of recreation is expected to be provided. This total of man-days of recreation provided (supplied) is consistent with the rough total of 100,000 man-days of demand for recreational boating derived in the previous section. The composition of this total supply is also taken to be roughly the relevant disaggregation of the total demand.

5.4 *A Classification System for Outdoor Recreational Activities*

With the disaggregation of demand now complete, we turn to the technical production side. The first task is to identify and define systematically relevant recreational activities. That is, we seek a classification of recreational activities that will: (1) facilitate data collection, (2) be meaningful in the context of recreational development policy analysis, and (3) be useful in terms of existing and new operational recreation models. Once this sectoring is accomplished, it will be necessary to construct input-output vectors for those sectors relevant to the proposed marina complex.

Recreational activities might be sectored in a manner similar to the Standard Industrial Classification system devised by the U.S. Bureau of the Budget.[74] In this system, all economic activities are divided into 10 major divisions. These divisions are shown in Table 5.4a.

Table 5.4a Major Divisions of the Standard Industrial Classification System

Division	Industries within Division
A	Agriculture, Forestry, and Fisheries
B	Mining
C	Contract Construction
D	Manufacturing
E	Transportation, Communication, Electric, Gas, and Sanitary Services
F	Wholesale and Retail Trade
G	Finance, Insurance, and Real Estate
H	Services
I	Government
J	Nonclassifiable Establishments

In turn, the divisions are subdivided into major groups. Whereas the first digit of the S.I.C. number identifies the division of the activity, the first two digits give the major group. Thus, within the Division H entitled "Services", there is Major Group 79, "Amusement and Recreation Services, except Motion Pictures."

The third digit used in the S.I.C. system subdivides the major group into groups. Thus, group number 794 refers to "Sports Promoters and Commercial Operators, and Miscellaneous Amusement Recreation Services." Finally, the fourth digit subdivides groups into industries, for example, Industry 7943 refers to "Bathing Beaches."

Table 5.4b Industry Groupings of S.I.C. Major Group 79, Amusement and Recreation Services Except Motion Pictures

Industry Number	Definition of Industry
7911	Dance Halls, Studios and Schools
7921	Theatrical Producers (except motion pictures), Bands, Orchestras, and Entertainers
7931	Bowling, Billiards, and Pool
7941	Baseball and Football Clubs, Athletics Fields, and Sports Promoters
7942	Public Golf Courses
7943	Bathing Beaches
7944	Swimming Pools
7945	Skating Rinks
7946	Riding Academies
7947	Golf Clubs and Country Clubs
7948	Race Track Operation, including Racing Stables
7949	Sports Promoters and Commercial Operators, and Amusement and Recreation Services, not elsewhere classified

In Table 5.4b, the industry numbers of Major Group 79 are listed. Notice that they consist of 4 digits, the first two of each being 7 and 9.

[74] U.S. Bureau of the Budget [25].

It is evident that many types of outdoor recreational activities, such as swimming, can fit directly into the Industry Groupings established by the S.I.C. system, while many others, particularly unorganized outdoor activities, cannot. What is sought then, is an extension of industry 7949 which would encompass these outdoor activities. The classification numbers to be employed will use the S.I.C. numbers where applicable. Most of the activities will fall into some subdivision of industry 7949. The subdivisions will be designated by a dash followed by three digits. The first digit following the dash will divide the outdoor recreational activities into 9 groups. A first preliminary set of groups is shown in Table 5.4c.

Table 5.4c Recreational Activities Extended from S.I.C. Industry 7949

Recreational Group Code	Group Description
7949–1	Water Sports: Pleasure Boating
7949–2	Water Sports: Sport Fishing
7949–3	Backwoods Sports: Camping, Hiking, Mountain Climbing
7949–4	Backwoods Sports: Hunting
7949–5	Winter Sports: Sledding, Tobogganing, Skiing,
7949–6	Bicycling
7949–7	Driving for Pleasure, Sightseeing
7949–8	Picnicking, Walking for Pleasure, Nature Walks
7949–9	Outdoor Recreation, n.e.c.

Table 5.4c lists primarily those outdoor activities investigated by the National Recreation Survey[75] which did not neatly fit into the established S.I.C. codes.

If two more digits are added to the code 7949–1 Water Sports: Pleasure Boating, as given in Table 5.4c, up to 99 types of boating activity can be classified. The same is true for each of the other 8 major groups. All told, close to 900 new outdoor recreational subcategories can be created.

Against the background of this tentative classification system, we may now focus on the various marine-oriented activities that might occur at the proposed marina, each being assigned an appropriate code. Table 5.4d lists these activities.

Table 5.4d A Classification of Selected Recreational Activities

Code	Description
RE 7949–101	*Pleasure Boating: Outboard, Seasonal.* This activity requires seasonal mooring, docking, launching, and operational marine facilities. The average size of craft with outboard motor is defined to be between 15–20 feet, with an average use by three persons.
RE 7949–102	*Pleasure Boating: Outboard, Transient.* This activity necessitates traveling to a boating site with boat trailer. Therefore, it requires a larger parking area than RE 7949–101 and a launching ramp with minor docking facilities. The average size of craft with outboard motor is defined to be between 15–20 feet, with an average use by three persons.
RE 7949–103	*Pleasure Boating: Inboard, Seasonal.* This activity requires seasonal mooring, docking, and hoist or marine railway facilities with more water surface space than outboard activities. It also requires more operational facilities than RE 7949–101 and RE 7949–102, such as major maintenance and fuel. The average number of participants per trip is

[75] Outdoor Recreation Resources Review Commission [21].

Table 5.4d (cont.)

Code	Description
	four. The average size of craft with inboard motor is defined to be between 25–35 feet.
RE 7949–104	*Pleasure Boating: Inboard, Transient.* This activity necessitates traveling to a boating site with a boat trailer. Therefore, it requires a larger parking area than RE 7949–103, and a launching ramp with minor docking facilities. The average number of participants per trip is four. The average size of craft with inboard motor is defined to be between 25–45 feet.
RE 7949–105	*Pleasure Boating: Rowboating, Rental.* This activity has the same requirements as RE 7949–102, except that the craft and motor (optional) are rented at a boat livery. Whereas outboards are usually not adaptable to rowing, rowboats can easily be converted to outboard power. The average size of rowboats is defined to lie between 10–15 feet, with an average use by three persons.
RE 7949–106	*Pleasure Boating: Rowboating, Transient.* This activity has the same spatial requirements as RE 7949–102. As it necessitates traveling to a boating site with a boat trailer, it requires a larger parking area and a launching ramp with minor docking facilities. The average size of rowboats is defined to lie between 10–15 feet, with an average use by three persons.
RE 7949–107	*Pleasure Boating: Party Boat.* This type of boating takes place on a craft with an approximate capacity of 40 persons. Seasonal mooring or docking is required for a 40-foot craft. Each party boat maintains two to three persons as crew, including the captain. A small ticket sales office and attendant is required.
RE 7949–108	*Pleasure Boating: Sailing, Seasonal.* This activity requires seasonal mooring, docking, and hoist facilities or marine railway with more maneuvering water space, but less operational facilities than inboard activity RE 7949–103. The average size of craft is defined to lie between 15–30 feet, with an average use by three persons.
RE 7949–109	*Pleasure Boating: Sailing, Transient.* This activity necessitates traveling to a boating site with a boat trailer. It requires a larger parking area than RE 7949–108, and a launching ramp. Likewise, more maneuvering water space but less operational facilities are needed than for RE 7949–103. The average size of craft is defined to lie between 15–30 feet, with an average use by three persons.
RE 7949–201	*Sport Fishing: Pier and Jetty.* This sport fishing activity requires land space adjacent to or extending over fishing waters in the form of piers, jetties, rock outcrops, bridges, etc. This activity requires little or no supporting facilities other than bait and parking.
RE 7949–202	*Sport Fishing: Outboard, Seasonal.* This fishing activity is performed from an outboard boat. Seasonal mooring, docking, launching, and operational marine facilities are required. The average size of craft with outboard motor is defined to lie between 15–20 feet, with an average use by three persons.
RE 7949–203	*Sport Fishing: Outboard, Transient.* This fishing activity is performed from a transient outboard boat. It necessitates traveling to a fishing and boating site with a boat trailer. Therefore, it requires a larger parking area than RE 7949–202, and a launching ramp with minor docking facilities. The average size of craft with outboard motor is defined to lie between 15–20 feet, with an average use by three persons.
RE 7949–204	*Sport Fishing: Inboard, Seasonal.* In this fishing activity, a seasonal inboard boat is used. It therefore requires seasonal

Table 5.4d (cont.)

Code	Description
	mooring, docking, and hoist or marine railway facilities with more water surface space than outboard fishing activities. It also requires more operational facilities than RE 7949–202 or RE 7949–203, such as major maintenance and fuel. The average number of participants per trip is four. The average size of craft with inboard motor is defined to lie between 25–35 feet.
RE 7949–205	*Sport Fishing: Inboard, Transient.* In this activity, fishing is performed from a transient inboard boat. The activity necessitates traveling to a fishing and boating site with a boat trailer. Therefore, it requires a larger parking area than RE 7949–204, and a launching ramp with minor docking facilities. The average number of participants per trip is four. The average size of craft with inboard motor is defined to lie between 25–35 feet.
RE 7949–206	*Sport Fishing: Charter Boat.* This fishing activity takes place from a boat which is chartered, and therefore requires operating labor. The charter boat requires seasonal mooring, docking, and hoist or marine railway facilties. The average number of participants per trip is four. The average size of an inboard charter boat is defined to lie between 25–35 feet.
RE 7949–207	*Sport Fishing: Rowboating, Rental.* This fishing activity takes place from a rented rowboat with motor optional. The average size of rowboats is defined to lie between 10–15 feet, with an average use by three persons.
RE 7949–208	*Sport Fishing: Rowboating, Transient.* This fishing activity takes place from a transient rowboat. It necessitates traveling to a fishing and boating site with a boat trailer and therefore requires a larger parking space than seasonal activities, as well as a launching ramp with minor docking facilities. The average size of rowboats is defined to lie between 10–15 feet, with an average use by three persons.
RE 7949–209	*Sport Fishing: Party Boat.* This fishing activity takes place from a craft capable of carrying approximately forty persons. Seasonal mooring or docking is required for a 40-foot craft. Each boat maintains two to three persons as crew, including the captain. A small ticket sales office and attendant is required.
RE 7949–210	*Sport Fishing: Surf.* This fishing activity involves fishing in the surf. It requires beach area and parking. Bait and tackle facilities are optional.
RE 7949–211	*Sport Fishing: Clamming.* This activity involves the collection of clams in low water areas. It is usually performed with a rake and bucket. Parking area is required.
RE 7949–801	*Picnicking: Provided Facilities.* This activity involves using facilities which exist for picnicking. It requires tables and parking area.
RE 7949–810	*Walking for Pleasure: Beach.* This activity involves walking for pleasure on beach areas. Parking may be required.
RE 7949–811	*Walking for Pleasure: Trails.* This activity involves walking for pleasure over marked trails. In addition to the trails, parking space may be required.
RE 7949–820	*Nature Walks: Beach.* This activity involves walking for pleasure and observation of nature in beach area. Parking may be required.
RE 7949–821	*Nature Walks: Trails.* This activity involves walking for pleasure and observation of nature over marked trails. In addition to trails, parking space may be required.
S.I.C. 7943	*Beach Activity: Swimming.* This activity involves swimming at the beach and sun bathing. It requires facilities such as bathhouses, picnic areas, and small related commercial areas.

From the definitions in Table 5.4d, it is evident that the classification scheme proposed is oriented toward the facilities required of a recreational development. This orientation is necessary when policy problems related to planning recreational facilities are encountered. Hence, fishing activities are characterized by such words as *outboard*, which identifies required facilities, rather than the specific service sought.

The classification code in Table 5.4d will be employed in the following sections of this book. Henceforth, for example, RE 7949–104 will refer to Pleasure Boating: Inboard, Transient.

5.5 *Inputs and Outputs of Recreational Activities*

In this section, we present preliminary input-output data on various recreational activities considered relevant for potential development in the Plymouth area. These data will provide the means for cost and revenue analysis in subsequent sections. Input-output data are examined for the following recreational activities: (1) Pleasure Boating, (2) Sport Fishing, and (3) Swimming.

The data presented are, for the most part, general estimates. The amount of relevant published data is limited. Therefore, studies by the staff are employed extensively. Although subject to major revision, these data can be extremely useful in making preliminary projections and plans for coastal recreational development.

5.5.1 Outputs of Recreational Activities

For purposes of definition, the levels of output of the various recreational activities are based on an arbitrary unit level of output. The output of each activity is measured in terms of man-days over a season. The unit level of each activity is set at 1,000 man-days (which may occur on any combination of days during the season). For all activities, a man-day is taken to be 5 hours of recreational participation in a day. For each activity, the unit level of output, designated by +1 and corresponding to 1,000 man-days, is entered at the top of each column of Table 5.5a. At the heads of the columns of this table are listed relevant activities and classification codes as recorded in Table 4.3. At the left-hand tab of this table are listed commodities, by classification number, as recorded in Table 4.3.

We now begin the derivation of the necessary inputs per unit level of each activity.

5.5.2 Land Requirements for Parking Space

Adequate parking area is required for participants in the various marina activities. With respect to parking area requirements, the activities of the marina can be divided into five groups. In each group the procedure for computing parking requirements follows the same line of reasoning.

We deal first with the group of boats associated with seasonal activities. It is assumed that inboard boats carry, on the average, 4 persons, while outboards and sailboats carry 3. Thus it seems reasonable that 4-man inboard boats may require more parking space than the 3-man boats. It is felt that the 4-man inboard boats should have 1.7 parking places per boat, while each 3-man boat should be allowed 1.4 parking places. One parking place, with the necessary maneuvering room, requires 435 square feet of space. Thus, for each 4-man boat, approximately 740 square feet of parking space are required; and for each 3-man boat, 609 square feet of parking space are required.

It is shown below (see Section 5.5.15) that in order to support one unit level of outboard and sailboat activity, or 1,000 man-days over a season, 6.17 boats are required. To support 1,000 man-days of inboard activity, 4.63 boats are required. Hence, the parking requirements for the seasonal activities are easily computed. The number of outboard and sailboats required to support one unit level of recreational activity, 6.17, times the required parking space per 3-man boat, 609 square feet, yields a unit level requirement of 3,757 square feet. This figure is entered in the appropriate columns of Table 5.5a, for RE 7949–101, Pleasure Boating: Outboard, Seasonal; RE 7949–108, Pleasure Boating: Sailing, Seasonal; and RE 7949–202, Sport Fishing: Outboard, Seasonal.

With regard to seasonal inboard activities RE 7949–103, Pleasure Boating: Inboard, Seasonal, and RE 7949–204, Sport Fishing: Inboard, Seasonal, a different requirement is computed. The number of inboard boats necessary to support one unit level, 4.63, multiplied by the parking space requirement per boat, 740 square feet, yields a unit level parking space requirement of 3,426 square feet. This figure is entered in the appropriate columns dealing with RE 7949–103 and RE 7949–204.

The second major group of boats are associated with transient activities. Of these activities, five deal with 3-man boats: RE 7949–102, Pleasure Boating: Outboard, Transient; RE 7949–109, Pleasure Boating: Sailing, Transient; RE 7949–203, Sport Fishing: Outboard, Transient; RE 7949–106, Pleasure Boating: Rowboating, Transient; and RE 7949–208, Sport Fishing: Rowboating, Transient. It is assumed that for each of these categories, one parking place is required per boat. In addition, a space equal in area to the parking place is needed for a trailer. Hence, in all, the parking space per 3-man transient boat is 870 square feet. As previously determined, 6.17 boats are required to support one unit level of each of these 3-man boat activities. When multiplied by the required parking space per boat, the total required area per unit level is derived. This figure is 5,368 square feet.

There are two transient activities which require 4-man boats. These are RE 7949–104, Pleasure Boating: Inboard, Transient, and RE 7949–205, Sport Fishing: Inboard, Transient. As previously computed, 4.63 boats support one unit level of each of these activities. As each boat requires 870 square feet of parking space, one unit level requires 4,028 square feet.

The third major group of boats is associated with rental activities. Each rental boat is assumed to carry three persons. Hence, 6.17 boats are required per unit level (1,000 man-days) of rental boat recreational activity. As no trailers are involved it is assumed that one parking place per rental boat, or 435 square feet, is adequate. Thus, 2,684 square feet of parking space are required per unit level of activity. This figure is recorded in the appropriate columns for RE 7949–105, Pleasure Boating: Rowboating, Rental, and RE 7949–207, Sport Fishing: Rowboating, Rental.

The fourth group concerns party boats. Each party boat has a capacity of 40 persons. On the average, each party boat is assumed to carry 25 persons per trip. If each is used 140 times per 20 week season, then 0.28 party boats support one unit level of 1,000 man-days of recreational activity. If it is assumed that one third of a parking space, or 145 square feet, is required per passenger, then with 40 passengers, 5,800 square feet are required. Then at unit level of this activity, 0.28 times 5,800 square feet, or 1,624 square feet of parking space, is required. This figure is recorded in the appropriate columns for RE 7949–107, Pleasure Boating: Party Boat and RE 7949–209, Sport Fishing: Party Boat.

Finally, there are sport fishing activities without boat requirements. They include the following: RE 7949–201, Sport Fishing: Pier and Jetty; RE 7949–210, Sport Fishing: Surf; and RE 7949–211, Sport Fishing: Clamming. For RE 7949–201, Sport Fishing: Pier and Jetty, parking space is derived by assuming that for every eight persons participating in this activity, parking space for one car will be needed. This assumes that many of the anglers will be children and other people from nearby neighborhoods. If we consider (1) that corresponding to a unit level

Table 5.5a Input-Output Coefficients. Proposed Marina

TABLE 5.5.a INPUT-OUTPUT COEFFICIENTS FOR SELECTED RECREATIONAL ACTIVITIES

CLASSIFI-CATION NUMBER	COMMODITY	UNIT	RE7949-101	RE7949-102	RE7949-103	RE7949-104	RE7949-105	RE7949-106	RE7949-107	RE7949-108	RE7949-109	RE7949-201	RE7949-202	RE7949-203	RE7949-204	RE7949-205	RE7949-207	RE7949-208	RE7949-209	RE7949-210	RE7949-211	SIC7943
		PROCESS	PLEASURE BOATING: OUTBOARD SEASONAL	" OUTBOARD TRANSIENT	" INBOARD SEASONAL	" INBOARD TRANSIENT	" ROWBOAT RENTAL	" ROWBOAT TRANSIENT	" PARTY BOAT	" SAILING SEASONAL	" SAILING TRANSIENT	SPORT FISHING: PIER & JETTY	" OUTBOARD SEASONAL	" OUTBOARD TRANSIENT	" INBOARD SEASONAL	" INBOARD TRANSIENT	" ROWBOAT RENTAL	" ROWBOAT TRANSIENT	" PARTY BOAT	" SURF	" CLAMMING	BEACH ACTIVITY: SWIMMING
M 794-0	RECREATION	1000 MAN-DAYS	+1	+1	+1	+1	+1	+1	+1	+1	+1	+1	+1	+1	+1	+1	+1	+1	+1	+1	+1	0
	LAND AREA FOR:	SQ. FT.																				
LX3101	PARKING	" "	-3757	-5368	-3426	-4028	-2684	-5368	-1624	-3757	-5368	-870	-3757	-5368	-3426	-4028	-2684	-5368	-1624	-1740	-1740	-3045
LX3102	TOTAL INDOOR STORAGE	" "	-229	-658	-771	-933	0	-658	0	-1064	-1242	0	-229	-658	-771	-933	0	-658	0	0	0	0
LX3103	LOCAL INDOOR STORAGE	" "	-165	0	-670	0	0	0	0	-950	0	0	-165	0	-670	0	0	0	0	0	0	0
LX3104	TOTAL REPAIRS	" "	-59	-23	-84	-34	0	-23	0	-111	-44	0	-59	-23	-84	-34	0	-23	0	0	0	0
LX3105	LOCAL REPAIRS	" "	-59	0	-84	0	0	0	0	-111	0	0	-59	0	-84	0	0	0	0	0	0	0
LX3106	BOAT & MOTOR SHOWROOM	" "	-31.8	-31.8	-31.8	-31.8	0	-31.8	0	-31.8	-31.8	0	-31.8	-31.8	-31.8	-31.8	0	-31.8	0	0	0	0
LX3107	SALES OF MARINE ACCESSORIES	" "	-9	-9	-9	-9	0	-9	0	-9	-9	0	-9	-9	-9	-9	0	-9	0	0	0	0
LX3108	REST ROOMS & LOUNGE	" "	-17.5	-17.5	-17.5	-17.5	-17.5	-17.5	-17.5	-17.5	-17.5	-17.5	-17.5	-17.5	-17.5	-17.5	-17.5	-17.5	-17.5	-17.5	-17.5	0
LX3109	GEAR STORAGE	" "	-9	-9	-9	-9	-9	-9	-9	-9	-9	-9	-9	-9	-9	-9	-9	-9	-9	-9	-9	0
LX3110	ADMINISTRATIVE OFFICE	" "	-4.4	-4.4	-4.4	-4.4	-4.4	-4.4	-4.4	-4.4	-4.4	-4.4	-4.4	-4.4	-4.4	-4.4	-4.4	-4.4	-4.4	-4.4	-4.4	0
LX3111	TRANSIENT & RENTAL OFFICE	" "	0	-7.86	0	-7.86	-7.86	-7.86	-7.86	0	-7.86	0	0	-7.86	-0	-7.86	-7.86	-7.86	-7.86	0	0	0
LX3112	BAIT & PACKAGED FOOD SALES	" "	-3.85	-3.85	-3.85	-3.85	-3.85	-3.85	-3.85	-3.85	-3.85	-8.94	-8.94	-8.94	-8.94	-8.94	-8.94	-8.94	-8.94	-8.94	-3.85	0
LX3113	FUEL SALES	" "	-1.38	-1.38	-1.38	-1.38	0	0	0	-1.10	-1.10	0	-1.38	-1.38	-1.38	-1.38	0	0	0	0	0	0
LX3114	RAMPS	" "	0	-3628	0	-3628	0	-3628	0	0	-3628	0	0	-3628	0	-3628	0	-3628	0	0	0	0
LX3115	BATH HOUSE	" "	0	0	0	0	0	0	0	0	0	0	0	0	0	0	0	0	0	0	0	-70
	FISH																					
MX725	COD	POUNDS	0	0	0	0	0	0	0	0	0	0	-6700	-6700	-26800	-26800	-6700	-6700	-13400	0	0	0
MX723	WINTER FLOUNDER	"	0	0	0	0	0	0	0	0	0	-1400	-3600	-3600	-1400	-1400	-3600	-3600	-1400	-1400	0	0
MX716	CLAMS	BUSHELS	0	0	0	0	0	0	0	0	0	0	0	0	0	0	0	0	0	0	-500	0
L 3732	BOATS (IN BOAT SEASON)		-6.17	-6.17	-4.63	-4.63	-6.17	-6.17	-0.28	-6.17	-6.17	0	-6.17	-6.17	-4.63	-4.63	-6.17	-6.17	-0.28	0	0	0
L 2911-1	FUEL	GALLONS	-2900	-2900	-5000	-5000	-1100	-1250	-940	-666	-666	0	-2900	-2900	-5000	-5000	-1100	-1250	-940	0	0	0

	LABOR																					
L L794-01	GENERAL MANAGER	MAN-HOURS	- 20	- 20	- 20	- 20	- 20	- 20	- 20	- 20	- 20	- 20	- 20	- 20	- 20	- 20	- 20	- 20	- 20	- 20	0	0
L L794-02	OTHER ADMINISTRATIVE	" "	- 37	- 37	- 37	- 37	- 37	- 37	- 37	- 37	- 37	- 37	- 37	- 37	- 37	- 37	- 37	- 37	- 37	- 37	0	0
L L794-03	DOCK MASTER	" "	- 30	0	- 30	0	0	0	0	- 30	0	0	- 30	0	- 30	0	0	0	0	0	0	0
L L794-04	DOCK OPERATIONS PERSONNEL	" "	- 110	- 110	- 110	- 110	- 110	- 110	0	- 110	- 110	0	- 110	- 110	- 110	- 110	- 110	- 110	0	0	0	0
L L794-05	BOAT SALES MANAGER	" "	- 24	- 24	- 24	- 24	0	- 24	0	- 24	- 24	0	- 24	- 24	- 24	- 24	0	- 24	0	0	0	0
L L794-06	BOAT SALESMAN	" "	- 24	- 24	- 24	- 24	0	- 24	0	- 24	- 24	0	- 24	- 24	- 24	- 24	0	- 24	0	0	0	0
L L794-07	MARINE SUPPLIES SALES MANAGER	" "	- 24	- 24	- 24	- 24	0	- 24	0	- 24	- 24	0	- 24	- 24	- 24	- 24	0	- 24	0	0	0	0
L L794-08	MARINE SUPPLIES SALESMAN	" "	- 8	- 8	- 8	- 8	0	- 8	0	- 8	- 8	0	- 8	- 8	- 8	- 8	0	- 8	0	0	0	0
L L794-09	PARTY BOAT CREWS	" "	0	0	0	0	0	0	- 714	0	0	0	0	0	0	0	0	0	- 714	0	0	0
L L794-10	PACKAGED FOOD & BAIT SALES PERSONNEL	" "	- 10	- 10	- 10	- 10	- 10	- 10	- 10	- 10	- 10	- 23	- 23	- 23	- 23	- 23	- 23	- 23	- 23	- 23	- 10	0
L L794-11	REPAIR SHOP PERSONNEL	" "	- 104	0	- 157	0	0	0	0	- 209	0	0	- 105	0	- 157	0	0	0	0	0	0	0
	WATER SURFACE AREA FOR:																					
MX3301	DOCKED BOATS	SQ. FT.	-5152	-1717	-5156	-5880	-2468	- 823	- 507	-7287	-7836	0	-5152	-1717	-5156	-5880	-2468	- 823	- 507	0	0	0
MX3302	MOORED BOATS	" "	0	0	-2493	0	0	0	0	-2820	0	0	0	0	-2493	0	0	0	0	0	0	0
MX3303	FOR SWIMMING	" "	0	0	0	0	0	0	0	0	0	0	0	0	0	0	0	0	0	0	0	-3000
	QUALITY CONSTRAINTS:																					
MX4501	COLIFORM INDEX (PER 100 ML. - MAX.)	PER 100 ML.	5000	5000	5000	5000	5000	5000	5000	5000	5000	5000	5000	5000	5000	5000	[illegible]000	5000	5000	5000	b	2400
MX4502	DISSOLVED OXYGEN (PPM. - AVE.)	PPM.	4.0	4.0	4.0	4.0	4.0	4.0	4.0	4.0	4.0	2.5[c]	2.5[c]	2.5[c]	2.5[c]	2.5[c]	2.5[c]	2.5[c]	2.5[c]	2.5[c]	b	7.0
MX4503	pH (RANGE)		6.0-8.5	6.0-8.5	6.0-8.5	6.0-8.5	6.0-8.5	6.0-8.5	6.0-8.5	6.0-8.5	6.0-8.5	6.7-8.6	6.7-8.6	6.7-8.6	6.7-8.6	6.7-8.6	6.7-8.6	6.7-8.6	6.7-8.6	6.7-8.6	b	6.5-8.5
MX4504	BOD (PPM. - MONTHLY AVERAGE)	PPM.	3.0	3.0	3.0	3.0	3.0	3.0	3.0	3.0	3.0	b	b	b	b	b	b	b	b	b	b	b
MX4505	BOD (PPM. - MAX.)	PPM.	5.0	5.0	5.0	5.0	5.0	5.0	5.0	5.0	5.0	b	b	b	b	b	b	b	b	b	b	b
MX4506	TURBIDITY (PPM. - MAX.)	PPM.	b	b	b	b	b	b	b	b	b	100000	100000	100000	100000	100000	100000	100000	100000	100000	b	20
MX4507	COLOR	UNITS	b	b	b	b	b	b	b	b	b	b	b	b	b	b	b	b	b	b	b	30
	TEMPERATURE:																					
MX4508	COD (DEGREES - MAX.)	DEGREES C.	-	-	-	-	-	-	-	-	-	-	b	b	b	b	b	b	b	-	-	-
MX4509	WINTER FLOUNDER (DEGREES - MAX.)	"	-	-	-	-	-	-	-	-	-	25	25	25	25	25	25	25	25	25	-	-
MX4510	CLAMS (DEGREES - RANGE)	"	-	-	-	-	-	-	-	-	-	-	-	-	-	-	-	-	-	-	10-20	-
	SALINITY																					
MX4511-1	COD (PARTS PER THOUSAND - RANGE)		-	-	-	-	-	-	-	-	-	-	4-30	4-30	4-30	4-30	4-30	4-30	4-30	-	-	-
MX4511-2	WINTER FLOUNDER (PARTS PER THOUSAND -	RANGE)	-	-	-	-	-	-	-	-	-	4-30	4-30	4-30	4-30	4-30	4-30	4-30	4-30	4-30	-	-
MX4511-3	CLAMS (PARTS PER THOUSAND - RANGE)		-	-	-	-	-	-	-	-	-	-	-	-	-	-	-	-	-	-	9-25	-
LX3116	BEACH AREA	SQ. FT.	0	0	0	0	0	0	0	0	0	0	0	0	0	0	0	0	0	0	0	-3000

b: Data not available c: this is a minimum for winter flounder fishing of 1,000 man-days there will, on the average, be 6.67 persons involved per day in this recreational activity over a 150-day season, and (2) that the daily range of persons participating in such recreation may be from zero to twenty, then two parking places are a reasonable requirement. One parking place, with the necessary maneuvering area, requires 435 square feet. Thus, for one unit level of this activity, 870 square feet of parking space is required. This figure is entered in the column designated RE 7949–201.

For RE 7949–210, Sport Fishing: Surf, and RE 7949–211, Sport Fishing: Clamming, 3 persons per car is assumed. If we again assume a 150-day season, a unit level of 1,000 man-days involves, on the average, the daily participation of 6.67 persons. Assuming that the daily range of persons participating in each activity to be from zero to twenty, parking places for 4 cars are a reasonable requirement. At 435 square feet per parking space, the unit level requirement for each of these activities is 1,740 square feet. This figure is recorded in the columns of necessary inputs for activities RE 7949–210 and RE 7949–211.

5.5.3 Land Requirements for Boat-Storage Activities

It is assumed that of the 160 boats in the outboard seasonal category, 75 percent will be stored at the marina throughout the year, while the remaining 25 percent will be stored elsewhere. Of the owners of these 120 outboards stored at the marina, about one-half, or 60, will be willing to pay the premium for storing their boats inside a structure. Of the 40 boats not stored at the marina, only 20 percent, or 8 boats, will be stored indoors. The remaining 60 boats stored at the marina and the 32 boats not stored at the marina will be stored outside. Outside storage requires no land beyond the marina parking lot or vacant backyards; the required land area for such storage is not considered.

We thus proceed to determine two estimates of land requirements for indoor storage. The first estimate is the total indoor storage required for all boats stored in this manner. The number of boats involved are the 60 stored indoors at the marina and the 8 stored indoors elsewhere. The second estimate concerns only the land needed at the marina for the facility in which only the 60 boats will be stored.

The average size of outboard boat at the marina fills an area of approximately 213 square feet. The 60 boats at the marina are stored on racks three deep. Thus each of these 60 boats is assigned an indoor storage area of 71 square feet. The remaining 8 boats stored indoors but not at the marina are assigned 213 square feet each. In all, 4,260 square feet of indoor storage area are required at the marina, and 1,704 square feet are required elsewhere, a total of 5,964 square feet.

Corresponding to this amount of storage area is the demand for RE 7949–101, Pleasure Boating: Outboard, Seasonal, and RE 7949–202, Sport Fishing: Outboard, Seasonal. In Table 5.3h this demand is estimated to be 25,920 man-days per annum, all of which is assumed will be met. Since the unit level of activities RE 7949–101, Pleasure Boating: Outboard, Seasonal, and RE 7949–202, Sport Fishing: Outboard, Seasonal, is set at 1,000 man-days, the total man-days demanded and supplied requires operation of these activities at levels which add to approximately 26. Dividing the total required area for indoor storage, 5,964, by the activity level, 26, yields the required total indoor storage space in square feet per unit level of RE 7949–101, Pleasure Boating: Outboard, Seasonal, and RE 7949–202, Sport Fishing: Outboard, Seasonal. This division reveals that approximately 229 square feet of indoor storage space are required for 1,000 man-days of seasonal outboard activity. This figure is recorded in the appropriate cell in Table 5.5a, for activities RE 7949–101 and RE 7949–202.

With regard to the row relating to indoor storage area supplied at the marina (local indoor storage), the sum of the levels of operation, 26, is still appropriate.

However, as previously computed, only 4,260 square feet of storage area are required at the marina. By division, the unit level requirement of 165 square feet of locally supplied indoor storage area for activities RE 7949–101 and RE 7949–202 is derived. This figure is entered in the appropriate cells.

Associated with RE 7949–103, Pleasure Boating: Inboard, Seasonal, and RE 7949–204, Sport Fishing: Inboard, Seasonal are 110 boats. It is felt that somewhat more than 75 percent of these would be stored at the marina throughout the year. Of the 80 boats stored at the marina, 40 inboards would be kept outside on the parking lot area, and 40 would require inside storage within a structure. Of the 30 boats not kept at the marina throughout the winter, 20 percent, or 6 boats, would require indoor storage. Thus, an indoor storage space requirement for 46 boats exists.

Assuming an average length of 30 feet for these inboard boats, each boat stored inside would require a storage space of 402 square feet. Due to their size, it would not be feasible to use a triple storage rack for the boats wintered at the marina. Thus, a total indoor storage area of 16,080 square feet is required for the 40 boats stored at the marina; and 2,412 square feet are required for the 6 boats stored indoors at places other than the marina. The total requirement is 18,492 square feet.

The required indoor storage area corresponds to the demand for RE 7949–103, Pleasure Boating: Inboard, Seasonal and RE 7949–204, Sport Fishing: Inboard, Seasonal. In Table 5.3h, this combined demand is estimated to be 23,760 man-days per annum. With unit level of each of these activities set at 1,000 man-days, the total number of man-days demanded and supplied requires operation of these activities at levels whose sum is roughly 24. Dividing the total required indoor storage area, 18,492 square feet, by the sum, 24, yields the total required indoor storage space in square feet per unit level of each activity. Approximately 771 square feet of indoor storage space are required per 1,000 man-days of seasonal inboard activity. This figure, as it refers to both RE 7949–103, Pleasure Boating: Inboard, Seasonal, and RE 7949–204, Sport Fishing: Inboard, Seasonal, is entered in the appropriate cells for these activities.

With regard to indoor storage space supplied at the marina, the sum of relevant activity levels is still 24. But, as computed, the marina furnishes only 16,080 square feet of indoor storage area. Thus at the unit level of RE 7949–103 and RE 7949–205, 670 square feet of indoor storage space are required at the marina.

Storage is required for some portion of the 105 seasonal sailing craft engaged in the activity RE 7949–108, Pleasure Boating: Sailing, Seasonal. If somewhat more than 75 percent of these boats, or 80 boats, are stored at the marina, half might require indoor storage. Of the 25 sailboats stored elsewhere, we assume that 20 percent, or 5 boats, will require indoor storage. Thus, in total, 45 sailboats require indoor storage.

Given the average length of these boats, 30 feet, each would require an indoor storage area of about 402 square feet. Thus, the boats kept at the marina would require 16,080 square feet of indoor storage space, while those not kept at the marina would require 2,010 square feet, for a total of 18,090 square feet.

The required indoor storage area corresponds to the demand for RE 7949–108, Pleasure Boating: Sailing, Seasonal. In Table 5.3h, this demand is estimated to be 17,010 man-days of recreational activity per year. If the unit level of this activity is set at 1,000 man-days, the total number of man-days demanded and supplied requires the operation of the activity at a level of 17. Dividing the required total indoor storage area, 18,090 square feet, by the activity level, 17, yields the required total indoor storage area per unit level of RE 7949–108. Approximately 1,064 square feet of indoor storage space in total is required per unit level of operation. This figure is entered in the column of inputs for RE 7949–108.

With regard to locally supplied indoor storage space for RE 7949–108, the relevant activity level is still 17. However, the marina furnishes only 16,080 square feet of indoor storage space. Thus, the locally supplied indoor storage space for RE 7949–108 per unit level of activity is 950 square feet.

We now turn to indoor storage requirements for the transient boats. By definition, none of these boats is stored at the marina. Thus, non-zero coefficients are entered only in the row labeled "Total Indoor Storage." However, a number of these boats which are relatively small will be stored indoors elsewhere. We assume that 50 percent of these boats will be so stored. Under the assumptions used in this study, boats carry, on the average, three or four persons. Inboard boats carry four, while the smaller boats—outboards, sailboats, and rowboats—carry only three.

We begin with indoor storage requirements for the three-man boats. These boats are used in transient activities RE 7949–102, Pleasure Boating: Outboard, Transient; RE 7949–106, Pleasure Boating: Rowboating, Transient; RE 7949–109, Pleasure Boating: Sailing, Transient; RE 7949–203, Sport Fishing: Outboard, Transient; and RE 7949–208, Sport Fishing: Rowboating, Transient.

In order to support 1,000 man-days of recreational activity in any of these activities, 6.17 boats are required. As each boat is assumed to be used on the average 54 days per year, and each carries 3 persons, then 6.17 boats times 54 days per season times 3 passengers equals 1,000 man-days of each activity. As it has been assumed that 50 percent of the boats will be stored indoors at places other than the marina, indoor storage space is required for 3.09 boats per unit level (1,000 man-days) of activity.

The boats in RE 7949–102, RE 7949–106, RE 7949–203, and RE 7949–208 are, on the average, 20 feet long and require a storage area of 213 square feet. Thus at the unit level of any one of these activities, 658 square feet of indoor storage space are required. This figure is recorded in the appropriate cells for these four activities.

The boats used for the transient sailing activity are, on the average, 30 feet long and require 402 square feet of storage area. As 3.09 boats will be stored indoors per unit level of this activity, 1,242 square feet will be required. This figure is recorded in the input column for RE 7949–109, Pleasure Boating: Sailing, Transient.

Four-man boats are used in two transient activities, RE 7949–104, Pleasure Boating: Inboard, Transient, and RE 7949–205, Sport Fishing: Inboard, Transient. In order to support one unit level of these activities, 4.63 boats are required. Since they are used, on the average, 54 days per season, 54 times 4 men per boat times 4.63 boats equals 1,000 man-days of inboard activities. Since 50 percent of these boats are assumed to be stored indoors, indoor storage for 2.32 boats is required for every 1,000 man-days in these two activities.

The average-size inboard boat is 30 feet, and it requires 402 square feet of storage space. Thus, at the unit level for these two transient activities, 933 feet of indoor storage space are required. This figure is recorded in the appropriate input columns for RE 7949–104 and RE 7949–205.

With regard to the rental boats and party boats used in RE 7949–105, Pleasure Boating: Rowboating, Rental; RE 7949–107, Pleasure Boating: Party Boat; RE 7949–207, Sport Fishing: Rowboating, Rental; and RE 7949–209, Sport Fishing: Party Boat, it is assumed that these boats are stored outdoors on the parking lot, or are in use elsewhere during the winter, or are kept at the docks. In each case, the land inputs for storage are zero; hence, zeros are recorded in the appropriate two cells in the columns for each of these activities.

5.5.4 Land Requirements for Boat and Engine Repair Services

Land space is also required for boat and engine repair. A repair shop would be an integral part of the marina under consideration. However, it is also recognized that some boats and engines would be serviced elsewhere. Thus, once again, two land requirements for repair operations are computed for each activity. One deals with the requirement for all repairs of the marina fleet, while the second concerns repairs supplied at the marina only—i.e., locally supplied repairs. We begin with a discussion of the land requirements for the locally supplied repairs.

In general, a boat repair operation tends to concentrate its activity during the winter off-season months in order to utilize labor more effectively. For a 400-boat marina, it would seem that on any one work day of the six off-season months, ten boats might be in process of being repaired, or proceeding to that stage. With approximately 150 work-days in this off-season period, and ten boats in the shop on any one day, there would be 1,500 boat work-days during this period. During the six in-season months of the year, with which we associate 160 work days, perhaps an average of three boats might be under repair per day, yielding 480 boat work-days during the boating season. The total for these two seasons of the year yields 1,980, or in round numbers, 2,000, boat work-days per year. This means that, on the average, a boat in a 400-boat fleet might be in the repair shop for 5 days per year, being under active repair for 3 days. Based on our knowledge of such operations, this appears to be a reasonable estimate.

Since the facility will operate at full capacity during the off-season months, and since only six rather than all ten boats in the repair shops are likely to be worked on simultaneously, then a repair space requirement of 560 square feet per boat, on the average, seems reasonable for efficient operations. This space assignment includes work and passage area around the boats, as well as area for engine repairs. For a daily capacity of ten boats, a facility of 5,600 square feet is therefore needed. It is assumed that this marina facility will supply repair services for all the seasonal boats which are at the marina.

As already indicated, approximately 2,000 boat-days of repair are locally supplied by the facility, and each of the 400 seasonal boats is in the repair shop 5 days per year. However, 30-foot boats take up more square footage than 20-foot boats, roughly by a factor of 1.9. Therefore, the 225 30-foot boats in our 395-boat fleet are in this respect equivalent to 427.5, or roughly 428 20-foot boats. Thus, the home, or seasonal, fleet consists of 603 "equivalent" 20-foot boats. Dividing 5,600 by 603 yields 9.29 square feet per 20-foot boat. Since each boat is on the average under repair 5 days during the season, dividing 9.29 square feet by 5 yields 1.9 square feet of space required per day of locally supplied repair services on a 20-foot boat. Multiplying 1.9 square feet by the factor 1.9 yields 3.6 square feet of marina facility space required per day of repair services on a 30-foot boat.

At the unit level (1,000 man-days) of operation for RE 7949–101, Pleasure Boating: Outboard, Seasonal, and RE 7949–202, Sport Fishing: Outboard, Seasonal, there is as previously stated a requirement of 6.17 boats. Each of these seasonal boats will be in the repair shop 5 days, yielding 30.9 boat-days of locally supplied repair. At 1.9 square feet per boat day of locally supplied repair, we obtain approximately 59 square feet to be assigned to the unit level of recreation in RE 7949–101, Pleasure Boating: Outboard, Seasonal, and RE 7949–202, Sport Fishing: Outboard, Seasonal. This figure is recorded in the appropriate input columns of Table 5.5a.

Since inboard boats are assumed to carry, on the average, 4 persons, a different space requirement is derived for them. As previously stated, 4.63 boats are required to operate RE 7949–103, Pleasure Boating: Inboard, Seasonal, and RE 7949–204, Sport Fishing: Inboard, Seasonal, at the unit level of 1,000 man-days. Retaining the assumption of 5 days of repair per boat per year, we obtain 23.2 boat-days of locally supplied repair. At 3.6 square feet per boat-day of repair, it is evident that approximately 84 square feet of marina facility repair space must be assigned to the unit level of 1,000 man-days of recreation in seasonal inboard boating. This figure is recorded in the appropriate columns in Table 5.5a.

The locally supplied space required for the repair of sailboats in RE 7949–108 is the same as that required in RE 7949–103, Pleasure Boating: Inboard, Seasonal, which is 3.6 square feet per day of local repair services. Since 6.17 boats are involved per unit level of this activity, 30.8 days of repair is required. Multiplying 30.8 times 3.6 yields 111 square feet of marina repair space which is the required input to a unit level of this activity. This figure is recorded in the input column of RE 7949–108.

Notice that for each of the seasonal activities, the input coefficient of space for total repair activity is the same as that for locally supplied repair activity. This is due to the stated assumption that all seasonal boat repair takes place at the marina, and is thus locally supplied. Strictly speaking, however, some of the repairs on the boats involved in seasonal activities may be done at other marinas and localities. But then, at the same time, the repair facility at the proposed marina may service boats which are associated with recreation operations at other marinas and sites. We assume that these imports and exports of repair services roughly balance out, so that the coefficients relating to local repair services, while ignoring imports and exports, do not lead to errors in the cost and revenue computations pertaining to the proposed marina.

With regard to the transient boats, it is assumed that they too require 5 boat-days of repair per year but that none of this takes place at the marina. This 5 days of repair is composed of 2 days in a repair shop at some place other than the marina, and 3 days of repair at the residence of the owner with the use of owner-supplied labor. The total repair space requirement for the transient boats is based only on the 2 days that such boats are in repair shops. Thus, in each case, the land input for repair with regard to a transient boating activity is $\frac{2}{5}$ths or 40 percent of the land input for repair services for the corresponding seasonal boating activity. These land input coefficients are listed in the input columns for RE 7949–102, Pleasure Boating: Outboard, Transient; RE 7949–104, Pleasure Boating: Inboard, Transient; RE 7949–109, Pleasure Boating: Sailing, Transient; RE 7949–203, Sport Fishing: Outboard, Transient; and RE 7949–205, Sport Fishing: Inboard, Transient.

Activities RE 7949–106, Pleasure Boating: Rowboating, Transient and RE 7949–208, Sport Fishing: Rowboating, Transient, are assumed to have the same requirements as the outboard transient activities.

5.5.5 Required Land Inputs for Sales and Showroom Facilities

Land is required for a structure which will house the boat showroom and sales area, as well as an area for motor and engine sales. Recall that the seasonal, or home, fleet of the marina under consideration consists of 395 boats. If the average boat has a life of approximately 12 years, and if we allow for sales to transient users of the marina, then approximately 40 boats might be sold in the showroom and sales area over the course of one year. For such a volume of sales, the showroom should be capable of holding 6 boats. At any one time, the size of the boats on show would roughly reflect the size of boats in the fleet. Thus, one might expect perhaps two 30-foot boats and four 20-foot boats in the showroom at any one time. The floor space required to display these six boats is approximately 1,900 square feet.

It is estimated that a floor area amounting to 40 percent of the boat showroom, or 750 square feet, should be sufficient for sales space for motors, engines, and related parts. The showroom and sales facility should then cover a total of 2,650 square feet.

The recreational activities which are served by this facility are:

RE 7949–101, Pleasure Boating: Outboard, Seasonal
RE 7949–102, Pleasure Boating: Outboard, Transient

RE 7949–103, Pleasure Boating: Inboard, Seasonal
RE 7949–104, Pleasure Boating: Inboard, Transient
RE 7949–106, Pleasure Boating: Rowboating, Transient
RE 7949–108, Pleasure Boating: Sailing, Seasonal
RE 7949–109, Pleasure Boating: Sailing, Transient
RE 7949–202, Sport Fishing: Outboard, Seasonal
RE 7949–203, Sport Fishing: Outboard, Transient
RE 7949–204, Sport Fishing: Inboard, Seasonal
RE 7949–205, Sport Fishing: Inboard, Transient
RE 7949–208, Sport Fishing: Rowboating, Transient

Those activities which are involved with docking, mooring, and dry-land berthing meet a demand of 70,200 man-days, while those involving transient ramp operations meet a demand of 13,230 man-days. In total, the 12 recreational activities listed above provide 83,430 man-days of recreation, which corresponds to 83.430 unit levels of operations. If we hypothesize that each unit level of operations requires the same input of floor space at the sales and showroom facility, then the total square feet of this facility, 2,650, when divided by the total number of activity unit levels, 83.430, yields a land input requirement per unit level of each activity of 31.8 square feet. This figure is then recorded in the appropriate cell of the column for each of the 12 using activities.

5.5.6 Land Requirements for the Sale of Boat Accessories

Land is also required for the display and sales of marina equipment other than boats and motors. Such items as anchors, hardware, lines, and pennants might be included. It is felt that the space requirements for this facility should be equal to that of the engine showroom space previously computed—namely, 750 square feet.

The boat accessory sales facility serves the same activities as the boat and engine showroom. These activities, when combined, provide 83.430 unit levels of recreation. Thus, the requirement per unit level for each of these 12 activities is equal to the floor space of the facility, 750 square feet, divided by the number of activity unit levels, 83.430, or 9 square feet. This coefficient is recorded in the appropriate input columns for each of the 12 using activities.

5.5.7 Required Land Inputs for Rest-Rooms and Customer Lounge

Land is required for various items which might be categorized as customer conveniences. These would include restrooms, a gear storage area, and a customer lounge. Certain of these items might be considered optional in planning a marina.

It is assumed that men's and women's restrooms, each with ten toilets, should adequately serve a marina of the scale visualized. At 15 square feet per toilet, and 200 square feet for lavatories and other passage space, 350 square feet per restroom should be sufficient. Since there are two restrooms, the land requirement would be 700 square feet. With regard to the customer lounge, it is felt that the lounge area should be approximately one and one-half times the size of the total restroom area, or 1,050 square feet. The combined area, then, for these two customer convenience activities, is 1,750 square feet.

It seems reasonable that all activities at the marina would use these customer conveniences on roughly the same basis per man-day of recreation provided. It was previously determined that in total, approximately 100,000 man-days of recreational activity would be provided by the marina. Since each activity has a unit level of 1,000 man-days, this signifies that in total, about 100 unit levels of recreational activity takes place at the marina.

Hence, to derive the land space requirements for restrooms and the customer lounge, the total square footage of these facilities, 1,750, divided by the number of unit levels, 100, equals the required square footage per unit level of activity—namely, 17.5. This figure is recorded in the input column of each activity which takes place at the marina.

5.5.8 Required Land Inputs for Gear Storage

Another customer convenience item to be considered is gear storage. Gear storage requires lockers which are approximately 1.5 feet by 3 feet in size, or 4.5 square feet. For a marina of the scale visualized, it seems reasonable to assume that 200 persons would demand lockers on a daily basis. Thus, an area for gear storage of approximately 900 square feet would be required. These lockers are assumed to be distributed about the dock area; hence, no specific passage space is required. Again, it is felt that all activities at the marina would use these lockers. Accordingly, the total square footage of the gear storage area, 900, divided by the total number of unit levels of recreational activity involved, 100, yields a per unit level requirement for each activity of 9 square feet. This figure is recorded in the input column for each activity at the marina.

5.5.9 Required Land Inputs for Administrative Office

Land inputs are also required for an administrative office. For the 400-boat marina, it is felt that administrative office space should be provided for four persons: the manager, a secretary and two bookkeepers. If on the average 110 square feet is a sufficient area per employee (full or part-time), then the administrative office should be 440 square feet.

Since all activities at the marina will demand administrative services, division by 100 unit levels, as in the case of the customer conveniences, yields 4.4 square feet as the unit level requirement of each activity for administrative office land inputs. This figure is recorded in the input column for each activity.

5.5.10 Required Land Inputs for Transient and Rental Office

Office space is required for conducting transient and rental operations. It is felt that for a 400-boat marina, two employees will be needed to conduct this business. Again, allowing 110 square feet per employee, we obtain a land input of 220 square feet.

The activities which demand these services are the transient operations, the rental operations, and the party-boat operation. For the marina under investigation, the total man-days of recreation provided by the operations just listed are 28,006. Dividing 220 square feet by this figure yields 7.86 per 1,000 man-days of recreation. This number is then the square feet of land for transient and rental office required per unit level of operation of each of the following activities:

RE 7949–102, Pleasure Boating: Outboard, Transient
RE 7949–104, Pleasure Boating: Inboard, Transient
RE 7949–105, Pleasure Boating: Rowboating, Rental
RE 7949–106, Pleasure Boating: Rowboating, Transient
RE 7949–107, Pleasure Boating: Party Boat

RE 7949–109, Pleasure Boating: Sailing, Transient
RE 7949–203, Sport Fishing: Outboard, Transient
RE 7949–205, Sport Fishing: Inboard, Transient
RE 7949–207, Sport Fishing: Rowboating, Rental
RE 7949–208, Sport Fishing: Rowboating, Transient
RE 7949–209, Sport Fishing: Party Boat

In all other activities this coefficient is zero.

5.5.11 Required Land Inputs for Bait and Packaged Food Sales

A reasonable amount of land for the sale of packaged food and bait for a 400-boat marina is 550 square feet. This area, however, must be further divided, because the sales of packaged food and bait are to two different sets of purchasers; bait sales are made only to those engaged in fishing activities.

It seems reasonable to assume that 70 percent of this area, or 385 square feet, will be for packaged food sales. It is posited that all activities will use the packaged food sales area. Since 100 unit levels of activity are involved, 3.85 square feet are required per unit level of each activity.

The bait-sales space comprises 30 percent of the facility, or 165 square feet. The activities which will demand the services of the bait shop are the following:

RE 7949–201, Sport Fishing: Pier and Jetty
RE 7949–202, Sport Fishing: Outboard, Seasonal
RE 7949–203, Sport Fishing: Outboard, Transient
RE 7949–204, Sport Fishing: Inboard, Seasonal
RE 7949–205, Sport Fishing: Inboard, Transient
RE 7949–207, Sport Fishing: Rowboating, Rental
RE 7949–208, Sport Fishing: Rowboating, Transient
RE 7949–209, Sport Fishing: Party Boat
RE 7949–210, Sport Fishing: Surf

Recall from Table 5.3h, in Section 5.3 dealing with the disaggregation of demand, that of those boats using the docking facilities, it was estimated that 50 seasonal outboards (from RE 7949–202), 4 transient outboards (a part of RE 7949–203), 4 seasonal inboards (from RE 7949–204), and 2 transient inboards (a part of RE 7949–205) would be used for fishing. Since the outboards are assumed to provide 162 man-days of fishing activity per season, then in total the boats using the docks will provide 17,820 man-days of fishing activity. Furthermore, as the seasonal equivalent of 17 fishing transient outboards (the remainder of RE 7949–203) will use the ramps on a daily basis, each providing 189 man-days, an additional 3,213 man-days are to be taken into account. Transient inboards using the ramps (the remainder of RE 7949–205) will provide another 567 man-days of fishing activity. Transient rowboats (RE 7949–208) will provide 567 man-days of fishing activity. The rental boats (from RE 7949–207) will provide 1,944 fishing activity man-days. Finally, it is assumed that the party-boat operations (RE 7949–209), pier and jetty fishing (RE 7949–201), and surf fishing (RE 7949–210) will provide 6,300, 1,200, and 800 fishing activity man-days, respectively. In total, for all activities, 32,411 man-days will be provided, which corresponds to 32.411 unit levels of activity. Dividing this last number into 165 square feet, the floor space of the bait shop, yields a unit level requirement for each activity involved of 5.09 square feet.

Thus, for the bait and packaged food facility, two different requirements are derived. For pleasure-boating activities, a land input for packaged food of 3.85 square feet per unit level is required. For sport-fishing activities, a land input for both packaged food and bait is required—namely, 3.85 plus 5.09, or 8.94 square feet.

For RE 7949–211, Sport Fishing: Clamming, no bait is required. It is, however, assumed that the packaged food facility land input should be assigned to this activity.

5.5.12 Required Land Inputs for Fuel Sales Facility

Land inputs are required for a fuel sales facility. It is felt that 110 square feet should be sufficient for this facility. The activities which will demand the services of this facility are those relating to inboards and outboards, both seasonal and transient, sport fishing, and pleasure boating. In addition, it is assumed that 80 percent of the sailboats at the marina have auxiliary engines, and hence, require fuel.

An estimate of the total numbers of man-days in these recreational activities is needed. Pleasure-boating seasonal outboards (RE 7949–101), pleasure-boating transient outboards (RE 7949–102), pleasure-boating seasonal inboards (RE 7949–103), pleasure-boating transient inboards (RE 7949–104), and pleasure-boating transient rowboats (RE 7949–106) account for 42,843 man-days of recreational activity. Pleasure-boating seasonal sailboats (RE 7949–108) and pleasure-boating transient sailboats (RE 7949–109) account for 18,198 man-days; since only 80 percent of the sailboats have auxiliary engines, the relevant number of man-days is 14,558. In the preceding section, it was determined that fishing activities that use seasonal and transient boats account for 22,167 man-days. Thus, in total, these fuel-using activities account for 79,568 man-days.

The floor space of the fuel sales facility, 110 square feet, divided by the number of unit levels of fuel-using activity involved, 79.568, yields a unit level requirement of 1.38 square feet. This coefficient is entered in the input column for all activities using this facility except those dealing with sailing activities, RE 7949–108 and RE 7949–109. Since only 80 percent of the boats involved in one unit level of these activities depend on the fuel facility, 1.38 square feet times 80 percent yields 1.10 square feet as the appropriate coefficient for these two activities.

5.5.13 Required Land Inputs for Ramps

In order to facilitate the transient launchings expected on a peak demand day at the marina, it is felt that a double ramp is needed. Such a ramp would have a capacity of 70 boats per day. The land area required for a double ramp is approximately $2\frac{1}{2}$ acres. This figure includes 60,900 square feet for parking space, and 48,000 square feet for the ramp and necessary maneuvering space. Parking space is taken into account elsewhere, so only the ramp space for transient operations is considered here.

In Table 5.3j of Section 5.3 dealing with disaggregation of recreational demand, it was estimated that the demand for transient facilities at the marina would be 13,230 man-days, or 13.230 unit levels. The required area for the ramps, 48,000 square feet, divided by this latter number yields the per unit level requirement of ramp land area for each of the transient activities, 3,628 square feet. This coefficient is recorded in the column of each transient operation.

5.5.14 Fish Inputs

The fishing activities depend on the availability of fish which can be caught. The input data on fish requirements were obtained by interviews and from the "Massachusetts Marine Sports Fisheries Inventory".[76] Table 5.5b summarizes the

[76] Fitzpatrick and Russell [7].

Table 5.5b Winter Flounder and Cod Caught per Man-Day by Sport Fishing Activity

Sport-Fishing Activity	Winter Flounder		Cod	
	No.	Lbs.	No.	Lbs.
RE 7949–201, Pier and Jetty	1.5	1.4	0	0.0
RE 7949–202, Outboard, Seasonal	4.0	3.6	1	6.7
RE 7949–203, Outboard, Transient	4.0	3.6	1	6.7
RE 7949–204, Inboard, Seasonal	1.5	1.4	4	26.8
RE 7949–205, Inboard, Transient	1.5	1.4	4	26.8
RE 7949–207, Rowboating, Rental	4.0	3.6	1	6.7
RE 7949–208, Rowboating, Transient	4.0	3.6	1	6.7
RE 7949–209, Party Boat	1.5	1.4	2	13.4
RE 7949–210, Surf	1.5	1.4	0	0.0

data on the number of pounds of winter flounder and cod caught by different recreational activities. It is assumed that the average winter flounder weighs 0.9 pound and the average cod, 6.7 pounds.[77] It is assumed that one man-day of RE 7949–211, Sport Fishing: Clamming, requires an input of 0.5 bushel of clams. The inputs by weight were then multiplied by 1,000 in order to derive the unit level requirements for the corresponding activities.

5.5.15 Boat Inputs

We have assumed that all boats at the marina will be either 3-man boats or 4-man boats and that all inboards, on the average, carry 4 persons, while outboards, sailboats, and rowboats, on the average, carry 3 persons. The boat input per unit level of each activity depends on the carrying capacity of each boat and the number of days it will be in use per season. In Section 5.3 we assumed that each boat would be used for an average of 4½ days per week throughout a 12-week season—that is, for 54 days. Thus, one boat, if it carries 4 persons, provides 216 man-days of recreation over a season. The problem of calculating boat inputs per unit level of activity, then, is to determine how many boats are required to support 1,000 man-days of recreational activity.

We begin the calculations with the 4-man boats. These are the inboards used in RE 7949–103, Pleasure Boating: Inboard, Seasonal; RE 7949–104, Pleasure Boating: Inboard, Transient; RE 7949–204, Sport Fishing: Inboard, Seasonal; and RE 7949–205, Sport Fishing: Inboard, Transient. If these inboard boats carry 4 persons, and are used, on the average, for 54 days per season (that is, provide 216 man-days of recreation per season), then 4.63 boats are required at the unit level of 1,000 man-days. This figure is recorded in the input columns of the corresponding activities.

We now turn to the 3-man boats used in RE 7949–101, Pleasure Boating: Outboard, Seasonal; RE 7949–102, Pleasure Boating: Outboard, Transient; RE 7949–105, Pleasure Boating: Rowboating, Rental; RE 7949–106, Pleasure Boating: Rowboating, Transient; RE 7949–108, Pleasure Boating: Sailing, Seasonal; RE 7949–109, Pleasure Boating: Sailing, Transient; RE 7949–202, Sport Fishing: Outboard, Seasonal; RE 7949–203, Sport Fishing: Outboard, Transient; RE 7949–207, Sport Fishing: Rowboating, Rental; and RE 7949–208, Sport Fishing: Rowboating, Transient. If these boats carry 3 persons, and are used, on the average, 54 days per season, then 6.17 boats are required at the unit level of activity—for 6.17 boats times 3 persons per boat times 54 days per season yields 1,000 man-days of recreational activity.

[77] *Ibid.*, p. 29.

Activities which make use of the party boats are RE 7949–107, Pleasure Boating: Party Boat, and RE 7949–209, Sport Fishing: Party Boats. Since these boats, on the average, make 140 trips per year and carry 25 passengers, on the average, then 0.28 party boat is required per unit level (1,000 man-days) of recreational activity.

5.5.16 Required Fuel Inputs

The next required input concerns fuel. Fuel is taken to include regular grade, unleaded, premium gasoline, diesel, and lubricating oil. Primary users of fuel are the inboard boats, the outboard boats, rowboats with motor, sailboats with auxiliary motors, and the party boats. For the outboard boats used in RE 7949–101, Pleasure Boating: Outboard, Seasonal; RE 7949–102, Pleasure Boating: Outboard, Transient; RE 7949–202, Sport Fishing: Outboard, Seasonal; and RE 7949–203, Sport Fishing: Outboard, Transient, the average number of gallons of fuel consumed per hour has been estimated at 2.25. However, this quantity would not be consumed during each of the five boating hours per day. Also, allowance should be made for fuel purchases made elsewhere. Therefore, it is estimated that, on net, 1.75 gallons of marina-purchased fuel are consumed for each hour of boating time, or 8.75 gallons per day. This latter figure, divided by the average number of persons per boat, namely 3, yields 2.9 gallons per man-day. Multiplying by 1,000 man-days yields 2,900 gallons per unit level of each of these four outboard boat activities.

In similar fashion, fuel inputs are calculated for the unit level of each other activity and recorded in Table 5.5c.[78]

Table 5.5c Fuel Inputs by Recreational Activity

Activity	Gallons per Hour of Full Use	Gallons per Hour of Average Use	Gallons per Day	Gallons per Unit Level
RE 7949–101	2.25	1.75	8.75	2,900
RE 7949–102	2.25	1.75	8.75	2,900
RE 7949–103	5.00	4.00	20.00	5,000
RE 7949–104	5.00	4.00	20.00	5,000
RE 7949–105[a]	1.00	0.88	4.38	1,100
RE 7949–106[b]	1.00	0.75	3.75	1,250
RE 7949–107	10.00	7.50	37.50	940
RE 7949–108	0.50	0.40	2.00	666
RE 7949–109	0.50	0.40	2.00	666
RE 7949–202	2.25	1.75	8.75	2,900
RE 7949–203	2.25	1.75	8.75	2,900
RE 7949–204	5.00	4.00	20.00	5,000
RE 7949–205	5.00	4.00	20.00	5,000
RE 7949–207[a]	1.00	0.88	4.38	1,100
RE 7949–208[b]	1.00	0.75	3.75	1,250
RE 7949–209	10.00	7.50	37.50	940

[a]The normal requirement for one rental rowboat with engine would be 2 gallons per hour at full use, 1.75 gallons per hour at average use, 8.75 gallons per day, and 2,200 gallons at unit level. We divide this number by 2 on the assumption that only one-half of the rental boats in RE 7949–105 and RE 7949–207 have engines.

[b]The normal requirement for a transient's rowboat with engine would be 2 gallons per hour at full use, 1.5 gallons per hour at average use, 7.5 gallons per day, and 2,500 gallons per unit level. We divide this number by 2 on the assumption that only one-half of the boats in RE 7949–106 and RE 7949–208 have engines.

5.5.17 General Approach to Derivation of Labor Input Coefficients

In order to obtain the various labor requirements per unit level of each activity,

[78] The fuel consumption in part was estimated by the authors, and in part was taken from Michigan State Waterways Commission [15], pp. 2–4.

the following general approach was used. First, a reasonable estimate of the required labor to service and maintain the proposed 395-boat marina was made. Second, the areas of responsibility for each employee were determined. Third, each employee's man-hours were allocated among the recreation activities using his labor. Finally, the pertinent man-hours in each activity were divided by the level of that activity proposed for the marina to yield the necessary number of man-hours of labor required per unit level.

It is felt that the labor required for a marina of the proposed size (395 boats) and composition should include the following:

1 General Manager
2 Bookkeepers (one full-time, one seasonal)
1 Secretary (half-time)
1 Dockmaster
9 Seasonal dock attendants
2 Equipment operators
1 Boat and motor sales manager
1 Boat and motor salesman
1 Marine supply sales manager
1 Seasonal marine supply salesman
2 Party boat crews (each with captain, mate, and one crew member)
2 Seasonal bait and packaged food salesmen
2 Mechanics
2 Carpenters
1 Painter

Each seasonal employee is assumed to work 4 months. Half-time employees work 6 months.

5.5.18 Required Labor Inputs: General Manager

We assume that the general manager works 40 hours per week for 50 weeks per year. Thus, the manager supplies 2,000 hours of labor per year. Since the general manager is concerned with all activities at the marina, he serves 100 unit levels of recreation. Therefore, each unit level of recreation requires 20 hours of the general manager's time. This figure is recorded in the appropriate cell of the column for each activity.

For deriving other labor inputs, it is now useful to allocate in an indirect manner the general manager labor among various using activities. To do so refer to Table 5.5d.

From discussion of previous sections, first, in column 1, the number of boats in each recreational activity is listed. Then, in column 2, the man-days per boat per season are listed. The data in this column are based upon the passengers per boat and the season that have previously been assumed. For example, for RE 7949–101, Pleasure Boating: Outboard, Seasonal, these boats carry 3 persons for 54 days per season. Multiplication yields 162 man-days per boat per season. With 110 boats in this category, a total of 17,820 man-days of recreation are expected to be provided. This figure is shown in column 3. For those sport-fishing activities which do not require boats, but which do require managerial supervision, the total number of man-days estimated also appears in column 3.

Then, the man-days from all activities are summed, and the percentage of the total accounted for by each recreational activity is derived and recorded in column 4. These percentages are then used as a basis for allocating among the recreational activities the 2,000 hours of labor supplied by the general manager. This man-hour allocation is shown in column 5.

Note that although party boat operations are, in practice, relatively independent

Table 5.5d Allocation of General Manager's Labor Among Various Recreational Activities

Activity Code	No. of Boats in Activity (1)	No. of Man-Days per Boat per Season (2)	Total Man-Days per Season (3)	Associated Level of Activity (3)	Percentage of Total Man-Days (4)	Hours of Managerial Time per Activity (5)
RE 7949–101	110	162	17,820	17.820	17.8	356
RE 7949–102 (at docks)	6	162	7,743	7.743	7.7	154
RE 7949–102 (ramps)	37	189				
RE 7949–103	70	216	15,120	15.120	15.1	302
RE 7949–104 (at docks)	3	216	1,593	1.593	1.6	32
RE 7949–104 (ramp)	5	189				
RE 7949–105	36	162	5,832	5.832	5.8	116
RE 7949–106	3	189	567	.567	0.6	12
RE 7949–108	105	162	17,010	17.010	17.0	340
RE 7949–109 (at docks)	5	162	1,188	1.188	1.2	24
RE 7949–109 (ramp)	2	189				
RE 7949–201	0	0	1,200	1.200	1.2	24
RE 7949–202	50	162	8,100	8.100	8.1	162
RE 7949–203 (at docks)	4	162	3,861	3.861	3.9	78
RE 7949–203 (ramps)	17	189				
RE 7949–204	40	216	8,640	8.640	8.6	172
RE 7949–205 (at docks)	2	216	999	.999	1.0	20
RE 7949–205 (ramps)	3	189				
RE 7949–207	12	162	1,944	1.944	2.0	40
RE 7949–208	3	189	567	.567	0.6	12
RE 7949–210	0	0	800	.800	0.8	16
RE 7949–211	0	0	0	.000	0.0	0
RE 7949–107	2	3,500	700	.700	0.7	14
RE 7949–209			6,300	6.300	6.3	126
Total			99,984[a]		100.0	2,000

[a]A small error due to rounding is involved in this number.

of other operations, it is assumed that they require some portion of the total administrative time.

Note also that certain code groupings have been broken into two parts. For example, RE 7949–102, Pleasure Boating: Outboard Transient, contains an "at docks" operation and a "ramp" operation. This division stems from the earlier assumption that dock space for six transient outboards was needed. These six boats, it will be recalled, were visualized as semi-transients, or seasonal equivalents. The other boats in the grouping are handled at the ramp.

Finally, although the manager works 2000 hours, per year, his most intensive period of work is during the boating season; that is, during four or five months during the summer. It was felt that his time should be allocated on the basis of peak-season demand, partly because the manager will probably average much more than 40 hours per week during the summer, and less during the winter.

In order to obtain indirectly the managerial labor input at the unit level of each activity, two approaches are possible. Either the number of boats in each grouping can be used with each type of boat appropriately weighted, or the number of unit levels of 1,000 man-days per season in column 3 can be used. We have employed the latter alternative. In round numbers, and as previously derived directly, 20 hours of managerial labor input are required per unit level of each activity.

5.5.19 Required Labor Inputs: Other Administrative

Other required administrative labor includes the bookkeepers and the secretary.

The full-time bookkeeper is expected to work 40 hours per week for 50 weeks per year, a total of 2,000 man-hours per year. The seasonal bookkeeper works 667 hours per year, and the half-time secretary, 1000 hours. The three employees are expected to account for 3,667 hours of labor per year. This additional administrative labor is associated with all the activities at the marina, or 100 unit levels of recreation. Thus, approximately 27 hours of bookkeeping time and 10 hours of secretarial time is required per unit level of each activity. In total, this amounts to 37 hours of other administrative labor input per unit level of each activity. This figure is then recorded in the appropriate cell in the column for each activity.

5.5.20 Required Labor Inputs: Dockmaster

The dockmaster is basically responsible for the smooth operation of those activities which involve the docks and piers at the marina. It is, therefore, reasonable to assign his services to the various seasonal boating activities which use the docks and piers. The man-days associated with these activities are given in Table 5.5e in

Table 5.5e Allocation of Dockmaster's Labor among Various Recreational Activities

Activity Code	Total Man-Days per Season (1)	Percentage of Total Man-Days (2)	Hours of Dockmaster Time per Activity (3)
RE 7949–101	17,820	26.7	534
RE 7949–103	15,120	22.7	454
RE 7949–108	17,010	25.5	510
RE 7949–202	8,100	12.1	242
RE 7949–204	8,640	13.0	260
Total	66,690	100.0	2,000

column 1. These figures originate in column 3 of Table 5.5d. The total of man-days listed in column 1 corresponds to 66.69 unit levels of activity. Since the dockmaster is a full-time employee, working 2,000 hours per year, 30 hours of his time are required by a unit level of each using activity.

For convenience, we list in columns 2 and 3 of Table 5.5e the allocation of the dockmaster's time, by percentage, and by numbers of hours, respectively. As in the case of the manager, the dockmaster is expected to be most busy during the summer months, and least busy during the winter. It is felt that his annual labor input should be allocated on the basis of peak-season demand.

5.5.21 Required Labor Inputs: Dock Operations Personnel

In order to assist the dockmaster and perform the necessary jobs that take place on the docks, it is felt that nine seasonal dock attendants and two equipment operators are necessary. Since each seasonal dock attendant works for four months per year, the nine seasonal dock attendants are taken to be equivalent to three full-time employees. Thus, in the course of one year, there are 6,000 hours of dock attendants' labor and 4,000 hours of equipment operators' labor. In total, then, dock operations personnel supply 10,000 hours of labor.

The responsibilities of the dock operations personnel concern the seasonal boating activities, the transient boating activities, and the rental boating activities. These various activities are listed in Table 5.5f. Altogether they are operated at

Table 5.5f Allocation of Dock Operation Labor Among Various Recreational Activities

Activity Code	Total Man-days per Season (1)	Percentage of Total Man-Days (2)	Hours of Dock Operation Time by Activity (3)
RE 7949–101	17,820	19.6	1,960
RE 7949–102	7,743	8.5	850
RE 7949–103	15,120	16.6	1,660
RE 7949–104	1,593	1.8	180
RE 7949–105	5,832	6.4	640
RE 7949–106	567	0.6	60
RE 7949–108	17,010	18.7	1,870
RE 7949–109	1,188	1.3	130
RE 7949–202	8,100	8.9	890
RE 7949–203	3,861	4.2	420
RE 7949–204	8,640	9.5	950
RE 7949–205	999	1.1	110
RE 7949–207	1,944	2.2	220
RE 7949–208	567	0.6	60
Total	90,984	100.0	10,000

90.984 unit levels. The 10,000 hours of labor of dock operations personnel divided by the 90.984 unit levels yields 110 hours of labor input per unit level of each using activity. This figure is recorded in the appropriate cell in the column for each activity. For convenience, we list in columns 2 and 3 of Table 5.5f the allocation of dock labor, by percentage, and by number of hours, respectively.

5.5.22 Required Labor Inputs: Boat and Motor Sales Personnel

In order to operate the facility which sells new and used boats and motors and trailers, a sales manager and a salesman are needed. As the rate of pay differs for these two persons, two labor input coefficients are computed, one for each.

The sales manager is a full-time employee, and thus works 2,000 hours per year. The salesman, as well, works 2,000 hours over the year.

Each of these employees is expected to make sales to those who participate in the seasonal and transient boating activities. The recreational activities involved are listed in Table 5.5g. Although Table 5.5g is constructed to allocate the 2,000 hours of sales manager labor, the allocation of hours is also appropriate for the salesman. Column 1 shows that 83.208 unit levels of recreation are served by both the sales manager and the salesman. The 2,000 man-hours worked by the sales manager divided by the 83.208 unit levels served by him yields 24 hours of labor input of the sales manager per unit level for each recreational activity involved. This figure is recorded in the appropriate cell in the column for each activity.

Since the salesman works the same number of hours, serving the same activities, the labor input coefficient for the salesman's time is exactly the same—namely, 24 hours for each recreational activity.

For convenience we list in columns 2 and 3 of Table 5.5g the allocation of the boat sales manager's labor, by percentage, and by number of hours, respectively.

5.5.23 Required Labor Inputs: Marine Supplies Sales Personnel

In addition to the new- and used-boat sales personnel, employees are needed to

Table 5.5g Allocation of Boat Sales Manager's Labor among Various Recreational Activities

Activity Code	Total Man-Days per Season (1)	Percentage of Total Man-Days (2)	Hours of Boat Sales Manager's Time per Activity (3)
RE 7949–101	17,820	21.4	428
RE 7949–102	7,743	9.3	186
RE 7949–103	15,120	18.2	364
RE 7949–104	1,593	1.9	38
RE 7949–106	567	0.7	14
RE 7949–108	17,010	20.4	408
RE 7949–109	1,188	1.4	28
RE 7949–202	8,100	9.7	194
RE 7949–203	3,861	4.6	92
RE 7949–204	8,640	10.5	210
RE 7949–205	999	1.2	24
RE 7949–208	567	0.7	14
Total	83,208	100.0	2,000

operate the marine supplies facility. It is felt that a marine supplies sales manager and one seasonal salesman are sufficient. Again, two labor input coefficients are calculated, one for each.

The marine supplies sales manager is assumed to supply 2,000 man-hours of labor per year. It is felt that the allocation percentages computed for the new- and used-boat sales personnel also are appropriate for the marine supplies sales manager. Consequently, the allocation of man-hours given in Table 5.5g for the boat sales manager is also appropriate for the marine supplies sales manager. Thus, at unit level of each using activity, an input of 24 hours of labor of a marine supplies sales manager is required.

Since the salesman works only for four months, or for one-third of a year, the unit level requirement of his services is one-third of 24 hours, or 8 hours for each using activity. These coefficients are recorded in the appropriate cells in the column for each of the 12 using activities.

5.5.24 Required Labor Inputs: Party Boat Crews

Crews are required for each of the two party boats which serve the marina. Each boat has a crew of 3, consisting of the captain, a mate, and a crew member. As each party boat operates roughly 5 months per year, this activity requires roughly 30 man-months of labor. As 30 man-months of labor is $2\frac{1}{2}$ man-years, a total labor input of 5,000 man-hours is required.

In total, 7,000 man-days of recreational activity corresponding to 7 unit levels of operation are provided by the two party-boat recreational activities RE 7949–107, Pleasure Boating: Party Boat, and RE 7949–209, Sport Fishing: Party Boat. Hence, per unit level, 714 man-hours of labor input are required. This figure is recorded in the input columns for RE 7949–107 and RE 7949–209.

5.5.25 Required Labor Inputs: Packaged Food and Bait Sales Personnel

To operate the packaged food and bait sales facility, it is felt that two seasonal salesmen are sufficient. These two salesmen work, in total, 35 man-weeks, so they provide a total of 1,400 man-hours of labor. As in the case of the required land input for the packaged food and bait sales facility, two coefficients are computed: one for the pleasure-boating activities and one for the sport-fishing activities. It was assumed that 70 percent of this facility would be for packaged food and 30 percent for bait. The labor input is also divided on the basis of these percentages. Hence, 980 man-hours are needed for packaged food sales, and 420 man-hours are needed for bait sales.

The sale of packaged food is assumed to be to participants of all activities. All activities in total provide 100,000 man-days of recreation, and are thus operated at 100 unit levels. Dividing 980 by 100 yields 9.8 hours of packaged food and bait sales labor per unit level of each activity. Since pleasure-boating activities require no bait and hence no bait sales labor, the relevant coefficient for each of these activities is then 9.8, or roughly 10.

With regard to the sport-fishing activities, labor for bait sales is required. From Table 5.5d, column 3, the sum of the recreational man-days provided by the nine sport-fishing activities is seen to be 32,411. The man-hours required for bait sales, 420, divided by the number of units at which sport-fishing activities are operated—namely 32.411—yields a requirement of 13.0 man-hours of bait shop labor per unit level of each using activity. Thus, since labor inputs for both packaged food and bait are required for sport-fishing activities, the relevant magnitude is 9.8 man-hours plus 13.0 man-hours, or in total, roughly 23 man-hours per unit level. This figure is recorded in the appropriate cell in the column of each sport-fishing activity.

5.5.26 Required Labor Inputs: Repair Shop Personnel

The final labor requirement is associated with the personnel required to operate the marina's repair shop. Two mechanics, two carpenters, and one painter are taken to constitute an adequate labor force for the facility. Working full time, 40 hours per week, 50 weeks per year, each furnishes 2,000 man-hours of labor per year. For five repair shop personnel, the total labor provided is 10,000 hours per year.

The repair facility is primarily oriented to the 400 boats which roughly comprise the marina's seasonal or home fleet. Hence a set of percentage allocations is required. These are derived in Table 5.5h.

Table 5.5h Allocation of Repair Shop Personnel Labor among Various Recreational Activities

Activity Code	Number of Boats (1)	Weighted Number of Boats (2)	Percentage of Total of Weighted Number of Boats (3)	Hours of Repair Labor (4)	Hours of Repair Labor per Unit Level of Activity (5)
RE 7949–101	110	110	18.6	1,860	104
RE 7949–103	70	140	23.7	2,370	157
RE 7949–108	105	210	35.6	3,560	209
RE 7949–202	50	50	8.5	850	105
RE 7949–204	40	80	13.6	1,360	157
Total		590	100.0	10,000	

It was judged that, on the average, repairs on sailboats and inboards take twice as long as repairs on outboards. (This repair time factor is similar to the repair space factor of 1.9 employed in computing space requirements for these boats.)

Thus, in Table 5.5h, column 2 is obtained from column 1 (which records the number of boats by activity) by applying a weight of 2 to each sailboat and inboard. The weighted number of boats by activity listed in column 2 is then converted to a percentage of the total of the weighted number of boats, as recorded in column 3. In column 4, the percentages of column 3 are used to allocate the 10,000 man-hours of repair labor. Finally, in column 5, the repair labor input per unit level of each recreational activity is listed. This requirement is then recorded in the appropriate cell of the column of that activity.

5.5.27 Required Water Surface Inputs

Water surface is needed for all boating activities carried on at the marina. In this section, separate coefficients for boats kept at docks and boats kept at moorings are computed. The first calculations concern those recreational activities in which all boats are kept at docks. Hence, for these activities, the requirement for water surface mooring is zero.

The water surface required for docked boats includes the square footage of the docks, the area of water between the docks, the maneuvering area between the rows of docks, and the area of the service channel within the marine facility basin.

For seasonal outboard activities (RE 7949–101 and RE 7949–202), all boats are kept at docks. It has been estimated that the required water surface per boat is 835 square feet.[79] Since one unit level of each of these two activities requires the use of 6.17 boats, this number times the required space per boat yields the relevant coefficient. This coefficient is 5,152 and is expressed in terms of square feet of water surface per unit level. It is recorded in the appropriate cell in the columns for RE 7949–101 and RE 7949–202.

For those transient activities which employ outboard boats (RE 7949–102 and RE 7949–203), no mooring space is required. The required water surface for transient outboards is less than for seasonal outboards, as boats utilizing ramp facilities require only a small dock for short periods of time and a short channel leading out of the basin. It is felt that the requirement is one-third that of the seasonal outboard requirement. This requirement is 278 square feet per boat, or 1,717 square feet per unit level of activity. This figure is recorded in the appropriate cell in the columns for RE 7949–102 and RE 7949–203.

For rental rowboating activity (RE 7949–105 and RE 7949–207), 400 square feet of water surface per boat is sufficient. As 6.17 rowboats are involved at one unit level of each of these activities, 2,468 square feet is required. No moorings are needed.

It is felt that the transient rowboats used in both pleasure boating and sport fishing (RE 7949–106 and RE 7949–208) require one-third of the water surface needed by the rental rowboats. Thus, at unit level of these two activities, 823 square feet of water surface is required. This coefficient is recorded in the input columns for RE 7949–106 and RE 7949–208. For these activities, no moorings are required.

Water surface is also required for the recreational activities RE 7949–107 and RE 7949–209, which use the party boats. Although these boats do not require docking slips, since they will be kept in the docked boat area, their water surface requirements are listed in this section.

It has been estimated that 1,775 square feet of water surface is needed per party boat.[80] Since there are two party boats, 3,550 square feet are to be reserved exclusively for party boat use. In total, the two party boats provide 7,000 man-days of recreational activity. Therefore, the required water space, 3,550 square feet, divided by 7, yields a water surface requirement per unit level of 507 square feet.

[79] Wisconsin Department of Resource Development [32], p. 27.
[80] *Ibid.*, p. 26.

This figure is recorded in the appropriate cells in the columns for RE 7949–107 and RE 7949–209. The coefficient for mooring water surface is zero.

For the seasonal inboard activities (RE 7949–103 and RE 7949–204), water surface is required for moorings as well as for boats kept at docks. For each of these two activities, it is estimated that 1,270 square feet of water surface is required per docked boat.[81] However, not all the seasonal inboards are kept at docks. Some are kept at moorings. In Table 5.3e and the related discussion in Section 5.3, it was assumed that there are 95 docked seasonal inboards. One-third of these boats, or 31.67, are fishing inboards, and thus are classified in RE 7949–204, while the remaining 63.33 are pleasure boating inboards, and classified in RE 7949–103.

In Table 5.3g in Section 5.3, it was assumed that 8 seasonal inboards are moored. Five of these boats are, on the average, 25 feet long, while three average 35 feet. Since one-third of the boat time is taken to be spent in fishing activities, this means that 1.67 25-foot moored boats and one 35-foot moored boat are used for fishing (RE 7949–204). Likewise, 3.33 25-foot boats and 2 35-foot boats are used for pleasure boating (RE 7949–103).

Thus, the total number of seasonal inboards used for sport fishing is 31.67 docked boats plus 1.67 25-foot moored boats plus 1 35-foot moored boat, or 34.33 boats in total. The total number of seasonal inboards used for pleasure boating is 63.33 docked boats plus 3.33 25-foot moored boats plus 2 35-foot moored boats, or 68.67 boats in total. In each case, 92 percent of the boats are docked boats, 5 percent are 25-foot moored boats, and 3 percent are 35-foot moored boats.

The water surface requirement per docked boat has already been set at 1,270 square feet. It is estimated that a 25-foot moored boat, when moored bow and stern, requires 5,880 square feet. A bow and stern moored 35-foot boat requires 8,150 square feet.[82]

At this stage, all the information necessary for computing unit level water surface requirements is on hand. As previously determined, 4.63 inboard 4-man boats are required to support one unit level (1,000 man-days) of activities RE 7949-103 and RE 7949–204. Therefore, for a unit level of these activities, the water surface requirement for the docked boats is 4.63 boats times 0.92 times 1,270 square feet per boat, or 5,156 square feet.

At unit level the required water surface for 25-foot moored boats is 4.63 boats times 0.05 times 5,880 square feet per boat, of 1,361 square feet. At unit level the required water surface for 35-foot moored boats is 4.63 boats times 0.03 times 8,150 square feet per boat, or 1,132 square feet. These two mooring requirements are added to obtain the total mooring requirement of 2,493 square feet per unit level of activity. This last figure, together with the figure of 5,156 square feet of water surface for docking space, is recorded in the appropriate cells in the columns for RE 7949–103 and RE 7949–204.

With respect to transient inboard recreational activities (RE 7949–104 and RE 7949–205), no water surface is required for mooring, but some is needed for docking. It is assumed that the required water surface per boat for docking is the same as that per boat engaged in seasonal inboard activities. Since 1,270 square feet of water surface is required per boat and since 4.63 boats are involved at unit level, 5,880 square feet are required per unit level of each of these two activities.

For the seasonal sailing activity RE 7949–108, water surface for both docked and moored boats is required. Although the average size of sailing boats is smaller than that of inboard boats, a greater maneuvering space between docks and in channel approaches is needed. It is therefore assumed that the water space at both docks and moorings per boat is the same as that required for inboard boats. This is 1,270 square feet per docked boat, 5,880 square feet per moored 25-foot boat, and 8,150 square feet per moored 35-foot boat.

In Table 5.3e and the discussion in Section 5.3, it was assumed that 87 seasonal

[81] *Ibid.*

[82] Tatlock [24], Section 1.1.

sailing boats use docking facilities. In Table 5.3g of that section, it was assumed that 7 boats are moored. Five are assumed to be 25-foot boats and 2 to be 35-foot boats. These assumptions yield a total of 94 boats at docks and moorings, 93 percent being docked boats, 5 percent being 25-foot moored boats, and 2 percent being 35-foot moored boats.

As previously stated, 6.17 sailboats of the 3-man category are required to support one unit level of sailing activity. Therefore, the water surface requirement per unit level for docked sailboats is 6.17 boats times 0.93 times 1,270 square feet per boat, or 7,287 square feet.

The water surface requirement per unit level for 25-foot moored sailboats is 6.17 boats times 0.05 times 5,880 square feet per boat, or 1,814 square feet. The water surface requirement per unit level for 35-foot moored sailboats is 6.17 boats times 0.02 times 8,150 square feet per boat, or 1,006 square feet. These two mooring requirements are added to yield the mooring space requirement of 2,820 square feet per unit level.

For the transient sailing activity RE 7949–109, water surface is required for docked boats, but not for moorings. Again, it is assumed that the water area required per boat is the same as that for inboard boats—namely, 1,270 square feet per boat. Since 6.17 sailboats are required per unit level of sailing activity, the relevant coefficient is 7,836. This coefficient is recorded in the input column for RE 7949–109.

5.5.28 Water Quality Constraints

With regard to water quality, the following criteria are used:[83]

	Boating	Fishing
Coliform index	5,000/100 ml. max.	5,000/100 ml. max.
Dissolved oxygen	4.0 ppm monthly average	—
pH	6.0–8.5	6.7–8.6
Biochemical oxygen demand	3.0 ppm monthly average	—
	5.0 max.	—
Turbidity	—	100,000 ppm max.

Also, water color, temperature, and salinity form relevant constraints for certain activities. Pertinent data on these environmental conditions are presented in Appendix B of this report and are entered in Table 5.5a where relevant.

5.5.29 Inputs for Beach Activity: Swimming

Although the recreation activity, Beach Activity: Swimming (S.I.C. 7943), is programed at zero level in the proposed marina development, the necessary inputs per unit level are determined. A reasonable unit level of output for the derivation of necessary inputs is 1,000 man-days of swimming activity. If this number of man-days is distributed over the 100-day swimming season, this step implies that on the average there are 10 swimmers per day. However, since most activity takes place during the weekend, a range of 5 to 20 swimmers per day appears reasonable. The maximum end of this range, 20 swimmers per day, is used to derive the inputs.

With regard to land for parking space, it is assumed that for every three swimmers, one parking space is needed. Thus, for a peak demand day, 7 parking places must be allocated per unit level of this activity. Since 435 square feet are required per parking space after allowance for adequate maneuvering area, 3,045 square feet of parking space are required per unit level.

It is assumed that 3.5 square feet of bathhouse space is needed per person.

[83] They are based on Wisconsin Department of Resource Development [32], pp. 46–47.

Since 20 swimmers might be at the marina on a weekend day per unit level, 70 square feet of bathhouse land input are required.

It has been estimated that there must be between 100 and 200 square feet, or an average of 150 square feet, of beach area per man-day of swimming activity at the beach.[84] Since a maximum of 20 persons per day are associated with one unit level of this activity, then 3,000 square feet of beach area are required per unit level. For water surface area, it is assumed that 150 square feet per person are needed.[85] Thus, at unit level, 3,000 square feet of water surface are required.

With regard to water quality constraints, it is specified that the average coliform index should be 1,000 per 100 ml., with a maximum of 2,400 per 100 ml. The minimum limit for amounts of dissolved oxygen should be 7.0 ppm. The pH range should be 6.5–8.5. The maximum turbidity should be 20 ppm. The maximum amount of color should be 30 units.[86] These conditions are listed in Table 5.5a, in the input column for S.I.C. 7943, Beach Activity: Swimming.

Table 5.5i Total Input Requirements, 395-Boat Marina

LAND (in square feet) for	
Parking	364,520
Total indoor storage	54,628
Local indoor storage	36,355
Total repairs	5,854
Local repairs	5,413
Boat and motor showroom	2,650
Sales of marine accessories	750
Rest rooms and lounge	1,750
Gear storage	900
Administrative office	440
Transient and rental office	220
Bait and packaged food sales	550
Fuel sales	110
FISH	
Cod (in pounds)	237,611
Winter flounder (in pounds)	90,806
Clams (in bushels)	0
BOATS (during season)	523
FUEL (in gallons)	269,251
LABOR (in man-hours)	
General manager	2,000
Other administrative	3,667
Dockmaster	2,000
Dock operations personnel	10,000
Boat sales manager	2,000
Boat salesman	2,000
Marine supplies sales manager	2,000
Marine supplies salesman	667
Party boat crews	5,000
Packaged food and bait sales personnel	1,400
Repair shop personnel	10,000
WATER SURFACE (in square feet)	
For docked boats	448,146
For moored boats	107,202

[84] Wisconsin Department of Resource Development [32], p. 32.

[85] For our study area, for every lineal foot of shoreline with a 100-foot-deep beach, we require a 100-foot band of swimming area. However, see *ibid.*, p. 34, for a less generous requirement.

[86] These criteria are based on data in *ibid.*, p. 45.

5.5.30 Total Input Requirements, 395-Boat Marina

We have now derived each of the input-output vectors which are relevant for the proposed 395-boat marina complex. Each is recorded in input-output format in Table 5.5a.

We have also indicated in Table 5.5d, column 3, the levels at which we run each activity in the proposed complex. If we then multiply these levels represented as a column vector, by the input-output coefficient matrix in Table 5.5a, we obtain the total input requirements. These requirements are listed in Table 5.5i. In the multiplication, we omit the rows in Table 5.5a which refer to water quality constraints.

5.6 *Capital Costs of the Marina Complex*

In Table 5.5i of Section 5.5.30, we have indicated input requirements for a 395-boat marina of the composition recorded in Table 5.3h of Section 5.3.2. We now proceed to estimate capital costs by type for the 395-boat marina complex. In the following section, we shall extend the computations in a highly simplified manner to project capital costs for marina complexes of different sizes.

In the subsequent analysis we frequently use a finer breakdown of sizes of boats than used in the derivation of the input vectors of the preceding section. Such a finer breakdown allows us to make somewhat more detailed estimates of costs and revenues.

5.6.1 Moorings

Table 5.3g of Section 5.3 indicates that for meeting the demands for the diverse recreational services to be provided, there will be a need for fifteen seasonal boats to be moored in the basin. For estimating mooring costs, the relevant criteria are type of boat and length.

We take the fifteen boats to comprise ten motor boats in the 20–30 foot range, averaging 25 feet; and five in the 30–40 foot range, averaging 35 feet. To conserve water surface space, we assume the boats to be moored by the bow and stern; hence, we require two moorings per boat.

To begin the cost estimation procedure, we calculate the maximum height of water in the basin by adding the dredged depth, 8 feet, to the extreme high tide, 11.1 feet, to obtain the approximate figure of 19 feet.[87] Next, we compute the lengths of chain and pennant rope which are dependent on the maximum height of water. We then assign unit costs to chain, pennant, mooring buoy, and hardware for the 25-foot and 35-foot length boats and multiply, respectively, by the numbers of these boats involved. Multiplying again by 2 yields a cost for the two moorings required per boat. For fifteen boats, we obtain $4,253 as the total cost of moorings.[88] This figure is listed in Table 5.6h.

5.6.2 Shore Protection

The marina complex site requires shore protection from waves and earth settling on four sides of the land fill. In Section 5.2, which compares key economic and ecologic costs for several sites, an outline of the procedure for calculating the quantities of materials required, unit costs, and total shore protection costs is given. Briefly, the following are taken to characterize the required shore protection:[89]

[87] See Tatlock [24], Section 1.1.
[88] Costs are from *ibid.*
[89] See *ibid.*, Section 1.2, for further details.

1. Bulkhead of timber and pile to mean low water level, with stone block revetment on plastic filtercloth on the slope.
2. Height of bulkhead at 32 feet for 1,315 lineal feet of shore and at 8 feet for 1,223 lineal feet of shore.[90]

At a cost per linear foot of $120 for shore protection of the 32-foot height, and $44 for shore protection of the 8-foot height, we estimate total shore protection costs for the Duxbury Nook site to be $211,600.[91] This figure is entered in Table 5.6h.

5.6.3 Dredging

For the marina complex, dredging of two types is required: channel and basin. The procedure for determining quantities of material to be dredged, dredged depths, and cubic yard unit costs has been outlined in Section 5.2, which compares key economic and ecologic costs for several sites. For the Duxbury Nook site, it was determined that 35,000 cubic yards of bottom material need to be dredged for the channel, and 116,000 cubic yards need to be dredged for the basin. At $2.00 per cubic yard for dumping spoil one mile east of Plymouth Bay harbor entrance, dredging cost for the channel was estimated at $70,000 and for the basin at $232,000. The total, then, is $302,000.[92]

5.6.4 Docks

For the 395-boat marina complex, we estimate that 300 boats will require berths at docks. Of the balance, 80 will be dry-land berthed and 15 moored. For these boats we shall consider only floating docks since the mean tide range of 9.6 feet precludes use of fixed docks.[93]

From Table 5.3e in Section 5.3, we classify boats by length ranges as indicated in the first two columns of Table 5.6a.

To derive an estimate of required square feet of docks, we employ our classification of boats by boat length ranges. For each length range, the largest boat in that range is taken to determine the square feet requirement for each boat in that range. Where dock configuration is taken to be Dock Type I[94] we thus have:

Table 5.6a Dock Area Requirements

Boat Length Ranges	Numbers	Sq. Ft./Boat	Total Sq. Ft.
10–20 feet	150	89.6	13,440
20–30 feet	90	109.8	9,882
30–40 feet	60	136.6	8,196
Total			31,518

At cost $4.01 per square foot, the 31,518 square feet of dock cost $126,388. To this figure must be added the costs of a fueling dock (800 square feet at $5.91 =

[90] After the analysis of Section 5.2.2 was completed, refinement of the initial design considered suggests lower figures for lineal feet of shore protection. See the discussion in Section 5.11. Here we use lower and somewhat more reasonable figures than in Section 5.2.2.

[91] Unit costs are from Tatlock [24], Section 1.2.

[92] At the time this section was written, it was not anticipated that any of the dredged material could be used for fill at the site. The analysis is based on the assumption that all the dredged material is dumped. Later, in Section 5.6.8, we do assume that 46,500 cubic yards of material dredged from the basin can be used for land fill. A more rigorous analysis should then have involved a modification of the dredging costs calculated in this section.

[93] Refer to Tatlock [24], Section 1.4.

[94] *Ibid.*

$4,728);[95] of a boat rental dock (of similar size and cost); and of a dinghy storage and boat ramp dock (again of similar size and cost). Thus, an additional outlay of $14,184 is required for docks.

Associated with docks are pilings. We set 21 feet as the maximum height of these docks. To calculate the required length of piling, we must add 5 feet to the height of the docks to allow for sufficient piling above the dock and another 11 feet to anchor the piling adequately within the bottom material. All told, the piling length is taken to be 37 feet on the average.[96]

To determine costs of piling, we assume that two boats use one dock catwalk. Since there are 300 docked boats, 150 catwalk piles are required. For every 15 linear feet of mainwalk, one anchorage pile is needed. Two boats, plus clearance, plus a 5-foot catwalk, take 30 feet of mainwalk. Since boats are docked on both sides of the mainwalk, two anchorage piles are required for every four boats. Thus, 150 anchorage piles are also required. Because economies of scale would be realizable when 300 piles are to be installed on the same job, we use the low linear foot cost of $2.61.[97] Each pile of 37 feet then costs $96.57; and the 300 cost $28,971. Another 12 pilings are required for the three small docks. Each of these averaging 37 feet in length costs $96.57; the twelve cost $1,158.84.

To complete the overall costs for dock installation, we must allow for an electrical system at a cost of $72.46 per boat,[98] and eight aluminum gangways of 20 feet at a cost of $417 each. The total of dock costs is derived in Table 5.6b.

Table 5.6b Dock Costs

Berthing docks	$126,388
Fueling, rental, and storage docks	14,184
Pilings for berthing docks	28,971
Pilings for other docks	1,159
Electrical system	21,738
Gangways	3,336
Total	$195,776

5.5.6 Breakwaters

For the Duxbury Nook site marina complex, a breakwater is required to mitigate the force of wind and waves acting on boats within the basin. The breakwater also provides sufficient area for the pier and jetty fishing activities. As developed in Section 5.2.2, which compares key economic and ecologic costs for several sites, a breakwater 600 feet in length, 30 feet wide at the bottom, and 6 feet high is required and would cost $25,920.

5.6.6 Ramps

For the transient boating activities, one double width ramp is required to accommodate boats launched from trailers. In addition, the forklift for the dry-land berthing operation requires a ramp for launching and picking up boats when the tide is low in the hoisting well.

A type of ramp construction that requires minimum land area is selected.[99] The ramp is designed to be 35 feet in width, with an end depth of 3 feet and ramp gradient of 12 percent. The length of a ramp with these dimensions is calculated to be

[95] Square feet and cost for the fueling, boat rental, and dinghy storage docks taken from suitable examples in *ibid.*, Section 1.4.
[96] *Ibid.* [97] Unit costs are from *ibid.* [98] Costs are from *ibid.* [99] See *ibid.*, Section 1.7.

122 feet.[100] At an average cost of $100 per lineal foot of cement concrete surface,[101] the total cost of the ramp is $12,200.

5.6.7 Ice-Free System

Although we do not include an ice-free system in our marina complex, one might assume that a certain percentage of the home fleet boats would be winter stored on the premises—some of indoor storage, and some in outdoor storage. The older, wooden boats which dry out when stored out of water and perhaps boats devoted to winter sports-fishing activities could be assumed to require wet storage.

To prevent icing conditions in the dock area, an air-bubbling ice-free system could be installed. The cost would be $140 for each 30-foot boat and $180 for each 40-foot boat.[102]

5.6.8 Site Improvement

For the 395-boat marina complex, it is estimated that 13.5 acres of land are required to service the recreational activities programmed. Various operations are involved in the development of this land; namely, excavation, filling, paving, drainage, utility installation, landscaping, sewage treatment, and diverse construction.

EXCAVATION

Costs of excavation are included in the cost of utility installation. As far as can be determined there is on the site no rock to be removed that would necessitate undue expense.

FILL COSTS

Fill costs along with paving costs is a major site improvement cost item. Since the site is low-lying marshland and since the level of the finished site must be above high-tide level, the area that needs filling is taken to be two-thirds of the land area, or 10.8 acres. The average depth to be filled is 4 feet.

Thus the volume of fill required is 69,522 cubic yards. Since we can assume that roughly 46,500 cubic yards of fill will be from basin dredging spoil, we need on net only 23,022 cubic yards. (This latter fill will be placed over the dredging spoil fill, and thereby be suitable for a paving base.) At an estimated cost of $3.50 per cubic yard, total fill costs are $80,297.

PAVING COSTS

Paving costs depend on the parking area requirements, which are 364,520 square feet (see Table 5.5i). In addition to the parking area, somewhat less than 1 acre is allotted for general circulation. In total, we estimate that 44,972 square yards are to be paved. This operation requires 6,425 tons of bituminous concrete, which at a cost of $8.00 per ton when put in place involves a total cost of $51,400.[103]

We estimate that improvements on existing roads and possible additions might cost an amount equal to the construction cost of one-quarter mile of a new road. This amount is $20,650.

DRAINAGE AND UTILITIES

Drainage costs and costs of utility installation cover facilities for fire protection water lines, outdoor lighting, electrical lines, storm drainage, and sewage collection lines. We estimate these costs at $1,000 per acre; the total is therefore $13,500.

[100] See *ibid.* for a full discussion of the procedure.
[101] *Ibid.*
[102] Costs for different length boats are from *ibid.*
[103] See *ibid.* [24], Section 1.10.

LANDSCAPING

Landscaping costs for 2 acres of the site in and around parking and walkway areas is estimated to be $14,076.

SEWAGE SYSTEMS

Sewage system costs and requirements are estimated in Section 5.2 to be $11,250.

FUELING FACILITIES

Fueling facilities for a 395-boat marina require four separate installations, since several types of fuel and separate locations to avoid congestion are desirable.[104] Each fueling facility costs approximately $4,000, yielding $16,000 as total cost.

The full list of site-improvement costs is given in Table 5.6c.[105]

Table 5.6c Site-Improvement Costs for the Marina Complex

Cost Item	Quantity	Unit Cost	Total
Fill	22,942 cu. yd.	$ 3.50	$ 80,297
Paving	6,425 tons	8.00	51,400
Drainage and utility installation	13.5 acres	1,000.00	13,500
Landscaping			
Fine grade	2.0 acres	1,650.00	
Top soil		4,200.00	
Seeding		688.00	
Trees		500.00	
		$7,038.00	14,076
Road improvements		(lump sum)	20,650
Sewage system		(lump sum)	11,250
Fueling facilities	4	4,000.00	16,000
Total Site Improvement Cost			$207,173

5.6.9 Equipment and Boats

BOAT-HANDLING EQUIPMENT

In order to haul and launch boats and help service the dry-land berthing operation, a vertical lift wheeled sling hoist and two forklift trucks are required. For general yard use one truck and boat trailer are required together with five boat trailers for rental purposes.

The cost of these equipment items depends on the length and types of boats to be handled. We here specify the size of equipment required in terms of the weight of the longest boat to be serviced.[106]

Since the longest boat in the home fleet to be handled is 40 feet (possibly 50 feet), and weighs approximately 22 tons, we specify that the vertical lift wheeled hoist have a capacity of 25 tons. Since the longest motorboat in the dry-land berthing operation is 25 feet and weighs 6 tons, we specify that the fork lift have a capacity of 8 tons. Also, we specify that the general yard trailer and 3 of the rental trailers be able to handle 25-foot boats, and the other 2 rental trailers be able to handle 20-foot

[104] Refer to *ibid.*, Section 1.8.
[105] Refer to *ibid.*, Section 1.10.
[106] Weight of boats are determined in *ibid.* [24], Section 1.6.

Table 5.6d Unit Costs of Boat-Handling Equipment

Type of Equipment (1)	Purchase Price (2)	Installation (3)	Shipping Charge (4)	Total Unit Cost (5)
Vertical lift wheeled sling hoist, 25 ton	$20,425	$8,000	$500	$28,925
1 new forklift, 8 ton	16,500	—	—	16,500
Used forklift, 8 ton	6,500	—	—	6,500
Heavy duty pickup truck	4,000	—	—	4,000
Boat trailers (for 25-foot boats)	560	—	20	580
Boat trailers (for 20-foot boats)	364	—	20	384

boats. The unit costs of these items of equipment are given in Table 5.6d.[107]

Since only one of each of the above items is required, except for boat trailers, and since 4 boat trailers to handle 25-foot boats and 2 boat trailers to handle 20-foot boats are required, total costs of boat-handling equipment comes to $59,013.

WORK AND PARTY BOAT COSTS

For servicing the 395-boat marina it is estimated that 3 workboats will be required. One heavy-duty workboat is needed for shifting boats, firefighting, patrol, towing, and salvage functions. Two light-duty workboats are required for servicing the rental boat operation and providing launch service to moored boats.

Two party boats are required to service the level of sports-fishing activity in the marina complex. Party boat and workboat costs are presented in Table 5.6e.[108]

Table 5.6e Party Boat and Workboat costs

Type of Boat; Length (1)	Type of Construction (2)	Power (3)	Equipment (4)	Cost (5)
One heavy duty workboat, 25 foot	Wood	Gasoline	Towing, fire-fighting	$15,000
One light duty workboat, "Boston Whaler," 13 feet 9 in.	Fiberglass reinforced plastic	Outboard	Steering station	1,120
One light duty workboat, 18-foot skiff	Wood	Outboard	Steering station	760
Two party boats, 40 foot	Wood	Diesel	All necessary for C.G. inspection; @ $35,000	70,000
Total				$86,880

RENTAL BOAT COSTS

We estimate that a total of 48 boats will be required for rental purposes. Of these, 12 are rowboats, 12 are rowboats with motors (small outboards), 12 are medium-size outboards, and 12 are sailboats. Further details and costs of these boats are given in Table 5.6f.

[107] Vertical lift wheeled sling hoist and forklift costs from *ibid*. Pickup truck cost estimated by authors. Boat trailer costs at retail prices, discounted to wholesale, are calculated from *ibid*.

[108] Heavy-duty workboat costs from *ibid*. [24], Section 1.11.

Table 5.6f Rental Boat Costs

Type (1)	Construction Material (2)	Unit Cost[a] (w/motor) (3)	Number (4)	Total Cost (5)
Rowboats 14 ft. "Cape Dory"	Fiberglass reinforced plastic	$ 475	12	$ 5,700
Rowboats w/motors 12 ft. "Alumnacraft"	Aluminum	634	12	7,608
Outboards 13 ft. 3 in. "Boston Whaler"	Fiberglass reinforced plastic	1,120	12	13,440
Small sailboats 15 ft. "Mercury" dinghy	Fiberglass reinforced plastic	1,258	6	7,548
Larger sailboats 19 ft. "Lightning" planing boat	Fiberglass reinforced plastic	3,050	6	18,300
Total				$52,596

[a]Rental boat costs from Tatlock [24] Section 1.12.

5.6.10 Land

For the 395-boat marina complex, our computations, based on land input requirements per unit level of activity and on the levels of activities specified in Table 5.5d, indicate that a total of 13.5 acres of land are required. The assessed valuation per acre of land for most of the 13.5-acre site required by the marina complex is $900, not including any buildings on the site. The market value is assumed to be $1,530 per acre for most of the acreage. At this market price, the 13.5 acres cost $20,655. If we assume that one building is on the site, and also that the price of land is considerably higher if all 13.5 acreas are to be assembled as one contiguous piece with proper dimensions, the cost of the land (including building) is $67,500.

5.6.11 Building Construction

Having determined square feet of land required for diverse activities, we now estimate the cost of constructing the buildings.[109] From Table 5.5i we obtain the space requirements indicated in column 2 of Table 5.6g.

For boat and motor sales, which require 2,650 square feet, we estimate the cost per square foot to be $9.00. This estimate lies within a range of costs quoted on the construction of typical "automotive sales" space. We estimate furnishings at $2,000.

For marine accessory sales, the cost for a 750-square-foot space is $11.00 per square foot. This higher unit cost figure reflects the larger amount of built-in equipment required for this type of sales compared to boat sales. Since a fair amount of sales counters, display fixtures, etc., are required, we estimate furnishings at $6,000.

For restroom-lounge space, we estimate the cost at the relatively high figure of

[109] Square-foot costs and some furnishings costs estimated from *ibid.*, Section 1.9.

Table 5.6g Square-Feet and Construction Costs, By Type Building Space

Type of Space (1)	Square Feet Required (2)	Square-Foot Cost (3)	Furnishings (4)	Total Costs (5)
Boat and motor sales	2,650	$ 9.00	$ 2,000	$ 25,850
Marine accessory sales	750	11.00	6,000	14,250
Restrooms and lounge	1,750	13.00	8,000	30,750
Gear storage	900	6.00	8,000	13,400
Administration	440	14.00	4,000	10,160
Transient and rental office	220	10.00	1,000	3,200
Fuel sales	110	10.00	800	1,900
Bait and packaged food sales	550	10.00	2,000	7,500
Indoor storage				
Single level	32,095	4.00	—	128,380
Triple level	4,260	4.50	32,000	51,170
	36,355			
Repair services	5,413	18.00	8,000	105,434
Total				$391,994

$13.00 per square foot. This figure reflects a fair number of luxury items. Fixtures (toilets, washbowls, etc., as well as sofas, soft chairs, etc.) are estimated at $8,000.

For gear storage, which is within the restroom-lounge area, we estimate the cost per square foot at $6.00. This figure reflects minimum structural needs. Two hundred lockers at $40.00 each cost $8,000.

For administrative space, the cost is set at $14.00 per square foot. This figure covers a fair amount of luxury-type items and materials. The figure of $14.00 is within the range of relevant quotations. Furnishings are estimated to cost $4,000.

For transient and rental office space, with minimum interior finish, the cost is set at $10.00 per square foot. The minimum cost for furnishings is $1,000.

For fuel sales space and bait and packaged food sales space, the cost per square foot is the same as for transient and rental office space. For fuel sales, furnishings are costed at $800 (exclusive of fueling equipment recorded elsewhere). For bait and packaged food sales, furnishings include sales counter, some refrigeration equipment for storing bait, and so on. Their cost is set at $2,000.

For indoor storage space, the cost per square foot of $4.00 for single-level storage is based on a manufacturer's quotation and published materials. The low cost is mainly due to the large floor area of the storage facility. Similarly, triple-level storage space, within the same building, is set at $4.50 per square foot. Triple-level storage space, however, does require boat racks, which for 4,260 square feet of space are estimated to cost $32,000.

Finally, for repair service space, the cost of $18.00 per square foot is based on a study of automotive maintenance shops at military installations, a similar type facility.[110] The cost is consistent with the scale of operations envisaged (since these costs do vary significantly with scale), and are adjusted to reflect New England prices. The cost of furnishings is based on published materials and judgment of the authors and is set at $8,000.

With the above square-foot and furnishing costs, we derive column 5 of Table 5.6g. Total building costs (inclusive of furnishings) are estimated to be $391,994.

[110] Costs adjusted for New England prices from procedure outlined in National Construction Estimator [17], pp. 175–177.

5.6.12 Total Capital Cost and Non-Recurring Planning Costs

The capital costs by item discussed above are now listed in column 2 of Table 5.6h. Their total is $1,616,905. In addition to these capital costs, which involve

Table 5.6h Capital Cost, Depreciation Rate, and Annual Depreciation by Item

Item (1)		Capital Cost (400-Boat Marina) (2)	Depreciation Rate (3)		Annual Depreciation (4)
1. Moorings		$ 4,253	7%		$ 298
2. Shore protection		211,600	6		12,696
3. Dredging		302,000	7		21,140
4. Docks		195,776	6		11,747
5. Breakwaters		25,920	5		1,296
6. Ramps		12,200	7		854
7. Ice-free system		0	0		0
8. Site improvement					
Fill	$80,297		0	$ 0	
Paving	51,400		10	5,140	
Utility / Drainage	13,500		6	810	
Landscaping	14,076		0	0	
Access road	20,650		6	1,239	
Sewage system	11,250		6	675	
Fueling facilities	16,000		12	1,920	
		207,173			9,784
9. Equipment and boats					
Boat-handling equipment	59,013		10	5,901	
Work and party boats	86,880		7	6,082	
Rental boats	52,596		10	5,260	
		198,489			17,243
10. Land		67,500	0		0
11. Building construction					
Boat and motor sales	25,850				
Marine accessory sales	14,250				
Restrooms and lounge	30,750				
Gear storage	13,400				
Administration	10,160				
Transient and rental office	3,200				
Fuel sales	1,900				
Boat and packaged food sales	7,500				
Indoor storage—single level	128,380				
Indoor storage—triple level	51,170				
Repair services	105,434				
		391,994	6		23,520
Grand Total		$1,616,905			$98,578

land, buildings, improvement on land and water area, and equipment, there is one additional cost that is not strictly a capital cost. However, it is a non-recurring cost which must be met initially. This is the planning cost.

Planning costs are estimated as follows:

Topographic surveys, at $50/acre	$ 675
Soil-borings, involving 5 days work at $583/day	2,915
Hydrographic surveys, with reference to 11 acres of water basin and channel area, at $40/acre	440
Meteorological consultation, 3 days at $160/day	480
Building permits at standard rates	1,019
Master planning at approximately 5 percent of construction and improvement cost (excluding boats, equipment, and land)	68,000
Total	$73,529

Thus, the total of capital cost and non-recurring planning costs is $1,690,434.

5.7 *Annual Costs*

With the estimates presented in the previous sections, we can proceed to the calculation of annual costs. They are presented by major item in Table 5.7a.

Table 5.7a Annual Costs for 395-Boat Marina complex

Fixed	
Depreciation	$ 98,578
Taxes on land and structures	35,000
Insurance	5,852
Public relations	3,000
Operating	
Labor	197,600
Utilities	11,650
Maintenance and supplies	66,567
Total	$418,247

5.7.1 Annual Depreciation Costs

The calculation of annual depreciation costs for the marina complex is based on published materials[111] and the judgement of the authors. These costs are based on annual rates of depreciation as listed in column 3 of Table 5.6h. The rates are depreciation rates, determined by simple division of 100 percent by the expected life of the facility, improvement, or equipment. In some cases, we use rates somewhat higher than the standard accounting rates; for example, our rates on buildings and structures are 6 percent whereas standard rates as published are 4 percent; our rates on paving are 10 percent, standard rates as published are 5 percent. We use higher rates in order to reflect a somewhat higher quality of services to be offered by the marina as well as to recognize the nonstatic nature of the demand for diverse types of recreational services.

In Table 5.6h, the annual depreciation rates listed in column 3 are applied to the capital costs of column 2 of that table to yield annual depreciation charges recorded in column 4 of that table. The sum of the charges in column 4 is $98,578 and represents the annual depreciation cost set down in Table 5.7a.

[111] See Tatlock [24], Section 2.4, for a more complete listing of depreciation rates.

5.7.2 Annual Taxes

The land and structures, inclusive of site improvement, are valued for tax purposes at approximately $1.4 million. On the basis of limited data and interviewing in an unpublished marina study for Salem, Massachusetts, we set the effective tax rate at $2\frac{1}{2}$ percent. We recognize that this rate varies greatly from locality to locality in an irregular, unpredictable fashion. Because of the possibility of special rates and of diverse political factors, it is not possible to set any firm rate for an area, particularly when it is subject to significant change in land use. Annual taxes are estimated to amount to $35,000.

5.7.3 Insurance

We obtain total annual insurance costs by summing the costs of the following six insurance items.[112]

Fire Insurance on Buildings. At a rate of $0.60 per $100 valuation, and at the valuation of $392,000 (replacement value), this insurance amounts to $2,352.

Ship Repairer's Liability. For the protection of customers' boats while they are being repaired, a rate of 1 percent of annual gross revenue from repairs and outfitting service—namely, $90,000—yields an annual cost of $900.

Motor Vehicle Coverage. For liability and property damage for the truck and eight boat trailers owned by the marine complex, we take the annual cost of insurance to be approximately $400.

Personal and Indemnity. For this insurance protection, we take the cost to be $1,000 annually.

Boat Dealer's and Commercial Hull Policies. The total for these two insurance items is estimated at roughly $1,200 per annum.

Annual insurance costs add up to $5,852.

5.7.4 Public Relations

A reasonable annual expense for this item, including advertising and promotional activities, is $3,000.

Table 5.7b Number of Employees, Salaries, and Labor Costs by Type for a 395-Boat Marina Complex

Type of Employee	Number of Employees	Annual Salary	Annual Cost
Manager	1	$16,000	$ 16,000
Bookkeeper	$1\frac{1}{3}$	6,000	8,000
Secretary	$\frac{1}{2}$	6,000	3,000
Dockmaster	1	10,500	10,500
Dock attendant	3	7,500	22,500
Equipment operators	2	7,500	15,000
Sales manager (boat)	1	14,000	14,000
Salesman (boat)	1	12,000	12,000
Party-boat crew	$2\frac{1}{2}$	13,440	33,600
Sales manager (marine supplies)	1	9,000	9,000
Salesman (marine supplies)	$\frac{1}{3}$	9,000	3,000
Salesman (bait, packaged food)	$\frac{2}{3}$	9,000	6,000
Mechanic	2	9,000	18,000
Carpenter	2	9,000	18,000
Painter	1	9,000	9,000
Total			$197,600

[112] See *ibid.*, Section 2.3, for further details concerning rates and guidelines for the determination of insurance costs.

5.7.5 Annual Labor Costs

From Section 5.5.17 we obtain the number and type of employees as listed in Table 5.7b. At the salary rates indicated, some of which are based on reported wages and salaries for the Northeast region[113] and some on staff judgement, we derive total labor costs as indicated in the last column of Table 5.7b. Our wages and salaries are set at a level somewhat higher than that prevailing at existing quality marinas for year 1968.

5.7.6 Annual Costs of Utilities

In column 1 of Table 5.7c, annual costs of utilities (primarily consisting of water, electricity, and telephone) are listed by type of revenue-yielding operation. (Certain minor utility costs are not specifically listed since in our marina complex they are associated with nonrevenue-yielding operations such as pier and jetty fishing. However, these costs are negligible.) The utilities cost for each revenue-yielding operation was estimated on the basis of staff judgement. Total annual cost for utilities is estimated at $11,650, and recorded in Table 5.7a.

Table 5.7c Costs of Utilities, Costs of Maintenance and Supplies, and Revenues, by Revenue-Yielding Operation

Revenue-Yielding Operation	Cost of Utilities (1)	Costs of Maintenance and Supplies (2)	Revenue (3)
1. Slip rentals	$ 3,000	$13,760	$ 86,040
2. Moorings	—	533	4,050
3. Dry-land berthing rentals	500	4,300	26,880
4. Boat storage			
Indoor	500	4,320	27,000
Outdoor	—	2,688	16,800
Wet	—	—	—
5. Boat handling			
Hauling and launching	} 500 (Hauling and launching, Trailer rental, Ramp use)	1,152	7,200
Trailer rental		813	4,650
Ramp use		441	8,820
6. Boat rental	250	12,560	60,264
7. Boat, motor and trailer sales, new	2,000	6,000	99,844
8. Boat, motor, and trailer sales, used	—	2,500	12,000
9. Party-boat fishing	300	7,000	56,000
10. Marine accessory supplies	1,000	4,000	36,000
11. Repair and outfitting services	3,000	5,000	60,000
12. Packaged food and bait sales	500	1,000	27,000
13. Fuel and other product sales	100	500	11,270
14. Snack bar and laundry service	—	—	3,000
15. Gear storage rent	—	—	5,000
Totals	$11,650	$66,567	$551,818

5.7.7 Annual Costs of Maintenance and Supplies

In column 2 of Table 5.7c, annual costs of maintenance and supplies (excluding inventories) are listed by type of revenue-yielding operation. (Again, certain minor

[113] See *ibid.*, Section 3.1.

costs are not specifically listed since in our marina complex they are associated with nonrevenue-yielding operations such as pier and jetty fishing. However, these costs are negligible.) For some of the operations, data on costs are available in the published literature.[114] These data are usually employed. Items for which data are not available are estimated on the basis of staff judgement. The total annual cost of maintenance and supplies is set at $66,567.

5.7.8 Total Annual Costs

We are now in a position to estimate total annual cost for the 395-boat marina complex. Each cost item has been estimated and recorded in Table 5.7a. Their sum is $418,247.

5.8 *Revenue Analysis for the 395-Boat Marina Complex*

In this section, we set down estimated revenues for the 395-boat marina complex. In Section 5.10 we shall consider revenues for marinas of other sizes. We discuss each revenue-yielding operation in order, as listed in Table 5.7c.

5.8.1 Seasonal and Transient Slip Rentals

Of the 395 boats in the home fleet of the marina complex, it is estimated that 300 will require slip rental service over a 150-day season. Therefore, dock area for 300 boats has been provided and costed in Section 5.6 on capital cost. Two major factors bear on estimating revenues from this service. One relates to average lengths and numbers of boats, and the other to the rates charged for seasonal and transient use.

Table 5.8a Revenues from Seasonal Slip Rentals

Length Range (1)	Average Length (2)	Number of Boats (3)	Rate per Boat per Season (4)	Seasonal Slip Revenue (5)
10–20 ft.	15 ft.	150	$200	$30,000
20–30	25	90	300	27,000
30–40	35	60	420	25,200
Total				$82,200

In Table 5.8a we set down in column 3 the number of boats estimated for each of the length ranges listed in column 1. The average length is noted in column 2. The season rate to be charged boats in each length range is indicated in column 4. (These rates are adjusted to depict New England conditions and are relatively high, reflecting in part a high quality of service to be offered;[115] the rates include normal services such as water and electrical power.) Revenues from each length range of boats is given in column 5. Total revenue is estimated at $82,200 annually.

For estimating revenues from transient slip rentals, we posit that, on the average, 5 slips are available and are rented on a daily basis. This assumes that 5 home-fleet boats will either be cruising or be on shore for repairs during each day, thereby

[114] See Section 5.5 of this book, and Tatlock [24], Section 6.

[115] See Tatlock [24], Section 4.1, for high and average rate determination guidelines. Rates are for the North Atlantic region.

leaving 5 slips free for transient use. If the slips are rented to larger boats which tend to cruise more extensively, a daily rate of $6.40 appears reasonable. Over a 120-day season, there will then be 600 rentals, which at the daily rate of $6.40 yield an additional rental of $3,840.[116]

The sum of seasonal and transient slip rentals on an annual basis is $86,040. This figure is entered in column 3 of Table 5.7c.

5.8.2 Seasonal and Transient Mooring Rentals

Of the 395 boats in the marina complex, it is estimated that 15 seasonal boats will require mooring rental services. At a season rate of $150 per boat, the 15 seasonal boats generate revenue of $2,250. Additionally, we estimate that on the average 5 transients will require mooring service per day. At a rate of $3.00 per day, for a 120-day season, mooring rentals from transient boats amount to $1,800.[117] In sum, seasonal and transient mooring rentals yield $4,050 annual revenue. Again, this figure is entered in column 3 of Table 5.7c.

5.8.3 Dry-Land Berthing Rentals

Of the 395 boats in the home fleet of the marina complex, it is estimated that 80 outboard, inboard, and small sailboats of 25 feet and less will require dry-land berthing service. For estimation purposes, we assume an average length of a boat to be 20 feet. The yearly rate for this service is set at a figure equal to 80 percent of the sum of the charge a boat would normally pay to rent a slip and rent indoor storage space. The seasonal slip rental rate is set at $240[118] for boats not exceeding 25 feet, and the indoor storage rate is set at $180.[119] Eighty percent of the sum of these two rates is $336. For 80 boats, we obtain $26,880.

5.8.4 Indoor and Outdoor Boat-Storage Revenues

The marina complex provides for winter storing of boats, indoors and outdoors.

Table 5.8b Revenues from Indoor and Outdoor Boat Storage

Boat Length Range (1)	Average Boat Length (2)	Number of Boats (3)	Season Rate (4)	Season Revenue (5)
		a. Indoor Storage		
10–20 ft.	15 ft.	60	$130	$ 7,800
20–30	25	40	180	7,200
30–40	35	40	300	12,000
Subtotal				$27,000
		b. Outdoor Storage		
10–20	15	60	$ 80	$ 4,800
20–30	25	40	120	4,800
30–40	35	40	180	7,200
Subtotal				$16,800

[116] Rates are determined from North Atlantic region data reported in *ibid.*, Section 4.1. They are also consistent with locally charged rates.

[117] Rates from *ibid.*, Section 4.2. [118] Rate estimated from data in *ibid.*, Section 4.1.

[119] Storage rate estimated from *ibid.*, Section 4.3.

In the particular complex under study, we do not allow for any wet storage that an ice-free system would permit.

For estimating revenue, we classify boats into three average lengths, as given in column 2 of Table 5.8b for the boat length ranges given in column 1. We then list in column 4 the relevant rates per boat for the storage operation, the highest being for indoor storage.[120] Multiplying the numbers of boats in column 3 by the rates of column 4 yields the revenues of column 5. Adding the revenue subtotals from each storage operation yields the sum of $43,800, annually.

5.8.5 Boat-Handling Revenues

Hauling and Launching. Hauling and launching services are to be provided for boats primarily within the 20–40 foot range. Smaller boats can be quickly hauled by forklift truck, or from the ramp by the boat owner. The smaller boats do not generate any revenue here.

While not all boats in the 20–40 foot range will use the marina's hauling and launching equipment, most will. At the same time, a substantial number of transient boats will require use of this equipment for repair services. Hence, we assume that the number of boats which will require both hauling and launching will be approximately equal to the number of boats in the 20–40 foot range to be stored on the premises, either indoors or outdoors. The number of boats in the two length ranges, 20–30 foot and 30–40 foot, which average 25 and 35 feet respectively, are listed in column 2 of Table 5.8c. Multiplying the rate for launching or hauling in column 3,[121] by the number of boats, yields the estimated launching and hauling revenues of columns 4 and 5. They total $7,200.

Table 5.8c Revenues from Launching and Hauling

Average Length (1)	Number of Boats (2)	Rate: Launching or Hauling (3)	Launching Revenues (4)	Hauling Revenues (5)
25 foot	80	$18.75	$1,500	$1,500
35 foot	80	26.25	2,100	2,100
Total			$3,600	$3,600

Boat Trailer Rental. It is estimated that three boat trailers each capable of handling 25 foot boats, and two trailers, each capable of handling 20-foot boats, are needed for a boat-trailer rental operation. Both trailer sizes are assumed to rent at the same rate. On the assumption that each of the five trailers will be rented 60 times per year on a full-day basis at $14.00, and 10 times per year on a half-day basis at $9.00,[122] each trailer yields a revenue of $930. The revenue for the five trailers is then $4,650.

Ramp Use Charges. For the transient outboard boating activities, we have already projected a demand for 13,230 man-days. (See Table 5.3j in Section 5.3.) At three men per boat this yields 4,410 boat uses per year. At a daily rate (covering both in-and-out use) of $2.00,[123] total gross revenue is $8,820.

5.8.6 Boat Rentals

A total of 48 boats has been specified to service the boat rental activities in the

[120] Rates are from data in *ibid.*, for the North Atlantic region.
[121] Rates from *ibid.*, Section 6.6. Rates are computed at a low figure of $0.75 per lineal foot.
[122] Rates from data in *ibid.* [123] Rate from data in *ibid.*

marina complex. We have classified the boats as follows: 12 rowboats; 12 rowboats with engines; 12 small outboards; and 12 sailboats. We assume that on the average each boat is in full use 4½ days per week, over a 12-week season. Each boat then is used 54 times per season; and the twelve boats of any given type are used a total of 648 times. Approximate daily rates by type of boat are listed in column 3 of Table 5.8d. The rates selected are rather high as daily rates. They partly reflect the higher

Table 5.8d Revenues from Boat Rentals

Boat Types (1)	Number of Days Usage for 12 Boats (2)	Rental Rate per Boat per Day (3)	Season Revenues (4)
Rowboats	648	$10	$ 6,480
Rowboats with engine	648	22	14,256
Small outboards	648	25	16,200
Sailboats	648	36	23,328
Total			$60,264

revenues obtainable by renting boats on an hourly basis, particularly on weekends. Also, the higher rates tend to compensate for the relatively short season assumed.[124] When these rates are multiplied by number of days of use per season, we obtain the revenue yields listed in column 4.

5.8.7 Revenues from New-Boat, Motor and Trailer Sales

Boat Sales. In the discussion in Section 5.5 on required land inputs for sales and showroom facilities, we provide for 1,900 square feet of boat sales display area. This area displays two 30-foot boats and four 20-foot boats.

It has already been indicated that 40 boat sales might be made during the course of the year. In view of the composition of the marina home fleet, a reasonable breakdown of sales by length and type of boat is indicated in column 3 of Table 5.8e. The 1968 retail selling price[125] of each length and type of boat is indicated in column 4 of the table, while gross revenues from boat sales of each length and type are indicated in the last column.

Table 5.8e Gross Revenues from Sales of New Boats

Boat Types (1)	Average Boat Length (2)	Number of Sales (3)	Retail Selling Price (4)	Gross Sales (5)
Outboard	15 ft.	10	$ 1,050	$ 10,500
Inboard runabout	20	9	5,000	45,000
Inboard cruisers	25	8	7,500	60,000
Cruising sail	30	4	12,000	48,000
Inboard cruisers	30	6	14,500	87,000
Inboard cruisers	35	3	24,500	73,500
Total		40		$324,000

Motor Sales. Motors may be classified into outboard motors, inboard gasoline engines (including outdrive engines), and inboard diesel engines. We estimate the number of sales for a current year on the basis that outboard motors of home-fleet

[124] Rates are from *ibid.*, Section 5.1.

[125] Retail prices from *ibid.*, Section 6.2. Prices of outboard boats do not include outboard motors; all others include motors.

boats would be traded for larger models every 3 to 5 years, and that some inboard gasoline engines are replaced by diesel units when boats are repowered. We estimate that 50 outboard and 16 inboard motors will be sold annually of the type and average horsepower indicated in columns 1, 2, and 3 of Table 5.8f. At the retail selling prices in column 4,[126] the gross revenues from sales are listed in the last column.

Table 5.8f Gross Revenues from Sales of New Inboard and Outboard Motors

Engine Type (1)	Average Horsepower (2)	Number of Sales (3)	Retail Selling Price (4)	Gross Sales (5)
Outboard	60	30	$ 780	$23,400
Outboard	100	20	1,240	24,800
Gasoline inboard	185	10	1,500	15,000
Diesel inboard	125	6	3,000	18,000
Total		66		$81,200

Trailer Sales. We assume that a dozen trailers capable of handling 15-foot boats and a dozen more capable of handling 25-foot boats will be sold annually. At retail prices of $400 and $800, respectively, this yields gross sales revenue of $4,800 and $9,600, respectively.[127]

Net Revenues from Boat, Motor, and Trailer Sales. Although margins set on boats, motors, and trailers vary considerably among manufacturers and under different circumstances, we present in column 3 of Table 5.8g the margins on sales prices we find reasonable from a study of the published literature. When these margins[128] are applied to the gross sales of column 2, they yield the net revenues of column 4. All told, net revenues amount to $99,844.

Table 5.8g Net Revenues from Sales of New Boats, Motors, and Trailers

Item (1)	Gross Sales (2)	Margin (3)	Net Revenue (4)	
15-ft. Outboard boat	$10,500	30%	$ 3,150	
20-ft. Inboard runabout	45,000	25	11,250	
25-ft. Inboard cruisers	60,000	20	12,000	
30-ft. Cruising sailboats	48,000	23	11,040	
30-ft. Inboard cruisers	87,000	20	17,400	
35-ft. Inboard cruisers	73,500	20	14,700	
				69,540
60-Hp. Outboard motor	23,400	32	7,488	
100-Hp. Outboard motor	24,800	32	7,936	
185-Hp. Gasoline inboard	15,000	32	4,800	
125-Hp. Diesel inboard	18,000	32	5,760	
				25,984
15-ft. Boat trailer	4,800	30	1,440	
25-ft. Boat trailer	9,600	30	2,880	
				4,320
Total				$99,844

[126] Outboard motor prices from *ibid.* Inboard engine costs from *Boat Owners' Buyers Guide, 1967*, [1] pp 146–152.

[127] Retail selling prices from Tatlock [24], Section 6.2.

[128] Margins are from guidelines presented in *ibid.*, Section 3.5.

5.8.8 Revenues from Used Boat, Motor and Trailer Sales

Gross sales of used boats of diverse length and type are estimated to reach $65,000, approximately 20 percent of gross sales of new boats, motors, and trailers. At a 10 percent margin on gross sales, net revenue is $6,500.

Gross sales of used motors of diverse horsepower and type are estimated at $17,000, somewhat more than 20 percent of gross sales of new motors. At a 20 percent margin on gross sales, net revenue is $3,400.

Gross sales of used trailers of diverse type are estimated at $7,000, somewhat less than 50 percent of gross sales of new trailers. At a 30 percent margin on gross sales, net revenue is $2,100.[129]

In total, net revenues from these three categories of sales is $12,000.

5.8.9 Party-Boat Revenues

Two boats, 40 feet long, are necessary to service the party-boat sports-fishing activities in the marina complex. We assume that the boats average 140 trips per season with an average of 25 persons per boat trip; hence they provide 7,000 man-days of recreation. With new equipment and a relatively large crew, a reasonable rate would be $8.00 per person per day.[130] Accordingly, a revenue of $56,000 is anticipated.

5.8.10 Revenues from Marine Accessory Supplies

On the basis of a survey of 97 marine facility installations,[131] it is found that gross sales for marine accessory supplies constitute about 54 percent of the sum of slip rentals (inclusive of mooring charges and dry-land berthing rentals) and indoor and outdoor storage revenues. In Table 5.7c, we estimate this sum to be $160,770. Taking 54 percent of this sum yields $86,816. We then can approximate gross sales in this category at roughly $90,000. At the established 1968 margin of 40 percent,[132] these gross sales yield a net revenue of $36,000.

5.8.11 Revenues from Repairs and Outfitting Services

Again, on the basis of the survey of 97 marine facility installations, it is found that gross revenues from repairs and outfitting services are 54 per cent of the sum of slip rentals (inclusive of mooring charges and dry-land berthing rentals) and indoor and outdoor storage revenues. This yields again approximate gross sales of $90,000.

Recall that we assumed that all boats of the seasonal home fleet would be in the repair shop for five days, and be actively worked on for three days (including hull, engine, and outboard motor repair). If we divide the gross sales, $90,000, by 395 boats, we obtain on the average an expense of $228 per boat. This average figure, which we take also to include installation charges on new engines, appears reasonable in view of the fact that the 20–30 foot and 30–40 foot boats require considerably more maintenance than the smaller boats.

While gross revenues from repairs and outfitting services may thus be set at $90,000 for our 395-boat marina complex, we estimate that an expense of $30,000 will be incurred for purchase of parts.[133] Thus, revenues net of parts is $60,000.

[129] See *ibid.*, Section 3.6, for further details concerning margins and Section 6.3. concerning sales.

[130] Rate from data in *ibid.*, Section 5.2

[131] See Table 2 in *ibid.* for data relative to the survey.

[132] See data in Section 3.4, in *ibid.*

[133] See data in *ibid.*, Section 3.8, for details concerning amount of parts and supplies for this revenue-yielding operation.

5.8.12 Revenues from Packaged Food and Bait Sales

Again, from the survey cited above, gross sales of packaged food and bait may be taken to be 27 percent of slip rentals (inclusive of mooring charges and dry-land berthing rentals) and indoor and outdoor storage revenues. In Table 5.7c we estimate this sum to be $160,770. Taking 27 percent of this sum yields $43,400, or roughly $45,000 as sales. From this $45,000 figure must be deducted cost of merchandise sold—namely, $18,000—which yields a net revenue of $27,000.[134]

5.8.13 Revenues from Fuel Sales

From the discussion in Section 5.5.16 a set of fuel input requirements was derived for the activities in our marina complex. When these fuel inputs are multiplied by the relevant levels of activity, as indicated in Table 5.5d, column 3, we obtain a total fuel input of 269,251 gallons annually.

Taking into account the fact that some of these fuel inputs will be purchased at other locations, while concomitantly, boats associated with other sites will purchase fuel at our facility, we estimate that *on net* 80 percent of the total—namely, 215,400 gallons—will be purchased at our marina complex. At an average markup of 5 cents per gallon of fuel, we obtain a net revenue of $10,770.[135] New revenue from oil and other petroleum products might constitute roughly 5 percent of the net revenue from fuel sales—namely, $500.

5.8.14 Revenues from Concessions for a Snack Bar and Laundry

It is estimated that a snack bar seating 25 persons would be in a position to pay a concession fee of $2,000, representing a charge of 15 cents per customer meal for a 14-week season. It is estimated that a laundry having 10 washers and 5 driers would be in a position to pay a concession fee of $1,000 on gross sales of $4,000–$5,000.

5.8.15 Revenues from Gear Storage

The facility provides 200 lockers for storing gear. The charge for a locker might be $5.00 per month for a 5-month season. Accordingly, a revenue of $5,000 is anticipated.

5.8.16 Total Annual Revenues

We may now estimate total annual revenue for the 395-boat marina complex. Each main revenue item has been estimated and recorded in column 3, Table 5.7c. Their sum is $551,818.

[134] See *ibid.*, Section 3.9, for details concerning cost of merchandise for this revenue-yielding operation.

[135] See data in *ibid.*, Section 3.7.

5.9 *Net Annual Gains and Surplus for the 395-Boat Marina*

In Section 5.7 annual operating costs have been determined to be $418,247. These costs are strictly economic-type costs. To them must be added annual ecological costs, which in Section 5.2 have been estimated to be roughly $9,400.00. Total annual costs are then $427,647.

In Section 5.8 total revenues are estimated to be $551,818. The difference, which may be viewed either as gross profit or annual surplus, is $124,171. This gross profit or annual surplus contrasts with a total capital cost (investment) of $1,616,904. If to this capital cost is added the planning cost, estimated at $73,529, we obtain the more relevant total of $1,690,433. Therefore, gross profit or annual surplus represents 7.35 percent of total capital costs and planning costs. Observe that this figure does not include interest charges for any capital that may be borrowed or any charge for normal returns on capital that might be assigned to capital privately invested. If an economist, regional planner, or investment house were to judge 7.35 percent to be a reasonable interest rate, or normal return, or both, then the marina development is to be considered feasible. If 7.35 percent represents too low a return, then the marina development cannot be justified unless other social gains or ecological benefits, or both, can be identified as associated with it. If 7.35 percent represents too high a rate of return, then the marina development might be viewed as yielding a true economic profit or surplus.

Implicit in all these statements is the assumption that all other non-economic costs—social, political, ecological, etc.—are either negligible or fully offset by other gains not yet identified. These statements are contingent too on the validity of the numerous assumptions we have made.

5.10 *Costs, Revenues, and Profit (Surplus) at Alternative Scales of Operation*

Hitherto, we have treated the input structures and cost analysis in a form suggestive of the input-output technique. We have frequently alluded to this technique, and often have computed our coefficients on either a per unit basis, or a per man-day basis, having in mind, however, appropriate levels for the diverse activities. Such bases do imply constant production coefficients. Nonetheless, we performed our computations in this manner not only because it eased the calculation, but more important, because in general this computation procedure is used in the literature on marina operations and thus facilitates the problem of obtaining relevant data for an initial analysis.

It reality, however, constant coefficients do not obtain for many items. Therefore, we now wish to introduce certain key nonlinearities and consider their implications for major changes in scales of operation.

5.10.1 The Nook Site: The Data and Rates of Return

First, we develop the materials for the alternative involving a location at The Nook site with spoil removed from the harbor. We look at the input items within the various major cost categories: construction, equipment, labor, etc. At this time, we do not have production functions which describe how each input (and thus cost) might vary as the level of output and other inputs into any activity vary. All we can do at this time is to specify, in a highly simplified manner, scale factors analogous to those widely used in engineering fields (e.g., chemical engineering). We shall employ these factors in estimating how the cost of each capital item and each input might vary with change in the scale of output.

The concept of the scale factor has been used in studies using the activity complex model.[136] In this section, given the costs associated with a 400-boat capacity marina, estimates will be made of the costs and revenues of a 600- and 800-boat marina. It is to be expected that a number of capital inputs, labor inputs, and other necessary inputs do not vary proportionately with the scale of an activity. Thus, if the combined level of activity were to double, say, from a 400-boat marina to one oriented to 800 boats, the cost of various inputs for the 800-boat marina may be less than, more than, or equal to, twice the cost for a 400-boat marina. In such a case, there are, respectively, economies, diseconomies, or constant costs to scale.

The scale factor constitutes a fairly simple device to express the way in which cost elements vary with the scale of operation over some given range. It is assumed that the scales of operations considered here are within this range.

With regard to capital inputs, the formulation for estimating the cost of an 800-boat marina might be expressed as follows:

$$I = I_k \left(\frac{O}{O_k}\right)^\alpha$$

In this formula, I, which is to be estimated, represents the investment in some capital item for the 800-boat marina under consideration, O denotes the projected output or capacity corresponding to the 800-boat marina, and I_k represents the value of the required investment for the item in a marina with capacity O_k (400 boats). For this item, α represents the scale factor.[137]

The value of α varies from item to item. If the value of the exponent α were set at zero, then a case of pure economies would be involved; the total cost of the item would remain unchanged, regardless of the scale of operation. If the value of α were set at unity, then a doubling of scale would lead to a doubling of the cost of the capital input. With exponent values between zero and unity, the total cost of the capital item would increase proportionately less than the scale of output. With values greater than unity, the cost of the item would increase proportionately more than the scale of output.

To illustrate the use of the above formula, assume that the cost of some capital item for a marina of scale 400 boats has been valued at \$100,000. If we are interested in projecting the cost of this item for marinas of scale 800, and if the scale factor is 0.1, then we have:

$$I = I_k \left(\frac{O}{O_k}\right)^\alpha$$

$$I = \$100{,}000 \left(\frac{800}{400}\right)^{0.1}$$

$$I = \$107{,}000$$

The use of different scale factors is illustrated in Chart 5.10a. In this chart, the scale factor, α, is measured along the horizontal axis. Along the vertical, capital cost is measured. The lower line on the chart shows how for a 600-boat marina the capital cost of an item costing \$100,000 for a 400-boat marina would increase with increase in scale factor. The upper line shows how for an 800-boat marina the capital cost for this same item would increase with increase in scale factor.

Given the cost for the various capital items associated with the 400-boat marina in Table 5.6h, we now proceed to estimate the relevant costs for marinas of scale 600 and 800. As the scale factors are not known precisely, the illustrative use of this technique assigns each capital item to one of four scale factors. This assignment is shown in the left-hand tab of Table 5.10a.

[136] For example, see Isard, Schooler, and Vietorisz [11], and Isard and Schooler [10]. Although in Section 5.3, the size of the hypothetical marina was computed to be 395 boats, in this section that figure is rounded to 400 boats in order to simplify the computations and to illustrate better the techniques employed.

[137] This formulation is based on that used by Isard, Schooler, and Vietorisz [11], pp. 52–58.

Chart 5.10a Effect of Scale Factor on Capital Cost of a $100,000 Item

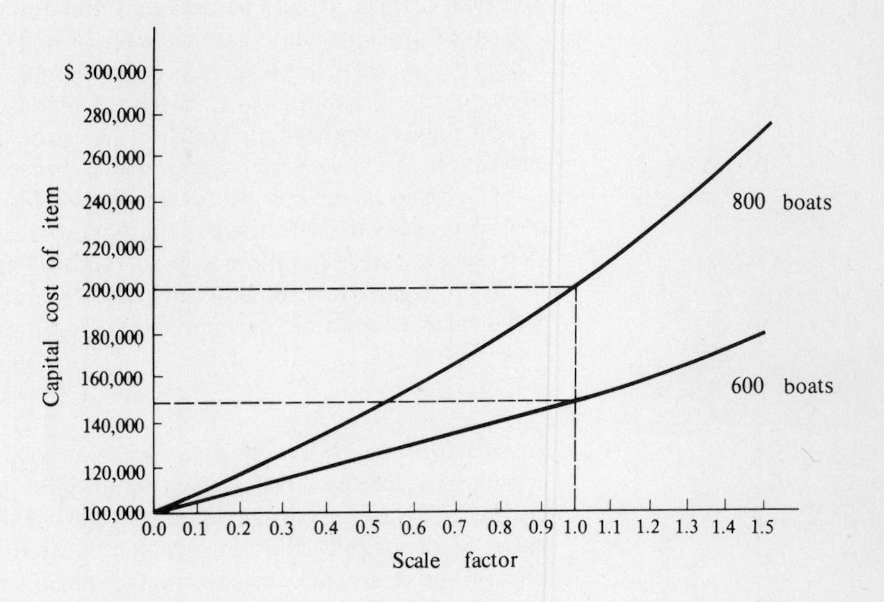

The lowest scale factor felt to be appropriate is 0.6. This factor is to be applied to the first group of capital items listed in Table 5.10a. For each item in this group, an increase in the scale of operation will lead to significantly less than proportional increases in its capital cost. Included in this group are such capital items as dredging, ramps, and the sewage disposal system.

The next scale factor used is 0.8. This factor is employed for capital items wherein moderate economies of scale are postulated to exist. Included in this group are such capital items as paving and docks.

A scale factor of unity signifies absence of either economies or diseconomies of scale. Where this factor applies to an item, the item, when calculated for a 600-boat marina, has a cost 1.5 times that for the 400-boat marina. A doubling of scale to 800 boats involves a doubling of capital cost over that of the 400-boat scale. The items included in this group are those which provide services which must proportionately increase with increase in output or which are directly linked to demand on a one-to-one basis. Among items in this category are moorings, shore protection, various types of boats, and storage area.

Finally, a scale factor of 1.2 is used for those items where diseconomies of scale are expected. The cost of these items increases more than proportionately with scale of operation. For example, since land prices might rise as larger contiguous parcels are needed, land is included in this category. Higher capacity and longer roads and utility lines are typically required as scale rises, and so roads and utilities are put in this group. Finally, it is judged that in order to provide a larger turning basin, deeper waters would be encountered. Thus, the breakwater would on the average need to be higher, although it may not need to be made proportionately longer.

Accordingly, as shown in Table 5.10a, the capital costs by item were derived for marinas of scale 600 and 800. These magnitudes are shown in columns 2 and 3. In column 4, the appropriate depreciation rate for each item is listed. In columns 5, 6, and 7, the annual depreciation costs are listed for the 400-, 600- and 800-boat marinas. They total $98,578, $140,849, and $182,068, respectively. Had the increase in capital cost been directly proportionate to the increase in capacity, the annual capital cost due to depreciation of the 600-boat marina would have been 1.5 times that of the 400-boat marina, or $147,867 (or $7,818 greater). For the 800-boat

Table 5.10a Capital Costs and Annual Capital Charges for Marinas of Scale 400, 600, and 800

Capital Items	Capital Cost per Item			Annual Depreciation Rate	Annual Depreciation Cost		
	400 Scale (1)	600 Scale (2)	800 Scale (3)	(4)	400 Scale (5)	600 Scale (6)	800 Scale (7)
Scale factor = 0.6							
Dredging	$ 302,000	$ 385,050	$ 458,134	7%	$21,140	$ 26,954	$ 32,070
Ramps	12,200	15,550	18,507	7	854	1,089	1,295
Sewage system	11,250	14,344	17,066	6	675	861	1,024
Transient and rental office building	3,200	4,080	4,854	6	192	245	292
Administrative building	10,160	12,954	15,413	6	610	777	925
Scale factor = 0.8							
Docks	195,775	270,757	341,040	6	11,747	16,245	20,462
Paving	51,400	71,086	89,713	10	5,140	7,109	8,971
Boat and motor-sales building	25,850	35,750	45,031	6	1,551	2,145	2,702
Scale factor = 1.0							
Moorings	4,253	6,380	8,506	7	298	447	595
Shore protection	211,600	317,400	423,200	6	12,696	19,044	25,392
Fill	80,297	120,446	160,594	—	—	—	—
Landscaping	14,076	21,114	28,152	—	—	—	—
Fuel facility site improvement	16,000	24,000	32,000	12	1,920	2,880	3,840
Fuel-sales building	1,900	2,850	3,800	6	114	171	228
Boat-handling equipment	59,013	88,519	118,026	10	5,901	8,852	11,803
Work and party boats	86,880	130,320	173,760	7	6,082	9,122	12,163
Rental boats	52,596	78,894	105,192	10	5,260	7,889	10,519
Marine accessory sales building	14,250	21,375	28,500	6	855	1,283	1,710
Restrooms and lounge	30,750	46,125	61,500	6	1,845	2,768	3,690
Gear storage	13,400	20,100	26,800	6	804	1,206	1,608
Packaged food and bait sale building	7,500	11,250	15,000	6	450	675	900
Single level indoor storage	128,380	192,570	256,760	6	7,703	11,554	15,406
Triple level indoor storage	51,170	76,755	102,340	6	3,070	4,605	6,140
Repair service	105,434	158,151	210,868	6	6,326	9,489	12,652
Scale factor = 1.2							
Breakwaters	25,920	42,145	59,512	5	1,296	2,107	2,976
Utilities	13,500	21,951	30,996	6	810	1,317	1,860
Access road	20,650	33,577	47,412	6	1,239	2,015	2,845
Land	67,500	109,755	154,990	—	—	—	—
Total	$1,616,904	$2,333,248	$3,037,666		$98,578	$140,849	$182,068

marina, had a doubling of capacity led to a doubling of capital investment, the annual cost of capital would have been $197,156 (or $15,088 greater). Thus, on net, significant economies of scale have been assumed to exist with respect to capital investment.

In brief, the cost of capital for the 400-boat marina was estimated at $1,616,904. Using the scale factors, the total capital cost of the 600-boat marina is estimated at $2,333,248, while that of the 800-boat marina is estimated at $3,037,666.

With this estimation of capital costs, we now turn to labor costs. The annual cost of labor for the 400-boat marina was estimated at $197,600. The exact scale factor to be applied to labor is difficult to specify since it depends in large measure on the amount and types of labor initially planned for the 400-boat marina. Consequently, for illustrative purposes, separate calculations for five different scale factors are shown in Table 5.10b. In that table, calculations are performed for scale factors of 0.5, 0.6, 0.7, 0.8, and 0.9. For example, if the appropriate scale factor is taken to be 0.5, then the annual labor cost for a 600-boat marina (given that the

Table 5.10b Annual Labor Costs for Selected Scales and Scale Factors

Scale Factor	Annual Labor Cost Scale = 400	Scale = 600	Scale = 800
0.5	$197,600	$242,455	$279,011
0.6	197,600	251,940	299,759
0.7	197,600	262,412	321,297
0.8	197,600	273,280	344,219
0.9	197,600	284,544	368,721

Table 5.10c Annual Operating Expenses for Diverse Items for Selected Scales and Scale Factors

Item	Scale Factor	Annual Expense 400 Scale	600 Scale	800 Scale
Taxes on land and structures	1.0	$35,000	$52,500	$70,000
Insurance	0.9	5,852	8,427	10,920
	1.0	5,852	8,778	11,704
Advertising	0.5	3,000	3,681	4,236
	0.6	3,000	3,825	4,551
	0.7	3,000	3,984	4,878
	0.8	3,000	4,149	5,226
	0.9	3,000	4,320	5,598
	1.0	3,000	4,500	6,000
Utilities	0.8	11,650	16,112	20,294
	0.9	11,650	16,776	21,739
	1.0	11,650	17,475	23,300
Maintenance and supplies	0.5	66,567	81,678	93,993
	0.6	66,567	84,873	100,982
	0.7	66,567	88,401	108,238
	0.8	66,567	92,062	115,960
	0.9	66,567	95,856	124,214
	1.0	66,567	99,851	133,134

annual labor cost of the 400-boat marina is $197,600) is $242,455, while for an 800-boat marina, it is $279,011.

For the 400-boat marina discussed in the foregoing sections of this manual, it is judged that 0.7 is, for the moment, the most appropriate scale factor. Thus, in deriving annual labor costs for the 600- and 800-boat marinas, these costs are set at $262,412 and $321,297, respectively.

In Table 5.10c, the remaining costs are estimated for the 600- and 800-boat marinas. In that table, they are treated in the same manner as the labor costs. Hence, several different scale factors are calculated for illustrative purposes. It is felt in this study that the scale factor of 1.0 is most appropriate for insurance, 0.6 for advertising, 0.8 for utilities, and 0.9 for maintenance and supplies. Taxes on land and structures are assumed to be proportional to output, and thus the scale factor is set at unity.

With the necessary data thus presented in Tables 5.10a, b, and c, we proceed to derive the total annual costs for the 600- and 800-boat marinas in Table 5.10d. This

Table 5.10d Total Annual Costs of Marinas for Selected Scales

		Annual Cost		
	Scale Factor	Scale = 400	Scale = 600	Scale = 800
Fixed Charge Items				
Depreciation	0.6, 0.8, 1.0, and 1.2	$ 98,578	$140,849	$182,068
Taxes on land and structures	1.0	35,000	52,500	70,000
Insurance	1.0	5,852	8,778	11,504
Advertising	0.6	3,000	3,825	4,551
Subtotal		$142,430	$205,952	$268,123
Variable Cost Items				
Labor	0.7	197,600	262,412	321,297
Utilities	0.8	11,650	16,112	20,294
Maintenance and supplies	0.9	66,567	95,856	124,214
Subtotal		$275,817	$374,380	$465,805
Total		$418,247	$580,332	$733,928

table records in summary form the costs for each fixed charge item and each variable cost item for the three different scales examined. Significant scale economies are reflected in both total fixed charges and total variable charges, and thus in overall annual costs. The overall annual cost of the 400-boat marina, as previously calculated, is $418,247. Using the scale factors, the total annual cost of the 600-boat marina is estimated at $580,332 while that of the 800-boat marina is set at $733,928. Had the cost of operation increased proportionately with capacity, the annual operating cost of the 600-boat marina would have been expected to be $627,371 (or $47,039 greater), and the annual operating cost of the 800-boat marina would have been $836,494 (or $102,566 greater). Thus, according to the assumptions of this study, sizeable economies of scale exist in marina construction and operation.

With our economic cost calculations now complete, we turn to the estimation of demand for larger marina facilities, and hence to their expected revenues.

The above discussion relates to the derivation of annual operating costs. Concurrently, however, a change in the scale of the marina affects total gross revenues. In the present analysis, the prices charged by our 400-boat marina are viewed as "fair" charges which every marina, regardless of size, sets. Thus, it is assumed that these charges are fairly constant; and the price for a service of a given quality at a 600- or 800-boat marina is the same as for the service of the same quality at a 400-

boat marina. With this assumption, the effect on revenues comes primarily from changes in demand. The normal fall in price which one might expect with an increase in supply is associated with a less than proportionate increase in demand in the sense that, vis à vis existing competition (sites), the new marina must reach farther and farther into its hinterland. In its attempt to operate its facilities at full capacity, it must go after customers at greater and greater distances or who are less and less inclined to patronize the new marina. Thus, the new marina becomes less and less able to compete with competitors. Consequently, at existing prices the demand for its services does not increase *pari passu* with capacity. In this manner, a decreasing rate of increase in gross revenue is introduced into the analysis.

Our problem, then, becomes one of estimating potential demand for marinas of scale 600 and 800 (that is, of 600-boat and 800-boat capacities, respectively). We employ the gravity model as previously used to estimate the potential demand for a marina of scale 400 (400-boat capacity). Recall that at the scale of 400 it was determined that the marina would attract approximately 123,751 man-days of recreational activity, assuming an exponent on distance of unity. Rerunning the gravity model with new marina weights rather than the original weight of 400 provides the estimated demand for man-days of recreation at the marina at the expanded capacities.

In order to illustrate the effect of changing the marina capacity, for diverse exponents applied to the distance variable, we present Table 5.10e. In the first

Table 5.10e Projected Demand for Selected Scales and Distance Exponents

Scale of Marina (in Boats)	**Number of Man-days**		
	Exponent = 1 (1)	Exponent = 2 (2)	Exponent = 3 (3)
0	0	0	0
100	31,349	24,262	14,378
200	62,421	47,819	27,120
300	93,221	70,735	38,573
400	123,751	93,069	48,990
500	154,016	114,870	58,565
600	184,020	136,180	67,444
700	213,766	157,039	75,741
800	243,257	177,479	83,546

column of that table, nine marina capacities are specified, ranging from zero to 800 boats. The effects of different capacities are shown in column 1 when the exponent on distance is unity, in column 2 when the exponent is 2, and in column 3 when the exponent is 3. Table 5.10e reveals that, if the exponent is set at unity, a doubling of capacity from 200 to 400 leads to an estimated 98 percent increase in demand. If the capacity is doubled from 400 to 800, demand increases 97 percent.

As larger exponents are used, the attenuating effect of distance on demand is intensified. With an exponent of 2, an increase in scale from 200 to 400 leads to an increase in demand of only 95 percent, while doubling the scale again increases demand only 91 percent. Finally, with an exponent of 3, an increase of scale from 200 to 400 leads to an increase in demand of just 81 percent, while an increase in scale from 400 to 800 leads to an increase in demand of just 71 percent. If the prices charged by the marinas of various scales are the same, it can be seen that with increase in scale, the total gross revenue increases at a decreasing rate.

In this study, it has been assumed that the relevant exponent on distance is unity. Hence, for the 400-boat marina, approximately 123,751 man-days of demand for recreational activity are estimated. For a scale of 600, there are 184,020 man-days expected, while for a scale of 800, there are 243,257 man-days anticipated. In effect,

Table 5.10f Rates of Return on Investment at Each of Three Marina Sites, at Scales 400, 600, and 800

	Jones River Site			Island Creek Site			The Nook Site		
	Scale = 400	Scale = 600	Scale = 800	Scale = 400	Scale = 600	Scale = 800	Scale = 400	Scale = 600	Scale = 800
1. Total annual revenues	$ 551,818	$ 820,553	$1,084,874	$ 551,818	$ 820,553	$1,084,874	$ 551,818	$ 820,553	$1,084,874
2. Annual operating costs at The Nook	418,247	580,332	733,928	418,247	580,332	733,928	418,247	580,332	733,928
3. Annual ecological costs at The Nook	9,160	14,900	21,040	9,160	14,900	21,040	9,160	14,900	21,040
4. Annual capital depreciation differentials	+23,952	+29,809	+34,766	+9,282	+11,033	+12,430	0	0	0
5. Annual ecological cost differentials	−6,095	−9,914	−14,000	−5,060	−8,230	−11,621	0	0	0
6. Annual tax differentials	+8,279	+10,235	+11,866	+3,276	+3,914	+4,406	0	0	0
7. Total annual cost (2+3+4+5+6)	453,543	625,362	787,600	434,905	601,949	760,183	427,407	595,232	754,968
8. Annual surplus (1–7)	98,275	195,191	297,274	116,913	218,604	324,691	124,411	225,321	329,906
9. Total capital cost	1,948,079	2,706,619	3,512,318	1,747,949	2,489,776	3,213,885	1,616,904	2,333,248	3,037,666
10. Planning cost	89,302	124,545	158,387	79,070	111,530	142,939	73,529	104,263	134,918
11. Rate of return (8÷(9+10)×100)	4.82%	6.90%	8.10%	6.40%	8.40%	9.67%	7.36%	9.24%	10.40%

then, by this process, scale factors are derived for the estimates of total revenues of the 600- and 800-boat marinas. Given the revenue of the 400-boat marina, the scale factor for estimating the revenues of the 600-boat marina is .978, while the scale factor for estimating the revenues of the 800-boat marina is .975. The revenue of the 600-boat marina is thus 148.7 percent of that of the 400-boat marina, while at a scale of 800, revenue is 196.6 percent that at the scale of 400. Total revenue for the 600-boat marina is estimated at $820.553 and for the 800-boat marina at $1,084,874.

With these total revenue estimates, we may now compare the annual costs, revenues and profit (surplus) of operating a marina at each of the three different scales for the alternative involving location at The Nook site with spoil removed from the harbor. We record in the last three columns of Table 5.10f the relevant data. (For the moment the data in the other columns are to be ignored.) These last three columns indicate in the first row total annual revenue, in the second row annual operating costs at The Nook, and in the third row annual ecological costs at The Nook. In the seventh row of the table are recorded total annual costs; and in the eighth row, annual surplus. In the last row this annual surplus is indicated as a rate of return on total investment, which is the sum of the items in the ninth and tenth rows. Notice that the rate of return increases from 7.36 percent to 9.23 percent and to 10.40 percent with increase in scale from 400 to 600, and from 400 to 800, respectively. Recall, however, that this rate does not cover a reasonable interest rate or normal return on capital investment. Also, we are not able to introduce into a comparison of the relative feasibility of the several scales of operation a factor which might explicitly reflect the different degrees of risk associated with the several scales of marina operation. Nonetheless, the estimated rates of return do suggest that the operation at The Nook of a marina at a scale greater than 400 is to be seriously considered.

Activity complex analysis, however, requires that we pursue the investigation still further. If we do consider several different scales of operation at any one location, we must consider such scales at all other locations. For, while at one scale of operation one location may be optimal, at another scale of operation a second location may be the best.

5.10.2 The Three Sites: Comparison of Rates of Returns at Different Scales of Operation

In this subsection we proceed, using our comparative cost approach, to a comparison of rates of return for different scales of operation at the three relevant sites in our study area—namely, Jones River, Island Creek, and The Nook. To effect this step, recall that we need to compare only differences among these sites in capital costs, in annual operating costs, and in annual revenues. Since we estimate that there will be only minor differences in the level of demand for the services which might be offered at the three sites, and since the same charges for services are to be expected for all three sites, we anticipate no differences among these three sites in annual revenues.

Likewise, for *many* of the capital items, we do not expect differences among the three sites in their cost. Thus for any given scale, these items will cost the same at all three sites. However, there are some capital items whose cost will vary among the three sites, and these have already been identified in Table 5.2j. One of these is dredging costs which, by summation of the appropriate cost estimates in Tables 5.2d and 5.2e, are $698,000, $482,000, and $302,000, respectively, for Jones River, Island Creek, and The Nook for a 400-boat marina. These figures are recorded in the appropriate cells of the first row of Table 5.10g. Applying the relevant scale factor of Table 5.10a allows us to fill the remaining cells of the first row.

Table 5.10g Costs of Capital Items Which Vary among Marina Sites

	Jones River Site			Island Creek Site			The Nook Site		
	400 Scale	600 Scale	800 Scale	400 Scale	600 Scale	800 Scale	400 Scale	600 Scale	800 Scale
Dredging	$698,000	$889,950	$1,058,866	$482,000	$614,550	$731,194	$302,000	$385,050	$458,134
Shore protection	159,000	238,500	318,000	159,000	238,500	318,000	211,600	317,400	423,200
Land[a]	69,795	113,487	160,249	74,385	120,950	170,788	67,500	109,755	154,990
Sewage disposal system	2,000	2,551	3,027	11,250	14,344	17,066	11,250	14,344	17,066
Breakwater	0	0	0	22,680	36,878	52,073	25,920	42,145	59,512
Access road	20,650	33,577	47,412	0	0	0	0	0	0

[a] The figures in this row for the 400-scale marina represent an increase of $46,845 over the relevant figure in Table 5.2g of Section 5.2. largely reflecting the assumption of a structure on each possible site.

Table 5.10h Annual Capital Cost Differentials on Variable Capital Items, for Three Sites and Three Scales

	Jones River Site			Island Creek Site			The Nook Site		
	400 Scale	600 Scale	800 Scale	400 Scale	600 Scale	800 Scale	400 Scale	600 Scale	800 Scale
Dredging	+ $27,720	+ $35,343	+ $42,051	+ $12,600	+ $16,030	+ $19,114	$0	$0	$0
Shore protection	−3,156	−4,734	−6,312	−3,156	−4,734	−6,312	0	0	0
Land	—	—	—	—	—	—	—	—	—
Sewage disposal system	−555	−708	−842	0	0	0	0	0	0
Breakwater	−1,296	−2,107	−2,976	−162	−263	−372	0	0	0
Access road	+1,239	+2,015	+2,845	0	0	0	0	0	0
Total	+ $23,952	+ $29,809	+ $34,766	+ $9,282	+ $11,033	+ $12,430	$0	$0	$0

The second capital item whose cost varies among the sites is shore protection. The relevant data are developed and presented in the second row of Table 5.10g. The data for a 400-boat marina for Jones River and Island Creek are obtained from Table 5.2f and that for The Nook from the discussion in Section 5.6.2; the data for the 600- and 800-boat marinas are derived by applying the relevant scale factor in Table 5.10a.

In a similar fashion, the data in Table 5.10g for land, sewage disposal system, breakwater, and access road were obtained from materials developed in Section 5.2.2 and from the application of the appropriate scale factor in Table 5.10a.

In addition to the capital costs which vary among sites, certain capital items are expected to be of the same cost regardless of the site. In this grouping are the remainder of the capital items shown in Table 5.6h. At scale 400, these items total $998,634, while at scales 600 and 800, they are $1,464,554 and $1,924,764, respectively.

With the capital cost thus derived by item, cost differentials can be computed. All differentials have been computed relative to The Nook site. Hence, the cost at The Nook is set equal to zero, and items at other sites which involve greater capital costs have a "plus" value, while those which are less have a "minus" value. The total capital cost differential of those items which vary from site to site, when multiplied by the appropriate depreciation rate of that item (as listed in Table 5.10a) yields an annual capital cost differential. These annual capital cost differentials are given in Table 5.10h. (Since for each item the total capital cost differential has been set at zero for The Nook, the annual capital cost differential for the Nook must also be zero.) The sum of these differentials at each site for each scale yields the difference between annual cost at The Nook and at other sites. The capital items whose costs are the same for any given scale regardless of site have no annual cost differential associated with them; therefore, they are not included.

In Table 5.10h, it can be seen that, at each of the other two sites, irrespective of the scale of operation, the annual cost of capital is greater than at The Nook. For example, at scale 400, the annual capital cost at the Jones River site is $23,952 greater than at The Nook, while at Island Creek, it is $9,282 greater. Notice that no depreciation is applied to land acquisition costs. However, these are treated as a part of total capital cost when the rate of return on total investment is computed.

With the annual capital cost differentials derived, we now turn to annual ecological cost differentials. Recall from Table 5.2t that annual ecological costs (with dredging spoil removed from the bay) were $3,065 at Jones River, $4,100 at Island Creek, and $9,160 at The Nook. With larger scales, it is felt that relatively greater ecological damage might occur. Hence, a scale factor of 1.2 was applied to ecological damage. Thus, at scale 600, ecological damage at the Jones River site is estimated at $4,986 while at Island Creek and The Nook, annual ecological damage amounts to $6,670 and $14,900, respectively. Finally, if an 800-boat marina were constructed at each of these three sites, annual ecological damage is estimated to be $7,040 at Jones River, $9,419 at Island Creek, and $21,040 at The Nook.

In Table 5.10i, the ecological cost differentials for each site at each scale are presented. Again, all calculations are made with respect to The Nook. Thus a "minus" sign means that the annual ecological cost at a given site is less than at The Nook. As is shown in Table 5.10h The Nook involves the most disruption to

Table 5.10i Annual Ecological Cost Differentials for Selected Scales

Scale of Operation	Jones River	Island Creek	The Nook
400	−$ 6,095	−$ 5,060	$0
600	− 9,914	− 8,230	0
800	− 14,000	− 11,621	0

the natural environment at each scale of operation. As the scale increases, the advantages of the other two sites become greater.

Calculating planning costs at each site and at each scale are exactly analogous to the calculations performed for the 400-boat marina at The Nook.[138] Recall that at The Nook, total planning costs for the 400-boat marina are $73,529. Of this amount $5,529 is for boring, hydrographic surveys, and topological surveys. It is assumed that this charge is the same at each of the three sites when the scale of operation is 400. To obtain the cost at alternative scales, a scale factor of 1.0 is applied.

The remaining $68,000 in planning costs is due to a 5 percent charge on capital cost, with the cost of land, moorings, boat-handling equipment, work and party boats, and rental boats excluded. For example, consider the calculation of planning cost at the Island Creek site when the planned marina is of scale 600. In Table 5.10g, it is estimated that the capital items listed there for a 600-boat Island Creek marina total $1,025,222. The remainder of the capital items (those that are the same at each site), total $1,464,554. Thus, the total capital cost is $2,489,776 for the 600-boat Island Creek marina. The cost of land is $120,950. Boat-handling equipment, moorings, work and party boats, and rental boats cost $304,113. When the last two figures are subtracted from the capital cost, $2,064,713 remains. Five percent of this amount is $103,236. The cost of borings and surveys at scale 400 was estimated at $5,529. Applying a scale factor of 1.0, the cost of borings and surveys at scale 600 is then $8,294. Thus total planning cost for the 600-boat marina at the Island Creek site is $103,236 plus $8,294, or $111,530.

Table 5.10j Total Planning Costs and Planning Cost Differentials

	Jones River	Island Creek	The Nook
Scale = 400			
Total costs	$ 89,302	$ 79,070	$ 73,529
Cost differential	+15,773	+5,541	0
Scale = 600			
Total costs	124,545	111,530	104,263
Cost differential	+20,282	+7,267	0
Scale = 800			
Total costs	158,387	142,939	134,918
Cost differential	+23,469	+8,021	0

These planning costs are shown in Table 5.10j. As this item is a non-recurring cost, an annual cost or amount of depreciation is not computed. Thus, the table shows the total planning cost at each site for each scale. The table also records the cost differentials relative to The Nook site, the cost differential at The Nook being set equal to zero, since of the three sites it involves the least planning costs.

The final cost items to be considered are the annual operating costs other than capital depreciation. For The Nook site, these costs have been shown in Tables 5.10b and 5.10c, and summarized in Table 5.10d. Table 5.10b relates to labor costs, while Table 5.10c covers the calculations for taxes, insurance, advertising, utilities, maintenance, and supplies. In Table 5.10d, assumptions concerning the most appropriate scale factors are made and totals are computed. For The Nook site, it is shown that for scale 400, total annual operating cost is $418,247, of which $98,578 is attributable to depreciation of capital. At scale 600, the annual operating cost is $580,332, of which $140,849 is capital depreciation; while at scale 800, annual operating cost is $733,928, of which $182,068 is capital depreciation.

[138] See Section 5.6.12.

At this point, it is felt that the differences in annual costs of insurance, advertising, labor, utilities, maintenance, and supplies among the three sites, when the scale of operation is the same, are too small to be considered. These differences are therefore set at zero. The annual cost of capital has been presented in Table 5.10h on a differential basis. Thus, the only item which is yet unknown relates to taxes on land and structures. This item is expected to vary from site to site as taxes are assumed to be 2½ percent of taxable capital investment.[139] Although the total value of capital at The Nook for the 400-boat marina is $1,616,904, the amount of taxable capital is estimated at $1,400,000. The various boats owned by the marina, and other minor items, are taken to be non-taxable. When the 2½ percent tax rate is applied to this amount, an annual tax bill of $35,000 is estimated.

From the data in the preceding paragraph, it is seen that $216,904 of the total capital investment at scale 400 is considered non-taxable. This non-taxable capital is the same at each of the three sites. Thus, for scale 400, total capital cost, minus $216,904, yields the tax base at each site.

In order to avoid extensive computations to estimate taxes for scales 600 and 800, a crude indirect procedure is used. First, a scale factor of 1.0 is applied to the non-taxable amount, $216,904. Second, at each level for each site, the non-taxable amount was subtracted from the total capital cost estimate, and the remainder was then multiplied by the tax rate to obtain an approximate estimate of the annual tax bill.

Once the nine estimates of annual taxes were obtained, they were reduced to a differential basis. Again, the annual tax bill at The Nook was set equal to zero, and differentials at other sites were derived relative to The Nook. The annual tax differentials are shown in Table 5.10k. At each scale, The Nook site has a cost advantage with regard to taxes.

Table 5.10k Annual Tax Differentials for Selected Scales

Scale	Jones River	Island Creek	The Nook
400	+$ 8,279	+$3,276	$0
600	+10,235	+3,914	0
800	+11,866	+4,406	0

At this stage, all the relevant revenue and cost data for computing rates of return at each site for each scale have been derived. The rates of return must be sufficient to cover interest charges on borrowed capital, a fair or normal rate on private capital, and a fair economic return on entrepreneurial investment. It is difficult to specify exactly what this rate of return should be, but it can be stated with certainty that it should exceed 6 percent for an investment to be feasible.

The calculations for rate of return are based upon total annual revenues less the total annual cost, expressed as a percentage of the total of investment cost plus planning cost. For The Nook, at each of the three scales, this calculation has already been done based on data in Table 5.10f. For the remaining two sites, since differentials have been computed for variable items vis à vis The Nook, the computations are relatively simple.

As already mentioned, the first row of Table 5.10f records total annual revenues for each of three scales, the revenues being the same for all three sites for any given scale. The second row lists the annual operating costs at The Nook for each of the three relevant scales. The third row lists the Annual Ecological Costs at The Nook for each of the three relevant scales. The fourth row recognizes that the data in the preceding rows for the Jones River and Island Creek sites must be adjusted. This row presents the annual capital depreciation differentials, which being all positive, represent upward adjustments to be made to the data of the second row on "Annual

[139] A tax rate of 2½ percent is used in the calculations for the 400-boat marina at The Nook. See Section 5.7.2.

Operating Costs at The Nook." For example, consider the data of the first column which relates to a 400-boat marina at the Jones River site. The annual operating costs listed for it in the second row are those which are relevant for The Nook. They must be adjusted upward by $23,952, which is listed in the fourth row, to reflect the higher total capital cost at Jones River and the consequent higher annual depreciation charges at the Jones River site.

The fifth row of Table 5.10f refers to annual ecological differences; since these are all negative they represent downward adjustments to be made on the data of the third row which pertains to annual ecological costs at The Nook. The sixth row refers to annual tax differentials; these are all positive and represent upward adjustments to be made to the data of the second row. The seventh row of Table 5.10f sums the data in rows 2 to 6. In short, it makes the necessary adjustments on The Nook data for all three scales to yield total annual cost data relevant for the other two sites.

The eighth row calculates the annual surplus by subtracting row 7 (on total annual costs) from row 1 (on total annual revenues). Annual surplus is then taken as a percentage of the sum of total capital cost (row 9) and planning cost (row 10) to yield the estimated rates of return for the different alternatives. For example, for the 400-boat marina at Jones River, the total annual revenue of $551,818 (row 1) less total annual costs of $453,543 (row 7) yield an annual surplus of $98,275 (row 8), which represents a 4.82 percent rate of return on the sum of its total capital cost of $1,948,079 (row 9) and its planning cost of $89,302 (row 10).

From Table 5.10f, it can be seen that the rate of return increases at each site as the scale of operation increases. This result is largely due to the assumption of significant economies in the use of both capital and labor with increase in the scale of the complex. Thus a 400-boat marina at Island Creek has a 6.40 percent return on investment, while an 800-boat marina at that site has a 9.67 percent return. The highest rate of return at each scale of operation is registered by The Nook. Thus, it appears that of these three sites, such an investment should be planned for The Nook, regardless of the scale of operation.

Although the results of our computations indicate the superiority of The Nook to the other two sites at each scale of operation, it should be emphasized that this finding simply reflects the particulars of the situation examined. For other bays or for other sets of prices and levels of demand, it could very well develop that at one scale of operation, one of several particular sites is best, while at a second scale of operation, another site is best. This result would have obtained in our Plymouth Bay area study had ecological costs risen sharply enough and had the ecological situation at The Nook been more restrictive than at the other two sites. Also, our findings would have been different had we made different assumptions about the involvement of public bodies in recreational development. In this study, we have assumed that such involvement was minimal and that the Federal government performed no dredging and offered no subsidies, and that local and state governments provided no tax rebates nor other financial incentives. In a real world, however, these factors do play a role. Certainly, if it were contended that Federal involvement is justifiable from the standpoint of social welfare, then clearly our computations of rates of return would have been different.

To conclude, despite the many qualifications one may wish to make about the assumptions and approach used in this study, the findings as succinctly presented in Table 5.10f, indicate a high likelihood that private investment in recreational development at The Nook site is feasible provided that no major political or other obstacles are placed in its way.

5.11

The Land-Water Use Plan: Some Major Considerations

5.11.1 Functional Organization of the Marina Complex

Thus far the marina complex is described only in terms of its component parts, their land, water area, and other requirements, and their economic costs. No attention has been given to the functional organization of the various activities which will comprise the marina development. This section describes the functional relationships which should be recognized in organizing the marina and presents diagrams useful for translating the important relationships and linkages into physical form.

The components of the marina complex have been described in previous sections and will only be briefly summarized here. They include:

1. berthing and mooring space for a variety of boat sizes and types;
2. parking facilities, of several types;
3. boat service and storage areas;
4. customer convenience and marina rental and sales buildings; and
5. launching and hoisting facilities.

Land and water surface area requirements for the various components are summarized in Section 5.5, Table 5.5i.

(a) Activity Groupings

In physically organizing the marina, it is useful to divide its component parts into groupings of related activities based on type of use. The goal of organization according to type of use-activity is to permit efficient use of the marina facilities with a minimum amount of conflict between unrelated or incompatible activities. In the proposed marina for Kingston Bay, three use-activity groups are defined:

I. Seasonal-oriented facilities;
II. Transient-oriented facilities; and
III. Operations-oriented activities.

Each use-activity group is characterized by particular linkages and functional requirements.

Group I, *Seasonal-Oriented Facilities*, are those facilities used by customers berthing boats in the marina for an entire boating season. In general, this group comprises the largest number of marina users (man-days of use) and therefore is the generator of the greatest amount of movement of vehicles, boats, and pedestrians. Linkages between vehicular access, parking areas, berthing and mooring areas, and water access must, therefore, be adequate to handle the various types of movement. These important linkages are termed "first-order linkages" in the functional diagram for seasonal-oriented facilities (see Chart 5.11a).

Group II, *Transient-Oriented Facilities*, are those facilities used by customers who either rent boats at the marina or transport their own boats to the marina by trailer. The number of transient marina users is relatively small compared to seasonal users, but the facilities required to serve them are more varied. First, because the facilities used by transient customers produce revenue through daily fees, the location of a central rental office is a critical element. Second, because transient customers are likely purchasers of boats and equipment, it is advantageous to place the sales office in an easily accessible position. Third, because some transient customers launch their own boats, it is necessary to provide both direct access to the water and a special parking area for car/boat trailer combinations. Chart 5.11b summarizes the important functional relationships for transient-oriented activities.

Group III, *Operations-Oriented Activities*, include the boat service and storage functions that the particular marina business engages in. These functions are not

Chart 5.11a Seasonal-Oriented Facilities (Group I)

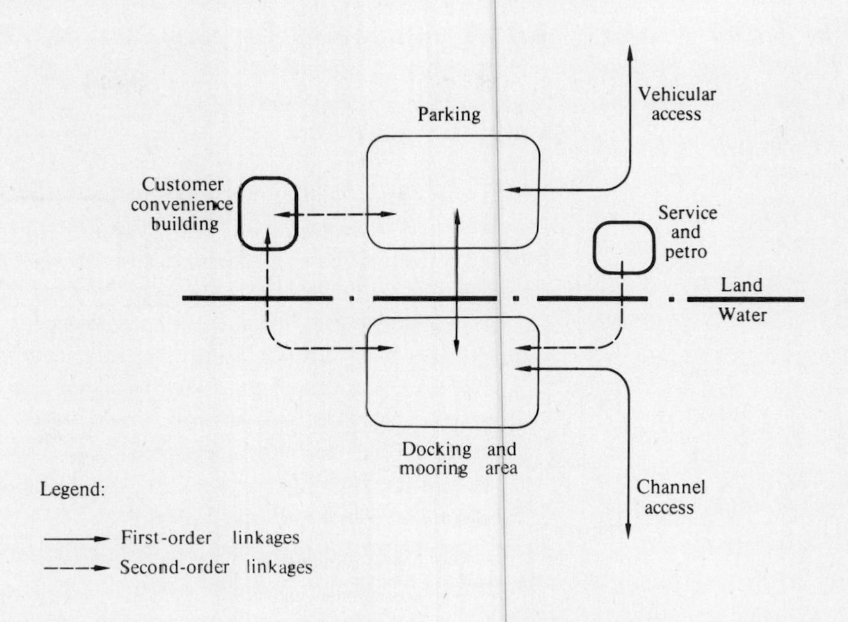

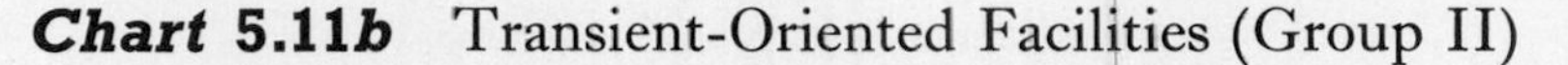

Chart 5.11b Transient-Oriented Facilities (Group II)

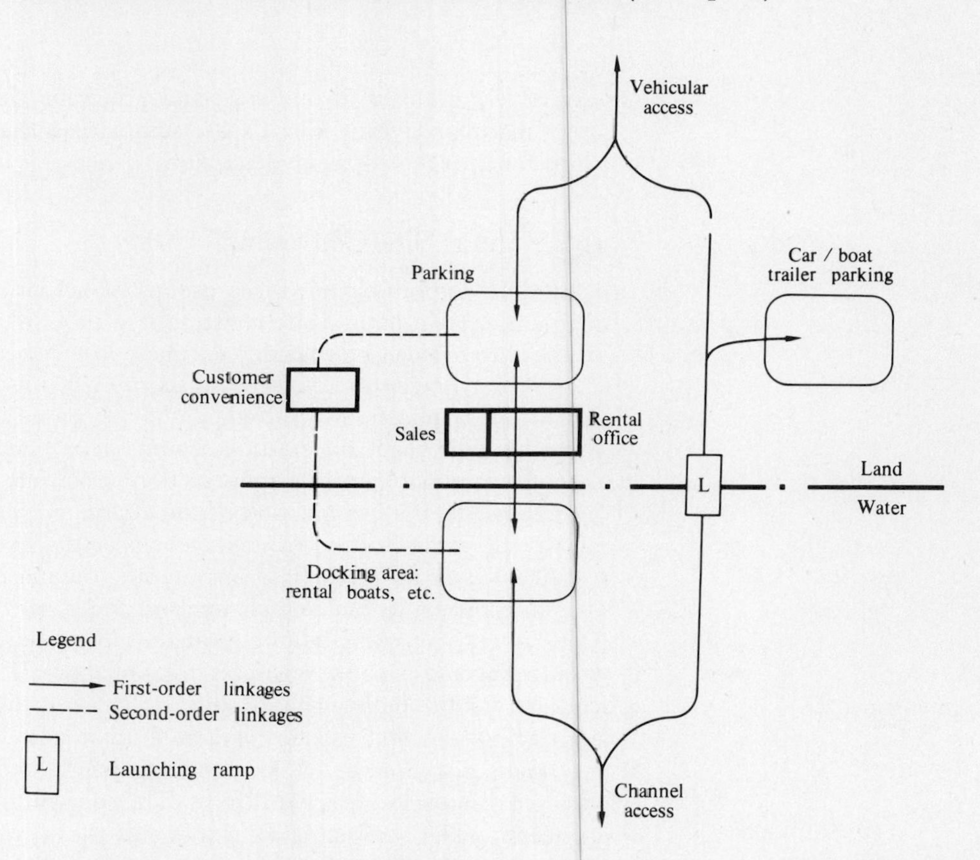

directly related to Group I or Group II activities, except for the periodical repair services the marina might provide for the privately-owned and rental boats. The main functional linkage between Group III activities and Group I and Group II activities is the launching ramp and hoist facility for transfering boats between water and land areas. In general, the operations-oriented activities should be

***Chart* 5.11c** Operations-Oriented Activities

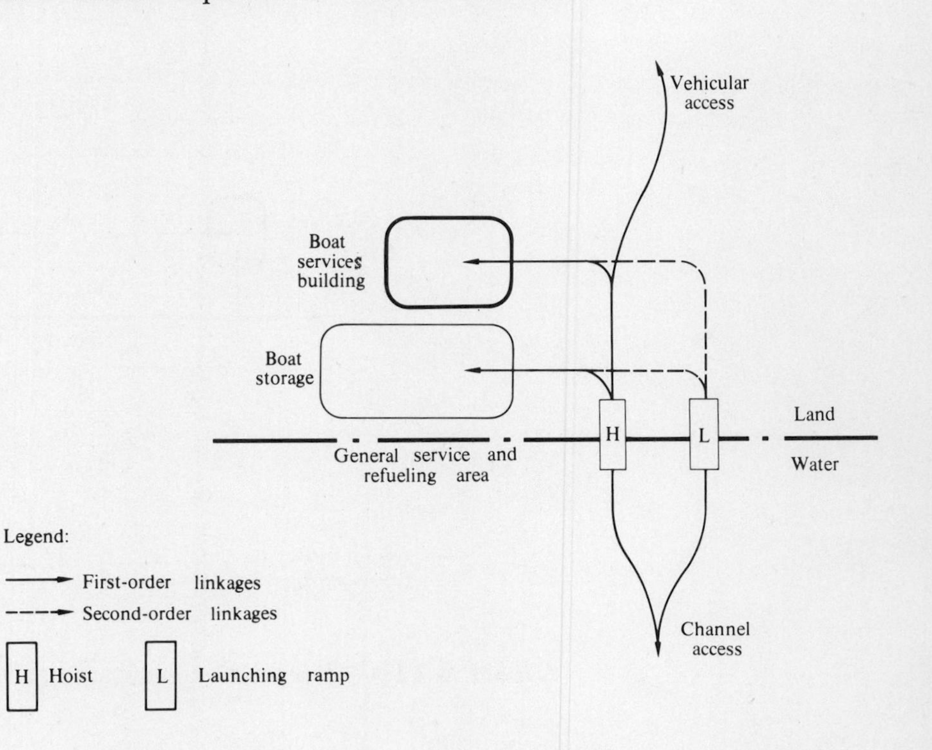

collectively grouped in one area, and preferably functionally separated from the other marina activities. Chart 5.11c summarizes the important functional relationships for operations-oriented activities.

(b) Natural Site Constraints

Before combining the three groups of activities into a composite functional diagram, certain natural site constraints which influence the physical organization of the marina must be considered. These influences are now summarized.

Tides. The nature of the tidal action in Kingston Bay is described in Section 5.1 and its implications for dredging have been described in Section 5.2. To minimize dredging costs, the existing channel near The Nook site is used to as large an extent as is possible, with a short section of new channel constructed to the marina basin area. In the examination of the alternative designs of the marina basin, the north end of this access channel is considered a fixed position.

At low tide the water area surrounding the marina will consist of exposed mud flats interrupted by isolated channels of water, such as the marina access channel. Consequently, boating will be limited at low tide to areas near the mouth of Plymouth Bay and to the open-water areas offshore. This limitation, combined with a concern for the biologically productive areas of the bay, suggests certain boating activity policies that will be elaborated upon later.

Winds and Storms. The prevailing winds and storms of the Kingston Bay area are discussed in Section 5.1.3b. The configuration of the land and water areas adjacent to The Nook site is such that only the prevailing winter and summer winds need to be considered for purposes of the marina design. The prevailing winter winds from the west and summer winds from the south-southwest approach The Nook site across a considerable area of open water and therefore can create significantly rough water conditions. The Nook site is protected from other wind directions by the Captains Hill land projection to the east. Breakwater construction is thus needed only on the west and south sides of the marina basin.

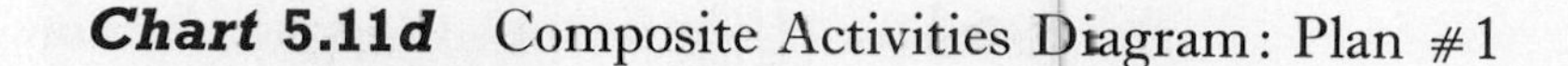

Chart* 5.11*d Composite Activities Diagram: Plan #1

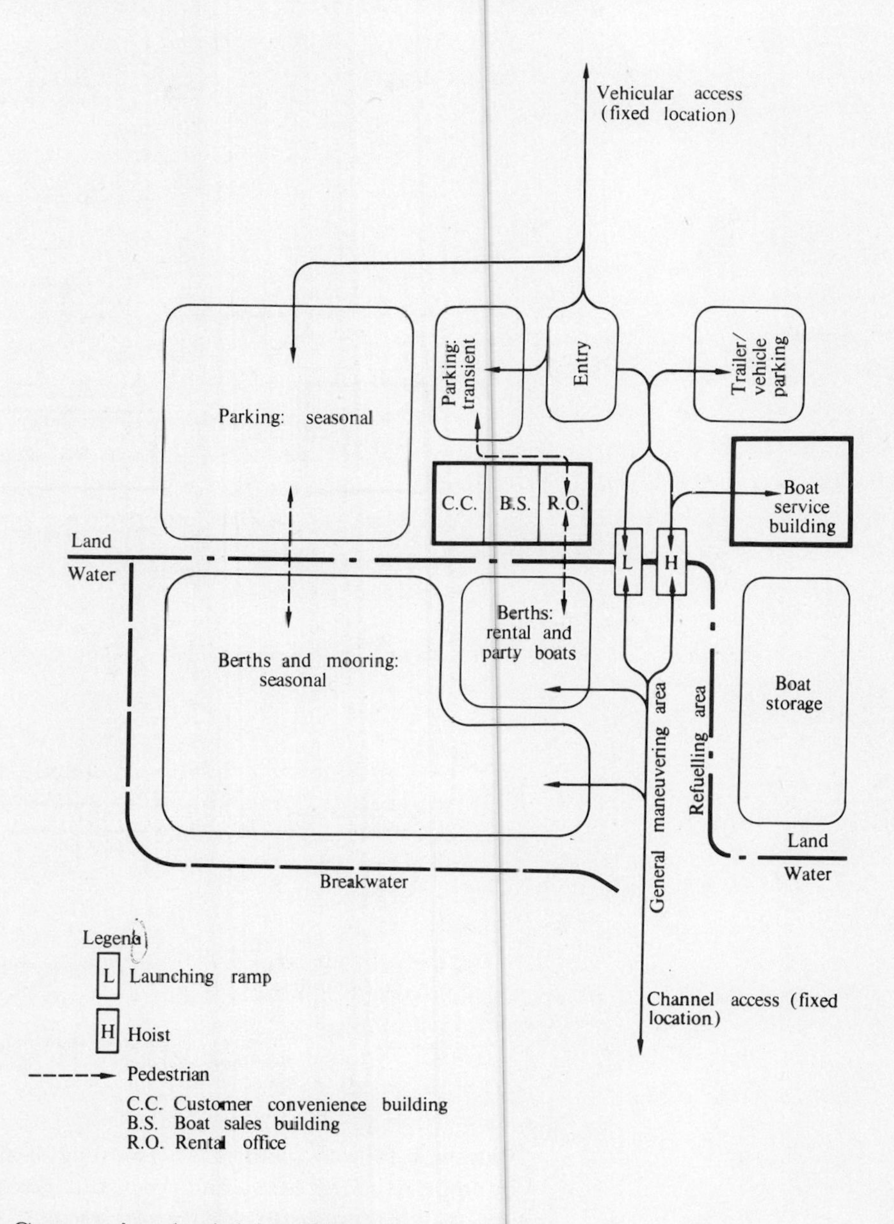

(c) Composite Activities Diagrams

Within the above site limitations, which should also include a relatively fixed point of vehicular access, alternative arrangements of the marina activities are possible. The following composite diagrams, Charts 5.11d and 5.11e, place the previously outlined functional requirements in relationship to each other and recognize the physical limitations at The Nook site.

Plan #1 (Chart 5.11d) illustrates a solution where service and transient-oriented activities are grouped near the channel entrance, thus minimizing the amount of service/transient circulation with the marina basin. Seasonal boating traffic is diverted at the channel entrance to a separate docking area.

Plan #2 (Chart 5.11e) reverses the relationships of channel entrance to boating-activity areas outlined in Plan #1. The service and transient-oriented activities are replaced at the channel entrance area by the larger seasonal docking and mooring area. Access to the service and transient-oriented activities is by way of an extended maneuvering area used by all boats in the marina.

Chart 5.11e Composite Activities Diagram: Plan #2

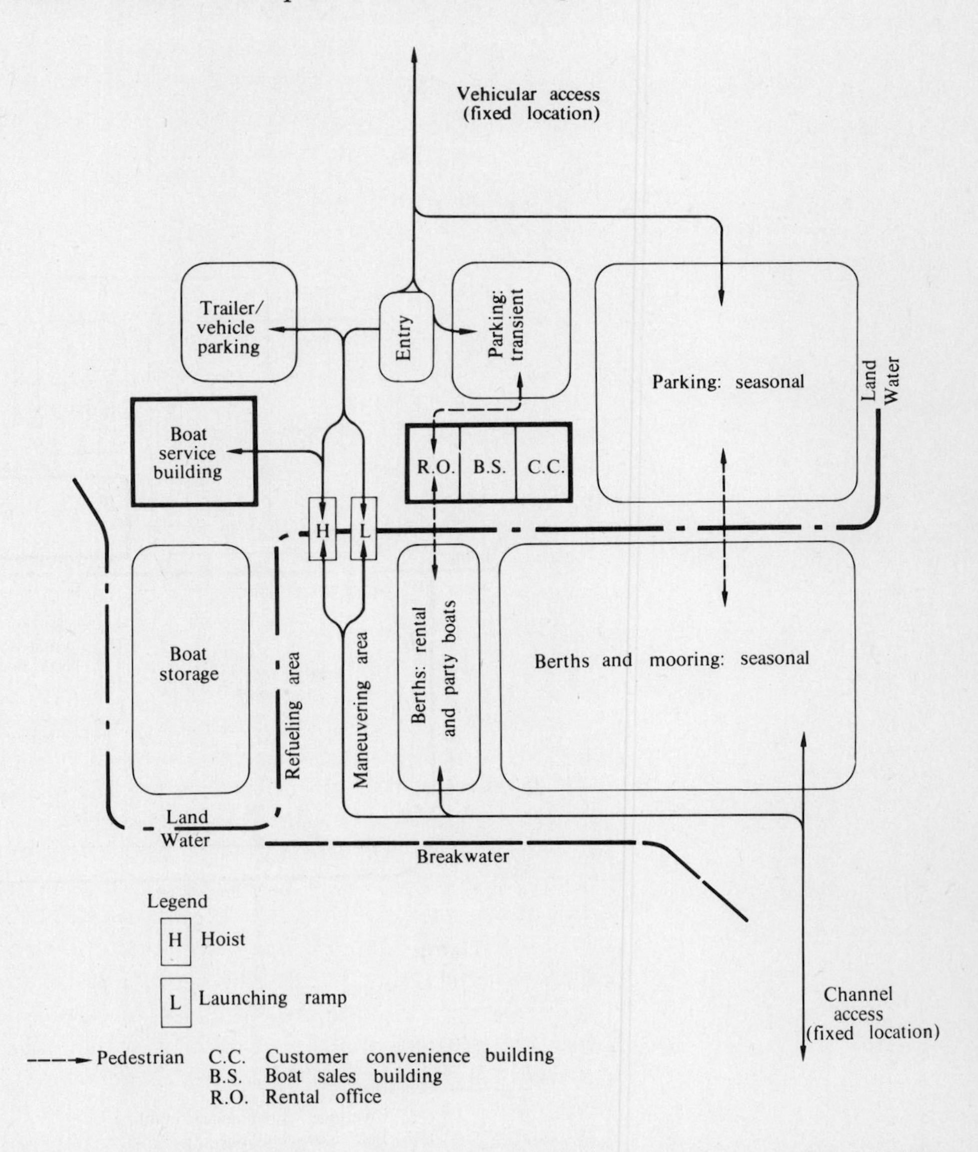

Common to both plans is the grouping of all boat-service and storage facilities on or adjacent to the small land projection designated "boat storage." The various operations that comprise "service and storage"—i.e., boat launching and servicing, land storage, refueling, and temporary docking require a flexible land/water edge with adjacent maneuvering areas. Flexibility in this context refers to areas with a minimum number of fixed structures which limit the type of activities which can be conducted. Plan #1 and Plan #2 differ in the relative positions of this service/storage grouping. In terms of functional considerations Plan #1 is superior to Plan #2. The transient/service-oriented traffic is terminated in Plan #1 near the channel entrance, thus minimizing the conflicts between different types of boat movement within the marina basin. Plan #2, however, actually extends the general use access channel into the restricted area of the marina without ordering and separating boat circulation according to type or destination.

The hypothetical choice of Plan #1 over Plan #2 is accompanied by certain additional capital costs. Site conditions require more bulkheading and breakwater installations in Plan #1 than in Plan #2. The comparative figures are summarized in Table 5.11a.

The choice of Plan #1 over Plan #2 is not central to the purposes of this paper.

Table 5.11a Comparison of Breakwater and Shore Protection Costs for Plans #1 and #2

	Plan #1		Total	Plan #2		Total
Breakwaters	1,200 lin. ft.	@ $43.20 per lin. ft.	$ 51,840	800 lin. ft.	@ $43.20 per lin. ft.	$ 34,560
Shore protection (32 ft.)	1,475 lin. ft.	@ $120.00 per lin. ft.	177,000	1,315 lin. ft.	@ $120.00 per lin. ft.	157,800
Shore protection (8 ft. height)	950 lin. ft.	@ $44.00 per lin. ft.	41,800	1,050 lin. ft.	@ $44.00 per lin. ft.	46,200
Total			$270,640			$238,560

It is more important, however, to illustrate the type of additional costs which may be incurred in achieving a functionally superior plan. Within the context of the marina complex outlined in this report and located at the proposed site, alternative plans with associated alternative costs are possible and must be considered. In this case, to achieve the safety and efficiency possible in Plan #1, $32,080 in additional capital investment is necessary.[140]

5.11.2 Relationship of Marina Activity to Kingston Bay Area

The relationship of the marina facility, as one type of activity, to other activities which exist or may potentially exist in the Kingston Bay area, has not been comprehensively explored in this case study. The focus has rather been on evaluating selected economic and non-economic costs associated with constructing the marina in a natural situation (Kingston Bay). In this section the relationships of the marina activity to other activities in the Kingston Bay area will be explored in general terms and certain unresolved problem areas will be identified.

In sections 5.1 and 5.2, the natural conditions and production activities which exist in Kingston Bay are considered in terms of the impact of a marina activity. The considerations are formulated primarily in terms of the impact of the construction process upon the natural environment, rather than in terms of a more dynamic situation which continues over time. As an example of the dynamic situation, the pollutants that may be released from the marina (e.g., gas and oil) may affect the marine life of the bay at peak seasons of boating, with residual effects at other seasons. Similarly, water turbulence caused by large numbers of motor boats may significantly change the water quality and bottom conditions of the bay and consequently affect the marine life that requires undisturbed conditions. In both cases the basic research necessary for projecting effects and establishing regulatory policies has not been completed. Nevertheless, certain preliminary guidelines can be suggested for minimizing the conflicts between the marina activity and the existing biological activities.

In Section 5.1 the three biological production units of an estuarine ecosystem

[140] Notice that both the plans described here are different from the preliminary plan discussed in Section 5.2.2. In that section, a preliminary plan was required in order to make a cost comparison between the three alternative sites in Kingston Bay which were considered. Plan #2 is about $15,000 cheaper than the plan described in Section 5.2.2, while Plan #1 is about $17,000 more expensive. The saving in Plan #2 is due mainly to a reduction in the amount of 8-ft bulkheading required. As this bulkheading is an expense which is peculiar to The Nook site, it seems reasonable to assume that corresponding savings could not be made at either of the other two sites. Accordingly, this saving will increase the comparative cost advantage of The Nook site as recorded in Table 5.2u of Section 5.2.2. Plan #1 involves capital costs which are about $32,000 greater than those for Plan #2, and about $17,000 greater than those calculated for The Nook site in Section 5.2.2. Plan #1, however, is considered functionally superior to Plan #2. Ideally, a quantitative evaluation of the benefits of this design should be made in order to determine whether its larger capital expenditure is economically justifiable.

Chart 5.11f Production Units in Kingston Bay

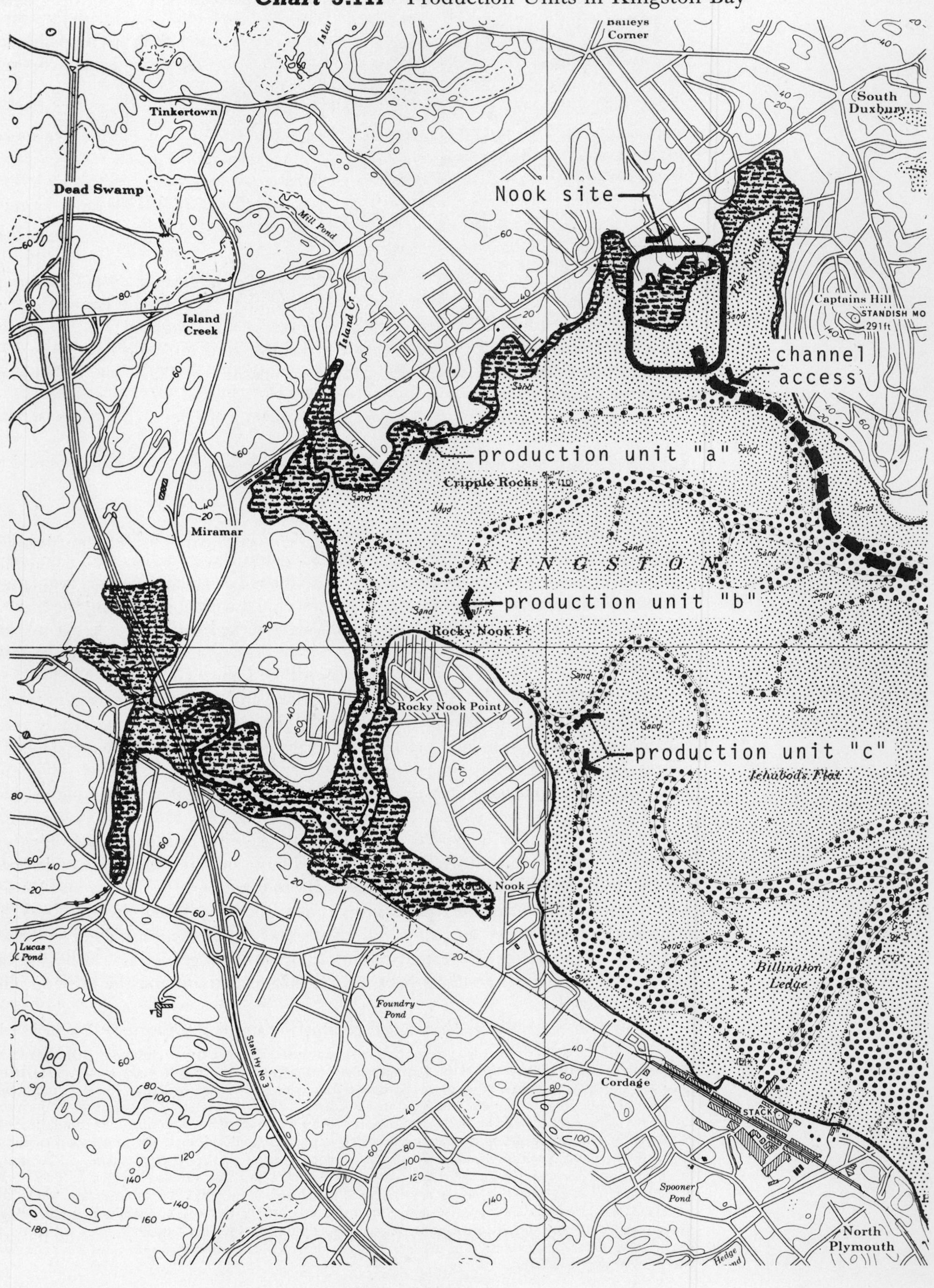

are defined, and in Chart 5.11f they are geographically located for the case-study area. The classification is formulated in terms of the most abundant producer organisms (green plants) of the particular area. Associated with each production unit are various animal species (consumers) related to each other and to the producer organisms according to the food-chain principles outlined in Section 3.4. If one of the goals of the general planning effort is to minimize the interference of the marina activity with the biological production activities of the bay, then two sets of precautions are appropriate:

1. Minimize the damage caused by the construction process.
2. Control those aspects of the marina operation which may have harmful effects on biological production over time.

The first set of precautions have been treated in Section 5.2. By selecting that site which requires the least amount of channel dredging, and by removing the dredged material from the bay, the destruction of biologically productive areas during the construction process is minimized.

The second set of precautions consists of regulatory policies applied to the marina operation over time. Assuming that the policy of maintaining the biological productivity of the bay is adopted, then any activity which reduces this productivity should either be prohibited from operating in the bay, or regulated in those aspects which are potentially harmful.

Marinas as an example of an activity with potentially harmful aspects could be regulated in the following ways and for the following reasons:

(a) *Restrict the number and size of marinas in the bay.* The larger the number of boats in the bay, the more severe the competition with other activities for the limited natural resources of the bay. It is necessary to identify the compatible and incompatible activities which can occur in the bay before assessing conflicts and establishing size limitations.

(b) *Specify those subareas of the bay (Kingston Bay) which may be used by motor boats.* The division of the bay into subareas would logically be on the basis of the three natural production units outlined previously. Particularly sensitive subareas (sensitive to disturbance by motor boats) would be placed off limits to motorboating while the use of other areas would not be restricted.

(c) *Specify those types of boats which may use the various subareas of the bay.* Rowboats and boats with very small motors may not be as damaging to biological productivity as larger boats. If in fact this statement is true, then subareas would be designated for certain types of boating, but prohibited to others.

These suggestions are intended to illustrate how the marina activity could be regulated to conform with the general policy initially stated; that is, to maintain the biological productivity of Kingston Bay. Activities which occur in the bay and can therefore be controlled in that local area may be handled in this manner. However, the dynamics of an estuary make it impossible to carry out the objectives of a locally formulated plan with only local cooperation and jurisdiction. For example, the continuous flow of water through Kingston Bay, including both stream flows and tidal action, closely links the bay with the adjacent land and water areas and their associated activities. In particular, the domestic and industrial activities located in the Jones River watershed (upstream from Kingston Bay) are directly linked to the activities in Kingston Bay through the existing and potential effects of pollution. Domestic and industrial wastes released into the Jones River eventually affect environmentally "sensitive" activities in Kingston Bay, such as biological production and water-oriented recreation, and render ineffective any locally formulated policies designed to encourage and protect these activities. This situation suggests that the planning procedures employed for a given situation must consider not only the conflicts between activities within a limited planning area, but also account for the influence of activities in adjacent areas interconnected by physical flows and natural processes.

5.11.3 Interregional Spatial and Sector Linkages

Our examination of The Nook site, as already indicated several times, must be placed in the broader context of the total structural-functional system in the Kingston Bay area. In a similar way our work must also be set in the larger contexts of the total Plymouth Bay area, the Boston region, the New England region, the United States, and in the world as a whole. In the context, or against the background of each of these successively larger scales, the key linkages or the key factors of our study change. Within the local area itself (Kingston Bay), the dynamic plan for The Nook site must be closely woven into the local system of interdependent environmental processes and systems. The work which we have attempted in sections 3.5 and 3.6 represents an initial attempt at setting down in systematic form (input-output type format) various environmental processes and their interrelationships. In Chapter 5 we have broadened our investigation to include certain proposed economic-social activities in Kingston Bay and their interrelationships with the environmental processes. The important point which we wish to reiterate here is that our work in this report moves in two primary directions: (1) to develop improved conceptual frameworks and new empirical materials for acquiring increased knowledge of the mutual dependencies of environmental processes, and (2) to develop techniques for identifying and analyzing the important linkages between environmental processes and economic-social systems at various scales.

In a local context, such as Kingston Bay, a dynamic plan for the development of a particular site does not consider the relationships among various economic sectors, as would be the case in a larger context, such as the Boston region. Rather, at the local scale the important relationships in a dynamic plan are between the particular development and the environmental systems of the area. The interdependent environmental systems which are subject to change in the plan must be identified, and the impact of these changes on the environment and ultimately on the limited number of other economic-social activities fully evaluated.

At a larger scale, for example that of the Boston region, the dynamic plan for a development must consider the effect of competing economic activities for the land that the particular development requires. Also, alternative sites for a particular development must be examined, with the use of tools such as comparative cost analysis to determine whether a site is most efficient for the particular development. However, when we consider the larger context it becomes necessary to reduce the amount of attention given to the intricacies of environmental processes in a local area. The fine detail which is possible when studying natural systems on a local scale becomes impractical in the larger context, simply because the resources for research are not available. Consistent comprehensive planning for the larger region must, therefore, work on a more aggregate basis, with detailed information reserved for decision-making at the local level.

As a dynamic land-water use plan for a local area is viewed in successively larger contexts, a shift of emphasis occurs from one set of variables to another. At the national scale, variables which are related to the composition of the total population will become important. For example, information on age structure, income distribution, and family size, when combined with information on the relative wealth of the country (gross national product), will indicate probable recreational demands by type and for future dates. It is only against the background of such national data that meaningful estimates can be obtained for the same variables in the New England and Boston regions. Also, consistent with our earlier statement, the larger the scale of concern, the more the information on local environmental processes must be treated in aggregated forms. For example, in the local situation at Kingston Bay, the attention given to climate is primarily in terms of specific temperature ranges, amounts of rainfall, and wind directions, and how these factors affect local environmental processes. At the national scale, climate is considered in terms of broad classes (i.e., Mediterranean type and non-Mediterranean type) and how these broad types lead to noticeable differences in behavior of groups and individuals and their demand for various types of recreational facilities.

It is also possible to ask how the dynamic land-water use plan is influenced by factors on the world-wide scale. The development of aircraft technology, for example, is affected by world, and not just national decisions. Such development not only increases mobility of the population and the availability of sites to satisfy its recreational needs, but also exerts a major influence on the state of the atmosphere in such areas as New York. In turn, the resulting air pollution, crowding of airways, sonic pollution, and the like, may have a major influence on the quality of the atmosphere and the environment in general in our local area.

All these considerations clearly point up the need for a multi-faceted approach to a dynamic land-water use plan. In this particular book we have started to probe into local interdependent environmental systems. That probe must certainly be developed and expanded. Particular attention must be given to how changes in magnitude of elements in the local plan affect the local natural systems. Moreover, a dynamic plan must be systematically redefined and re-"viewed" in terms of larger contexts and the variables which are pertinent in each. In short, a dynamic plan must be written in different variables and different magnitudes in each of the different contexts. This report is thus a mere beginning in the development of such a plan.

Bibliography

1. *Boat Owner's Buyers Guide, 1967.* Yachting Publishing Corporation, New York, 1967.
2. *Boating Almanac, 1967, Vol. I: Massachusetts, Maine and New Hampshire*, New York, G.W. Bromley and Company, Inc., 1967.
3. *Boating Almanac, 1967, Vol. 2: Long Island, Connecticut and Rhode Island*, New York, G. W. Bromley and Company, Inc., 1967.
4. Boating Industry Association, *Outboard Motor Sales by County*, Chicago, 1965.
5. Caspers, Hubert, "Estuaries: Analysis of Definitions and Biological Considerations," in George H. Lauff (ed.), *Estuaries*, Publication No. 83, American Association for the Advancement of Science, Washington, D.C., 1967.
6. Emery, K. O. and R. E. Stevenson, "Estuaries and Lagoons," Chapter 23 in Joel W. Hedgpeth (ed.), *Treatise on Marine Ecology and Paleoecology, Vol. 1—Ecology*, The Geological Society of America, Memoir 67, 1957.
7. Fitzpatrick, William A. and Sargent Russell, *Massachusetts Marine Sport Fisheries Inventory*, Massachusetts Division of Fisheries and Game, Fisheries Bulletin No. 36, 1961.
8. Foster, John H., *The Private Outdoor Recreation Industry in Essex County, Massachusetts, 1963*, Publication 427 (mimeographed), Amherst, Massachusetts, Cooperative Extension Service, University of Massachusetts, 1965.
9. ———, *The Private Outdoor Recreation Industry in Plymouth County, Massachusetts, 1963.* Publication 431 (mimeographed), Amherst, Massachusetts, Cooperative Extension Service, University of Massachusetts, 1965.
10. Isard, Walter and Eugene W. Schooler, "Industrial Complex Analysis, Agglomeration Economies and Regional Development," *Journal of Regional Science*, I (1959).
11. ———, Eugene W. Schooler and Thomas Vietorisz, *Industrial Complex Analysis and Regional Development*, Cambridge, Mass., M.I.T. Press, 1959.
12. Massachusetts, Commonwealth of, *Report of the Department of Natural Resources Relative to the Coastal Wetlands in the Commonwealth*, Senate Document No. 855, January, 1964.
13. ———, Department of Natural Resources, Division of Marine Fisheries, *A Study of the Marine Resources of Plymouth-Kingston-Duxbury Bay*, unpublished report.
14. ———, Department of Natural Resources, Public Access Board, *Public Access to the Waters of Massachusetts, Progress Report, 1967.*

15. Michigan State Waterways Commission, *Recreational Boating Needs of 1980, Fuel Consumption Appendix*, 1965.
16. Moore, Hilary B., *Marine Ecology*, New York, John Wiley and Sons, 1958.
17. *National Construction Estimator, Sixteenth Edition, 1968*, Los Angeles, Craftsman Book Company, 1968.
18. Niering, William A., *The Life of the Marsh*, New York, McGraw Hill, 1966.
19. Odum, Eugene P., *Fundamentals of Ecology*, 2nd ed., W. B. Saunders Company, Philadelphia, 1959.
20. ———, "The Role of Tidal Marshes in Estuarine Production," *Conservationist*, The State of New York Conservation Department, Vol. 15, (June–July), 1961.
21. Outdoor Recreation Resources Review Commission, *National Recreation Survey*, Report No. 19, Washington, D.C., U.S. Government Printing Office, 1962.
22. Pritchard, Donald W., "What is an Estuary: Physical Viewpoint," in George H. Lauff (ed.), *Estuaries*, Publication No. 83, American Association for the Advancement of Science, Washington, D.C., 1967.
23. Robert Snow Means Company, Inc., *Building Construction Cost Data*, 26th Annual Edition, Duxbury, Massachusetts, 1968.
24. Tatlock, Richard, *Cost and Revenue Notes for Marine Facility Development*, mimeographed, 1968, Department of Landscape Architecture—Research Office, Harvard University, Cambridge, Massachusetts.
25. U.S. Bureau of the Budget, Executive Office of the President, *Standard Industrial Classification Manual*, Washington, D.C., U.S. Government Printing Office, 1957.
26. U.S. Bureau of the Census, *U.S. Census of Population: 1960, General Social and Economic Characteristics, Massachusetts*, 1961.
27. ———, *U.S. Census of Population: 1960, General Social and Economic Characteristics, Rhode Island*, 1961.
28. U.S., 89th Congress, 1st Session, *Massachusetts Coastal and Tidal Areas*, House Document No. 293, Washington, D.C., U.S. Government Printing Office, 1965.
29. U.S., 86th Congress, 2nd Session, *The Shore Between Pemberton Point and Cape Cod Canal, Massachusetts, Beach Erosion Control Study*, House Document No. 272, Washington, D.C., U.S. Government Printing Office.
30. U.S. Department of Commerce, Coast and Geodetic Survey, *Harbors of Plymouth, Kingston, and Duxbury*, Chart #245.
31. ———, Coast and Geodetic Survey, *United States Coast Pilot #1—Atlantic Coast—Eastport to Cape Cod*, Seventh Edition (April 3, 1965).
32. Wisconsin Department of Resource Development, "Waterfront Renewal: Technical Supplement," Wisconsin Department of Resource Management, Madison, 1964.

Recommendations and Conclusions

6.1
Recommendations

We now wish to close this report by making a set of recommendations and stating certain conclusions.

1. The cost and revenue analysis of The Nook site in the Plymouth-Kingston-Duxbury area indicates that a marina could be profitably operated, with full account taken of the ecological costs involved. For a 400-boat marina the investment required (including planning cost) would be $1.69 million. The rate of return on the investment would be 7.36 percent before incomes taxes. For a 600-boat marina the total investment would be $2.44 million. The rate of return on investment before income taxes would be 9.24 percent. Finally, for an 800-boat marina the total investment would be $3.17 million. The rate of return on investment before income taxes would be 10.40 percent. We therefore recommend that a marina of at least 400-boat capacity be seriously considered for construction at The Nook site.

2. The analysis pursued for the Nook site specifically, and for the Plymouth-Kingston-Duxbury area in general, represents the minimum amount of analysis that should be undertaken when any development is contemplated for the Continental Shelf. By using this prototype study as a guide, it should be feasible, in subsequent studies, to extend the analysis toward a more comprehensive consideration of the critical links between the economic and ecologic systems.

6.2
Conclusions

1. In carrying through the research for this study, a considerable amount of progress was made in developing a more appropriate methodology for economic-ecologic analysis. In Chapter 2, we summarily presented and illustrated four basic techniques for economic and regional science analysis. These four analytic tools are the comparative cost approach, the input-output technique, industrial complex analysis, and the gravity model. We could have also presented a fifth technique—namely, linear programming, which is also generally considered valid in certain contexts and is frequently employed. However, we chose not to do so since we do not have occasion to use the linear programming approach in our case study.

It is significant that in the development of the study, it was possible to extend the field of application of these techniques to cover the ecologic system. A modified version of the input-output technique, which could be adapted for programming, was employed in Chapter 3 for a description of the data and relationships of an ecologic system. Three food chains were incorporated into this format, as well as the basic photosynthesis process and certain sub-cycles in the phosphorus cycle. In Chapter 4 we developed a fused framework for an input-output, activity analysis approach to the combined economic-ecologic system. In Chapter 5, we employed this framework, although in a very limited manner, when we examined the problem of the proper development of a marina complex in the Kingston Bay area. We did not use a programming approach to identify an optimal size and composition for the complex. However, it is clear that this could be done since the constraints of the system can be specified, since an objective function to maximize return on investment can be formulated, and since, at least within a small range, the variation of most of the basic magnitudes can be approximated with linear relationships.

Moreover, in Chapter 5, we illustrated, in the selection of a best site, how the comparative cost approach could be used for ecologic analysis. We specifically calculated certain ecological costs for the sites examined. Furthermore, we developed analysis for a recreational complex following the traditional industrial complex approach. Although our recreational complex does not encompass the full range of relevant ecological processes and their relationships, one can see how such a complex approach could be applied more extensively to the ecologic system. The usefulness of the activity-complex methodology is even clearer when we recognize that it represents a hybrid approach. It is a combination of comparative cost analysis and the input-output technique, and it has been demonstrated that each is applicable to the ecologic system.

Finally, a few words may be said about the gravity and other spatial interrelation models. Although their application to the ecologic system was not attempted in this report, they could perhaps be used for studying ecologic diffusion processes. Since there are many diffusion processes in the ecologic system (for example, in air and water systems) comparable to social diffusion processes (for example, communications, commodity and population flows, and rumor spread), the potentiality of gravity-type models for ecologic analysis is evident.

In short, perhaps the most important contribution of this research does lie in its development of methodology. It is suggested that many of the techniques employed in economics and regional science can be extended and reformulated without major difficulty for use in the study of the ecologic system. (This point was completely unanticipated at the outset of the research.) Thus, a number of advances in ecologic analysis might be possible. But perhaps the most significant result of this research is the discovery that by such extension and reformulation, it is feasible to handle jointly, and in combined fashion, both the economic and ecologic systems with all their mutual relationships and interdependencies. We should be able to approach the critical problems which arise from such interdependencies—such problems as air pollution, water pollution, and erosion—much more effectively.

2. While we point up the potential for adapting and developing new methodology for economic-ecologic analysis, one should at the same time recognize that the system of linkages governing natural and social phenomena is extremely complex. There are, for all practical purposes, few, if any, systems which are simple. We are operating in a world in which variables are all intricately interrelated. It is for this reason that there are some investigators who avoid empirical investigations because this approach cannot possibly portray accurately and comprehensively the interdependent web of real life.

While this view has its merits, in many situations critical decisions must be made. Water quality must be regulated, air pollution must be controlled, open space must be preserved. We cannot afford the luxury of postponing decisions until we have developed models of reality with a high potential for accurate prediction. We need some basis on which to make decisions *now*. We generally accept the hypothesis that decisions based on limited information and simplified relationships coupled with intuition and good judgement are frequently better than decisions based on intuition and good judgment alone.

It is in this spirit that we present methodology to examine and quantify the interrelationships of the economic and ecologic systems. None of the authors would be willing to state that these systems and their interrelationships are simple. Indeed, they are exceedingly involved. Yet, recalling the poor and ill-advised decisions concerning resource development which have been made in the past, we feel that models of simple relationships, when judiciously employed, and when based on the best available data, cannot help but improve the quality of decision-making.

Accordingly, we offer the methodology which we have just described. It is also in full recognition of the shortcomings of such methodology that we look forward to its early obsolesence and replacement by superior methodology.

3. Having made a number of specific recommendations and observations on methodological advances, it is also appropriate to consider the general problem of coastal zoning, particularly with reference to the Continental Shelf resources. We have indicated that if the necessary precautions are taken to protect the ecologically sensitive areas of Kingston Bay, the ecological damage resulting from the marina development could be kept within acceptable limits.

In recent years, there has been a growing concern for the protection and conservation of coastal wetlands and other areas of ecological value. This is a welcome change from the earlier attitude that marshes were of no value unless they could be drained and developed. It would however be wrong to assume that wetlands should not be developed under any circumstances, or that ecological resources should be protected regardless of the economic costs involved.

Since the intertidal area available for all purposes is limited, it would seem unwise to use such areas for purposes which could well be satisfied inland, such as housing. However, it must be recognized that certain kinds of development, including ports and marine recreation, can only occur on the coast; and that the demand for this type of development may be expected to increase as population increases. The population of the United States enjoys and expects a rising standard of living, and those expectations can only be met if a price in ecologically valuable marine resources is paid.

What is required is a procedure for assigning conservation priorities for various sections of the coastline. Since the value of the ecological resources of any particular coastal wetland will depend in part on the amount of wetlands still in existence elsewhere along the same coast, the conservation priority assignment must be performed on a comprehensive basis. It is very important to recognize here that: (1) a zoning scheme will be found acceptable by investors and land owners only if it is stable, and not subject to frequent change; and (2) that it can be stable only if it takes basic economic factors into account, for if it does not it will be forced to yield and change due to economic pressures. Consequently, zoning plans should, if at all possible, avoid assigning high conservation priorities to areas with major economic potential.

While the establishment by law in the state of Massachusetts of a system of priorities represents a step in the right direction, clearly a set of independent actions, one by each state or other political authority, is inadequate. For one or more states may be tempted to delay enacting zoning restrictions or some other control on its economic development in order to achieve economic growth at the expense of neighboring states less inclined to defer action. Furthermore, any one state may command insufficient resources to conduct the careful overall inventory and analysis of ecologically valuable coastal resources required by competent marine biologists and other scientists. Moreover, failure to coordinate statutes and other actions of states may lead to inefficiencies and incongruencies not clearly perceivable by the political leaders of any one state. Finally, uncertainty about the final set of statutes and controls which may be anticipated when each political authority acts independently may lead recreational and commercial developers and other private investors to overdevelop or underdevelop, and otherwise make decisions inconsistent with optimal resource use. In short, a comprehensive system of priorities established systematically and in coordinate fashion by all political authorities involved is to be highly desired. Such is in fact the only sound way of achieving viable and effective coastal zoning simultaneously sensitive to ecological productivity, economic development possibilities, accessibility to potential users, and other pertinent factors.

4. Finally, we must reiterate that the entire concept of regional planning must be changed. The old, narrow, economic approach no longer can prevail. Henceforth, regional planning must, at the minimum, consider both economic and ecologic analysis and encompass the key interrelationships between the two systems.

Appendix A

Summary of Studies on Mineral Resources of the Continental Shelf

A.1

The Economic Potential of Phosphorite Recovery

Phosphorite is not presently produced from the Continental Shelf, but the commercial potential of offshore production has aroused considerable interest. Phosphorite, like phosphate rock, is a source of P_2O_5, valuable as agricultural fertilizer. About three-fourths of the currently produced phosphate rock is used for agricultural purposes, while the remainder is used in the manufacture of organic and inorganic chemicals.

At present, 41 percent of world phosphate rock production takes place in Florida. Other sizeable producers include Tunisia, Algeria, Morocco, and the Pacific Islands of Makatea, Nauru and Ocean Island.[1]

Oceanographic surveys have shown that phosphorite occurs widely on the Continental Shelves. Available evidence indicates that in the United States' Continental Shelf regions, major potentials for phosphorite recovery are off the California coast.[2]

In our detailed study[3] the cost of dredging phosphorite nodules in the vicinity of the Forty Mile Bank (forty miles west of San Diego) was assessed. Although these phosphorite nodules occur in this area at depths of 190 to 600 feet, calculations were made for mining at depths of 600 feet. Once these calculations were made, it was then possible to compare the unit costs of production and delivery to an onshore fertilizer producer in the Los Angeles-San Francisco area with the delivered cost of phosphate rock from Florida and Idaho. Inland California agricultural markets for the fertilizer were hypothesized.

The cost calculations were patterned after those made by Hess[4] and Mero.[5] A drag-dredge operation, based on existing technology, was employed. The dredge bucket would be dropped into the mining area and pulled along the bottom to pick up the nodules which lie on the bottom. It would then be raised to the surface to be emptied into a barge.

The annual charges covering rent and depreciation of the offshore dredging equipment (consisting of a leased dredging ship and storage barge, a winch, and other necessary items) was estimated to be about $1,444,500.[6] Other operating expenses, including labor, supervision, power, cable, overhead and other expenses, were estimated to be $809,700 per year.[7] Thus, total annual costs might be $2,254,200.

Under the assumptions of the study, total annual output would be approximately 192,900 tons of phosphorite nodules.

If these estimates are correct, they would imply a cost per ton of $11.69. Transportation of the nodules to a fertilizer producer onshore would amount to about $1 per ton, giving a delivered cost of $12.69 per ton.

[1] Sweeney and Bradley [8], p. 161.
[2] Emery [2]; and Deitz, Emery, and Shepard [1], pp. 815–848.
[3] Isard, Bassett, Choguill, *et al.* [5], Appendix A.
[4] Hess [4], pp. 79–96.
[5] Mero [6], pp. 252–260, and Mero [7].
[6] For details, see Isard, Bassett, Choguill, *et al.* [5], Appendix A.
[7] For details, see *ibid.*

At this stage, comparison can be made with the costs of other production sites. Idaho phosphate rock could be delivered to the California market for a total cost of $15.50 per ton.[8] Thus, California off-shore nodules would be in a competitive position with this source for the coastal markets of California. However, it is estimated that Florida rock of superior quality could be delivered to coastal California points for less than $12.50 per ton. Thus, relative to Florida, the off-shore potential is inferior. Its major transport cost advantage is more than offset by its unfavorable production cost position.

Admittedly the cost data that have been collected and processed are almost entirely crude estimates. These cost data can be expected to change, perhaps drastically, with experience in off-shore mining and with development of technology. This might be especially true if more productive dredging equipment were developed.

Should the cost estimates prove to be valid, and should the various data that have been published also be accurate, it would seem that the competitive potential for offshore phosphorite mining in California would not lead to major resource savings and contributions to gross national product. With respect to markets at Los Angeles, San Francisco, and elsewhere on the West Coast, there does not seem to be any major advantage that the offshore California phosphorite deposits would have relative to Florida phosphate deposits.[9] With respect to inland markets, the offshore mining of phosphorite would not seem to be very economically favorable, if at all, relative to Idaho deposits. In fact, one might speculate that if offshore phosphorite deposits could compete with Idaho mines in interior markets, then the Florida phosphate rock could compete with the same Idaho mines still more favorably.

Bibliography

1. Deitz, R.S., K.O. Emery, and F.P. Shepard, "Phosphorite Deposits on the Sea Floor of Southern California," *Bulletin LIII*, The Geological Society of America, 1942, pp. 815–848.
2. Emery, K.O., *The Sea off Southern California*, New York, John Wiley & Sons, 1960.
3. Ensign, Chester O., Jr., "Economic Barriers Delay Underseas Mining," *Mining Engineer* (September, 1966), 59–62, 73.
4. Hess, H.D., "The Ocean: Mining's Newest Frontier," *Engineering and Mining Journal*, CLXVI (August, 1965), 79–96.
5. Isard, Walter, Kenneth E. Bassett, Charles L. Choguill, John G. Furtado, Ronald M. Izumita, John Kissin, Richard H. Seyfarth, and Richard Tatlock, *Report on Ecologic-Economic Analysis for Regional Development: Some Initial Explorations with Particular Reference to Recreational Resource Use and Environmental Planning*, Regional Science, and Landscape Analysis Project, Department of Landscape Architecture—Research Office, Graduate School of Design, Harvard University, December, 1968.
6. Mero, John L., *The Marine Resources of the Sea*, Amsterdam, Elsevier Publishing Company, 1965.
7. ———, *A Preliminary Report of an Economic Analysis of Mining Deep-Sea Phosphorite from the California Borderland Area*, Institute of Marine Resources, University of California at Berkeley (processed), March, 1960.
8. Sweeney, George C., Jr. and James W. Bradley, "An Economic Evaluation of Markets for California Phosphorite Deposits," in *Symposia on Economic Importance of Chemicals from the Sea*, American Chemical Society, Chemical Marketing and Economics Division, 1963, pp. 160–167.

[8] Sweeney and Bradley [8], p. 165.

[9] The Florida deposits are estimated to be 2 billion long tons, capable of supplying domestic consumption well into the next century. See Ensign [3], p. 61.

A.2

The Economic Potential of the Seawater Magnesia Industry

Magnesium, the fifth most common element in seawater, is present to the amount of 1,300 mg. per liter of ocean water.[10] This proportion indicates that 1 cubic mile of seawater contains 6 million tons of magnesium. It is not surprising, then, that magnesium was among the earlier elements exploited in the ocean environment.

This study examines a part of the seawater magnesia industry, with particular reference to the needs of the refractory brick industry, which in turn sells brick to the steel industry.[11]

In this study, a comparison is made between an East Coast seawater magnesia plant and an onshore mine producing magnesite in Nevada, where magnesite deposits occur.[12] Since in 1965, 50 precent of the refractory grade magnesia produced in the United States was derived from seawater processes,[13] it is to be expected that a comparative cost analysis will reveal that seawater processing is economically feasible.

Seawater magnesia extraction plants produce two basic grades of product. The first of these, which is of greatest importance to the refractory industry, is deadburned magnesia. This product is the result of heating magnesium hydroxide at a temperature of about 3,500°F. The other product, caustic calcined magnesia, is a reactive magnesium oxide made by calcining magnesium hydroxide or magnesium carbonate at 1,650°F or lower.[14] This latter product is used in the manufacture of fertilizer, paper, cement, rubber, rayon, pharmaceuticals, sugar, and in chemical processing.

Most seawater magnesia plants employ the same general industrial process. Seawater, containing 0.13 percent magnesium,[15] is screened, and pretreated to remove calcium bicarbonate hardness by addition of hydrated lime and removal of calcium carbonate.[16] Treated water is then mixed in a reactor with calcium hydroxide, obtained by calcining and hydrating dolomite or oyster shells to precipitate magnesium hydroxide. When dolomite is used, as in the East Coast plant visualized, the calcined dolomite furnishes about one half of the magnesium content. The magnesium hydroxide, after settling and processing in thickeners and filters, becomes the raw material of the later products.

The magnesium hydroxide is then treated to produce the final product. Until 1961, the traditional calcining process consisted of placing the magnesium hydroxide paste, or filter cake, into a rotary kiln, with the product being either refractory magnesia of about 92–95 percent purity, or caustic calcined magnesia, depending on the heat employed in the process and the time allowed. Since 1961, with demand for higher purity refractory magnesia increasing from the steel industry, a different burning process has become increasingly important. In this process, wet magnesium hydroxide is calcined to caustic calcined magnesia, which takes the form of a powder. This powder is then formed into briquets under pressure and fed to a vertical shaft kiln capable of reaching temperatures of 3,500° to 4,000°F. This process leads to a refractory grade magnesia that is 96–98 percent magnesium oxide. At present, about one-fourth of the seawater refractory magnesia is produced by this two-stage process, or a modification of it, and the percentage is increasing.

In attempting to assess the costs encountered by a seawater magnesia extraction plant, an annual plant capacity of 54,000 short tons of refractory magnesia was considered. With this capacity, capital costs for a plant utilizing a vertical calciner would approach $220 per annual ton of capacity. Thus, total capital cost would be

[10] See "Chemistry and the Oceans" [2], p. 12A.
[11] The full details of this study are found in Isard, Bassett, Choguill, *et al.* [5], Appendix A.
[12] Williams [6], p. 10. [13] Industry sources. [14] Williams [6], p. 4.
[15] Comstock [3], p. 27.
[16] The information included in this section is from various interviews with industry sources. Walter W. Cooper of Northwest Magnesite Company was especially helpful.

approximately $12 million. Of this $12 million, $6.6 million is for the capital equipment required for the production of magnesium hydroxide, $3.4 is for a rotary kiln for the preliminary calcining operation, and $2 million is for briquetting and dead-burning equipment for achieving high quality output. At a depreciation rate of 10 percent, the annual cost of capital would amount to $1.2 million.

Operating costs were computed per ton of output. The delivered cost of the 3.2 tons of dolomite needed per ton of magnesia output would be $16. Fuel and power would cost $15.88 per ton, while the necessary three man-hours of labor would cost $17.20. Annual depreciation would amount to $22.22 per ton and maintenance on plant to $9 per ton. Profit and taxes, which were excluded because these are not true resource costs, amounted to $10 per ton. Transportation to a representative market, which was taken to be Cleveland, was estimated at $8.40 per ton. The total delivered cost of refractory magnesia, then, capital depreciation included, would be about $88.40 per ton.[17]

The cost of the seawater process was then compared with a land-based mining operation located in Nevada or Washington. Again, a Cleveland market was assumed. As before, a 54,000-ton capacity was examined. Dolomite cost is taken at $8.00 per ton. Fuel and labor was estimated at $18.00 per ton, concentrating and upgrading costs at $13.50 per ton. Maintenance was computed at $9, depreciation at $15, and transportation to the market at $20.48 per ton. Thus, in total, the cost of production and delivery was $83.98.

At first, it appears that the seawater process is more expensive relative to the Cleveland market. Its transport cost advantage does not fully offset its major disadvantages in annual capital cost and raw material costs. However, the land-based operation produces an inferior grade of product. Under current technology, the land-produced product can be upgraded to 95 percent, while the seawater refractory magnesia has a purity of 98 percent.

According to industry sources, this quality differential is critical and accounts for the increasing use of a slightly more expensive, higher quality finished product.[18]

Despite the crudeness of the data used, the conclusion here seems to be that there is a significant locational advantage for seawater type magnesia plants on the East Coast, particularly to serve Eastern Seaboard markets. As industrial consumers continue to grow in this region, especially the steel industry, the competitive strength of East Coast seawater type magnesia plants should be still further enhanced.

Bibliography

1. Birch, R. E., "Refractories in Transition," *Iron and Steel Engineer* (October, 1966), 143–150.
2. "Chemistry and the Oceans," *Chemical and Engineering News* (June, 1964), 1A–48A.
3. Comstock, Hazel B., *Magnesium and Magnesium Compounds: A Materials Survey*, U.S. Bureau of the Mines Information Circular 8201, Washington, D.C., 1963.
4. Fulkerson, Frank B. and Jerry J. Gray, *The Magnesium Industry and its Relation to the Pacific Northwest.* A Report Prepared by the U.S. Bureau of Mines for the Bonneville Power Authority, Portland, Oregon, 1965.
5. Isard, Walter, Kenneth E. Bassett, Charles L. Choguill, John G. Furtado, Ronald M. Izumita, John Kissin, Richard H. Seyfarth, and Richard Tatlock, *Report on Ecologic-Economic Analysis for Regional Development: Some Initial Explorations with Particular Reference to Recreational Resource Use and Environmental Planning*, Regional Science and Landscape Analysis Project, Department of Landscape Architecture—Research Office, Graduate School of Design, Harvard University, December, 1968.

[17] For further details, see Isard, Bassett, Choguill, *et al.* [5], Appendix A; and Fulkerson and Gray [4].

[18] Birch [1].

6. Williams, Lloyd R., "Magnesium and Magnesium Compounds," U.S. Bureau of Mines Reprint from Bulletin 630, 1965.

A.3

The Economics of Offshore Sulfur Recovery

Since 1963, the demand for elemental sulfur, which includes marketable sulfur in solid or molten form, has increased at a rate which has exceeded supply. This imbalance between supply and demand has resulted in price increases, technical innovations, and extensive exploration for new supply sources. With these developments, sulfur producers have given increased attention to expanding production from offshore Continental Shelf areas.

Although the United States is by far the largest producer of elemental sulfur, deposits are scattered throughout the world. Nearly 40 percent of world production, which amounted to about 17.2 million long tons in 1967,[19] takes place in the United States. Other major producers include Mexico, France, Canada, and the Soviet Union.[20]

Most United States production is obtained from the Frasch process. In the Frasch process, water, superheated to temperatures as high as 325°F, is pumped into deposits which are contained in porous limestone formations. Sulfur melts at 240°F, and since it is heavier than water, it sinks to the bottom of the cavity. Molten sulfur is then pumped to the surface at purities exceeding 99 percent pure crude sulfur. There are, at present, ten Frasch sulfur mines in operation, four in Louisiana and six in Texas.[21] During the period these mines have been in operation, over 115 million long tons of elemental sulfur have been produced.[22]

Of the operational mines, one of the most interesting lies offshore, about seven miles off the coast of Grand Isle, Jefferson Parish, Louisiana. This is the Freeport Sulphur Company's Grand Isle Mine. The problems involved in tapping offshore sulfur domes are far more complex than in landward areas. As in offshore petroleum drilling, some type of drilling platform must be constructed. Whereas in landward sulfur mines, superheated non-corrosive fresh water is pumped into the deposit, at sea, fresh water does not exist. Finally, the offshore Louisiana sulfur area is frequently subject to severe hurricanes, which pose a menace to both equipment and to human life.

In this study, a comparison was made between an offshore mine, such as the Grand Isle Mine, and the marginal onshore mines that would have to be expanded if production were increased from onshore sources.[23] As in the other mineral studies an attempt was made to determine, from industry sources and published materials, the major differences in the per ton cost between offshore production and onshore production.

A major part of the cost of offshore production is the required capital investment for a drilling platform. The mining platform for the Grand Isle Mine is about 1 mile across, and costs about $30 million to construct. Of this amount, $8 million is estimated to be the extra cost incurred because the facility is offshore.[24] As the heating capacity of the plant is designed to produce an average of 5 million gallons of hot water per day, this would indicate that the plants' output would be about 1.2 million tons of sulfur per year. This estimate is based on an assumed hot water to sulfur ratio of 1,500 gallons per ton. Such a water ratio would mean that the offshore plant is fairly efficient. Efficient, low-cost operations maintain water ratios of 1,200–1,500 gallons per ton of sulfur, while some mines now in operation have water ratios of 1,500 to 3,000 gallons per ton of sulfur.[25] If these estimates of

[19] U.S. Bureau of Mines [6], p. 1087.
[20] *Ibid.*, p. 1098.
[21] Hawkins and Jirik [2], p. 35.
[22] *Ibid.*
[23] For full details of the study see Isard, Bassett, Choguill, *et al.* [4], Appendix A.
[24] Lee, Bartlett, and Feierabend [5], p. 578.
[25] Ambrose [1], p. 5.

investment and output are reasonable, then the total capital cost per ton of annual offshore output is $24.66.

Variable costs at the offshore mine would include natural gas, treated water, operating supplies, cost of production wells, loading costs, labor and overheads, and a severance tax. It is estimated that for the offshore mine, these items amount to $9.44 per ton of sulfur produced. Fixed costs, including maintenance, supervision, taxes, insurance, and depreciation on the $30-million capital investment, would amount to $3.42 per ton produced. Thus, in total, for the mine under examination, total production costs would amount to $12.86 per ton of sulfur produced.

Although little published data exist for the cost structure of the offshore operations, onshore operations have been fairly well documented by Hazelton.[26] In this analysis, comparison was made with the Hazelton data for two marginal onshore operations.[27]

The onshore plants were of considerably smaller scale, producing 350,000 and 155,400 tons of sulfur per year. Such marginal onshore plants represent a rather realistic alternative open to producers, which is to continue to operate existing and new marginal domes onshore rather than search for richer production areas offshore.

For the mine with production of 350,000 tons per year, variable costs amounted to $8.74 per ton, while fixed costs were $1.94, yielding a total per ton cost of $10.68. For the production unit which produced 155,400 tons of sulfur per year, variable costs were found to be $17.66 per ton, while fixed costs were $4.36 per ton. Thus, total cost was $22.02 per ton of sulfur produced.

It can be seen that one of the onshore plants has a somewhat lower unit cost per ton than the offshore mine. This lower cost reflects a favorable cost differential with respect to total variable cost and annual fixed costs. However, the comparison of offshore with the existing marginal operation is not the proper one for evaluating offshore sulfur resources. No unexploited high sulfur-producing salt domes are known to exist onshore. If sulfur production were to expand onshore, it would have to be based on increasingly poorer deposits and at significantly higher costs. Both the favorable variable cost and the fixed-cost differentials of onshore mines are likely to disappear, and may even become highly unfavorable. If offshore deposits are exploited to meet increasing demand for sulfur, the savings per ton over onshore operations might well run from $1–10 per ton. The savings will not be precisely known until further experience is gained in the offshore environment.

Hence, we conclude that if quality offshore deposits can be found and if the demand pressures for sulfur continue to mount, then given current technology, the search for offshore sulfur will continue and its production should increase significantly in the coming decade.

Bibliography

1. Ambrose, Paul M., "Sulphur and Pyrites," U.S. Bureau of Mines Preprint of Bulletin 630, 1965.
2. Hawkins, M.E., and C.J. Jirik, *Salt Domes in Texas, Louisiana, Mississippi, Alabama, and Offshore Tidelands: A Survey*, U.S. Bureau of Mines Information Circular 8313, 1966.
3. Hazelton, Jared E., *Sulphur, The Industry and the Resource* (forthcoming from Resources for the Future, Inc.) (Processed).
4. Isard, Walter, Kenneth E. Bassett, Charles L. Choguill, John G. Furtado, Ronald M. Izumita, John Kissin, Richard H. Seyfarth, and Richard Tatlock, *Report on Ecologic-Economic Analysis for Regional Development: Some Initial Explorations with Particular Reference to Recreational Resource Use and Environmental Planning*, Regional Science

[26] Hazelton [3].

[27] *Ibid.*, pp. 77–92.

and Landscape Analysis Project, Department of Landscape Architecture—Research Office, Graduate School of Design, Harvard University, December, 1968.

5. Lee, C.O., Z.W. Bartlett, and R.H. Feierabend, "The Grand Isle Mine," *Mining Engineering* (June 1960), 578–590.
6. U.S. Bureau of Mines, *Mineral Yearbook*, 1967, Vol. I-11.

Appendix B

Notes on Finfish and Shellfish Production Processes

This appendix discusses the derivation of the food-chain data presented in sections 3.6.2, 3.6.3, and 3.6.4, of the text. The data are based on conditions characteristic of the case study areas of Salem and Plymouth-Kingston-Duxbury Bay in Massachusetts. Some of the data are, however, applicable to the marine areas off New England generally.

B.1 *Winter Flounder Production*

The unit level of winter flounder production was set for convenience at 1,000,000 pounds since our study related to areas in the state of Massachusetts, and since it was estimated that the actual sport fishing catch of winter flounder in that state was 1,029,500 pounds in 1961.[1]

The quantity of food consumed by the winter flounder was based on a ratio of 10:1 as suggested by one of Petersen's studies.[2] Other studies by Petersen and others have indicated ratios of the same order of magnitude. Thus 10,000,000 pounds of winter flounder food are taken to be required for the production of 1,000,000 million pounds of winter flounder. Thus 10,000,000 pounds was specifically allocated among the five food types—annelida (3,360,000 pounds), algae (2,730,000 pounds), mollusca (2,300,000 pounds), crustacea (710,000 pounds), and other miscellaneous foods (900,000 pounds)[3]—on the basis of various reports of stomach contents of winter flounder.[4]

[1] Fitzpatrick and Russell [15], p. 29.

[2] Petersen [37], table facing p. 22. Petersen's quantitative samples seem to be the best developed to date and are accepted by many marine ecologists. Thorson [42], p. 468 states: "Most marine ecologists who have worked with quantitative bottom samples on a large scale have accepted Petersen's animal communities as statistical units. A good demonstration of the reality and value of Petersen's concept of communities is that his provisions map (Petersen, 1914) of the hypothetical distribution of the level bottom communities throughout the North Atlantic has proved to be essentially true today after nearly 40 years of continued research." Petersen's primary intention was to procure these quantitative bottom samples to calculate the quantity of fish food available for bottom fish (especially the flounder). Other sources such as Sverdrup, *et al.* [41], pp. 936–937, support Thorson in using Petersen. Also, the materials in Hedgpeth [19], pp. 38–39, roughly support the 10 to 1 ratio.

[3] Miscellaneous food was assumed to take the form of a variety of small fish, egg larvae, plants and detritus material that the flounder may have swallowed.

[4] Reports on winter flounder food habits by Bigelow and Schroeder [4], p. 279; Pearcy [35], Chapter 4; and Lux [28] suggest that in the *adult* winter flounder the five food types listed are typical and that the main types consumed in order of importance seem to be polychaeta (annelida), algae and mollusca. Small crustaceans and egg larvae and other small fish were also commonly found; but these were more important in the juvenile stages. Since we define 2–3 year old flounder (which average 0.8 pounds) as a relevant catch in sport fishing, we use the data on adult winter flounder stomach contents. Lux [28], p. 1, states: "The winter flounder eats a wide range of foods, and its diet is probably as much related to what is available to eat as it is to the tastes of the fish." However, Raymont [38], p. 607, states that lemon sole, which many marine biologists believe to be adult winter flounder, rely primarily on polychaeta (annelida). This statement together with information from other sources suggests that the winter flounder evidently prefer annelida (which have the highest

The requirement of 40,000 surface acres of bay or estuary area per million pounds of winter flounder is based on estimated catch of 25 pounds of fish per acre.[5]

We also record the following *environmental conditions*[6] as necessary for winter flounder production:

1. Temperature range (surface)[7]	32°F–77°F
2. Salinity[8]	4.0–30 ppm

dry organic weight) over all other foods and where possible, would most likely migrate to waters with this food type. Lux suggests that the Woods Hole findings can be used as a typical Massachusetts bay or estuarine situation.

[5] The 25 pounds figure was estimated by the authors from unpublished data gathered by Lux at Woods Hole. The method of fish collection was by otter trawl in shoal waters of depths between 2 and 15 feet, which was assumed to represent a typical Massachusetts Bay and estuarine environment for winter flounder. Accordingly, the data collected were then assumed to be indicative of flounder catch potential and to allow for natality, in and out migration, fish not caught, other potential mortality, etc. The following is a list of data and steps used in estimating yearly potential pounds production of winter flounder for fishing per acre of bay or estuary.

A. Data:

1. Total towing time in minutes (9-month fishing season)	1,651
2. Number of flounder caught (9-month fishing season)	1,180
3. Square feet covered per minute of tow time	1,584
4. Average weight in pounds per adult flounder taken	0.8
5. Rated efficiency factor of trawl (estimated in discussion with Lux)	0.50

B. Steps:

1. $1{,}651 \times 1{,}584 =$ *2,615,184* square feet covered by trawl per season
2. $2{,}615{,}184 + 43{,}560 =$ *60.0* acres estuary or bay
3. $1{,}180 \div 60.0 =$ *19.7* flounder per acre, per season
4. $19.7 \times 0.8 =$ *15.76* pounds per acre per season
5. $15.76 \div .50 =$ *31.52* pounds, the adjusted estimate of flounder per acre per season.

Comparison of this estimate with Petersen's findings in Danish waters on similar flounder-type species suggests that this estimate is rather high. Accordingly, *25* pounds per acre was chosen as a more reasonable estimate.

The figure of 25 pounds is consistent with estimates quoted by Pearcy [35]. Pearcy [35], p. 59, cites estimates of 7–33 pounds per acre per year on Georges Bank; Georges Bank is a deep-water area and, as deep water, would be expected to be less productive than the shoal waters of bays and estuaries. Pearcy also quotes an estimate of 0.001 gm. dry weight per square meter per day in the English Channel (which is about 20 pounds per acre per year of wet weight). Moreover, the figure of 25 pounds, when translated into indirect requirements of organic matter, is well within the available supply of such food as reported by Odum. See footnote 16.

[6] It was found through interviews with experts that the winter flounder tolerates an extreme variation in water quality factors and, in fact, seems to thrive in waters with some degree of pollution. Their value as a major food in New England is not decreased by the consumption of polluted foods, because organs of winter flounder, unlike those of shellfish, are not consumed, winter flounder being consumed as filet (flesh). There are, however, three water quality inputs—surface water temperature, salinity, and bottom condition—that seem to be of primary importance in determining winter flounder distribution and abundance. Factors such as dissolved oxygen, free carbon dioxide, and detergent pollutant are relevant for marine life in general; they seem to be less critically significant for the winter flounder.

[7] Pearcy [35], p. 47, suggests 0° to 25°C as an approximate range of temperature within which flounder survive. Studies by the Massachusetts Division of Marine Resources, however, found flounder to exist in temperatures lower than 0°C, but the data indicate that this was not normal. It appears to be the unanimous opinion that if temperatures exceed 25°C, the flounder (especially adult) move from the very warm shoal waters to the cooler and deeper offshore waters. In fact, Bigelow and Schroeder [4], p. 279, state that "they sometimes perish by the thousands in very hot spells of summer weather, if they are trapped in shallow enclosed bays, as happened in Moriches Bay, Long Island, N.Y., in 1917, between July 29 and August 4, when the air temperature rose to 82°–89°, and the temperature of the water on the very shallow flats nearly as high probably." It thus seems that temperature is one of the most important water quality requirements of the winter flounder.

[8] Pearcy [35], p. 47, and the Massachusetts Division of Marine Fisheries reports [14, 22, 23] give similar figures for salinity tolerances for winter flounder. The Massachusetts reports suggest tolerable salinity ranges which vary, according to specific area, from 0–34 ppm. Pearcy, however, suggests definite lethal extremes which fall barely outside the Massachusetts findings. Pearcy's recommendations of range extremes between 4.0–30 ppm salinity are used.

3. Depth (ideal)[9]	2–20 ft. plus muddy and sandy bottom
4. Dissolved oxygen[10]	Minimum 2.5 ppm
5. Free carbon dioxide[11]	Maximum 3.0 cc/liter
6. pH range[12]	6.0–9.0
7. Alkyl benzene sulfonate[13]	Maximum 8.2 ppm

For purposes of planning recreational development, it is seen that, while a variety of conditions must be met for any given level of winter flounder production, only a few of these are likely to act as effective constraints.

The winter flounder is fairly tolerant of variations in water conditions, but temperatures of much over 25°C are considered lethal; and care must be taken to ensure that such temperatures do not occur, even locally. This constraint may affect the permissible level of industrial cooling, especially in summer. Food supply is likely to be constrained by annelida supply; it may possibly be desirable to raise this artificially (perhaps by creating conditions less favorable to the annelida's competititors) to achieve, for example, a higher level of sport fishing.

Other forms of pollution (besides heat) do not appear to be a serious problem to winter flounder production. The winter flounder's tolerance for acidity variations seems adequate; in any case, the acidity of the water should be controllable locally. Winter flounder can tolerate lower levels of oxygen supply than most other species, including its competitors, so that lack of oxygen, within limits, may be beneficial. The concentration of certain organic chemical pollutants could, however, become critical.

B.2

Production of Food for Winter Flounder

As indicated in Section 3.6.2 in the text, we use Petersen's ratio of 10:1 to estimate the amounts of detritus required by the annelida, mollusca, and crustacea[14] which are consumed directly by the winter flounder.

We derive the requirements of muddy and sandy bottom area for these bottom invertebrates as follows: From Petersen and Blegvad[15] we estimate that *concurrently*

[9] Winter flounder have been found in depths up to 20–70 fathoms; however, most experts tend to agree that this species is primarily a shoal-water fish. Lux and Jerome in interviews have suggested that for winter flounder an ideal range of water depth (especially for sport fishing) is between 2–20 feet, if the bottom condition is muddy and sandy (especially if eel grass is prominent).

[10] An ORRRC Report [34], p. 17, states that "a well rounded fish population does not occur where dissolved oxygen is less than 3 ppm." Jerome suggests that winter flounder tolerate a lower oxygen content than most other fish; thus the figure of 2.5 was taken.

[11] This figure was taken from *ibid.*, in reference to fish in general, and therefore constitutes an ideal maximum.

[12] This figure was estimated by comparing the Massachusetts Division of Marine Fisheries data that correlated flounder caught to pH ranges with that of the ORRRC Report [34], p. 17, on fish in general.

[13] This figure was taken from Eisler [11], p. 26, who, from empirical data, found that winter flounder (primarily juvenile) were intermediate in susceptibility to alkyl benzene sulfonate at 8.2 ppm. Accordingly, this figure was used to assume ideal maximum tolerance for this detergent pollutant.

[14] These bottom invertebrates consume both living and dead bottom plants, and algae. As dead algae and dead bottom plants are both classed as detritus (see Blegvad [2], p. 46), and as the production coefficients for dead and living bottom flora are identical, we classify all the foods for bottom feeding invertebrates as detritus.

[15] Petersen's estimates ([37], p. 17) of bottom communities are of similar compositions as those described by Lux [28]. Given Blegvad's [3] estimate on plaice (flounder-type specie) food availability in Danish waters, the authors defined winter flounder food—namely, annelida, mollusca, and crustacea—to be *a bottom community* with an average density of 80 grams per square meter of estuary bottom. The breakdown is as follows:

1. Annelida (*polychaeta*)	15 gm. per m^2
2. Mollusca (small bivalves)	50 gm. per m^2
3. Crustacea (small crustaceans)	15 gm. per m^2

Note that the estimate of 80 grams per square meter is high compared to Petersen's [37], p. 36, estimate of 64 grams per square meter of plaice food. However, it was assumed that Massachusetts waters are more productive in "winter flounder" food.

15 grams of annelida are produced per square meter, or 60 kg. per acre of bottom area per year
50 grams of mollusca are produced per square meter, or 200 kg. per acre per year
15 grams of crustacea are produced per square meter, or 60 kg. per acre per year

Since the various food types can grow concurrently over the whole sea bottom, 25,000 acres represents the actual requirement of sea bottom. (See the total area requirements noted in Section 3.6.2.)

We derive the water-area requirements of the remaining 2 food types—namely, algae and "other"—as follows.[16] Odum [33], p. 13, gives an estimate of a productivity per acre of estuary of 20,000 pounds of dry organic matter per year. Petersen [37] p. 8, gives a dry weight factor of 0.16 for eel grass; we have taken this to hold for algae. Accordingly, 1 acre of intertidal and subtidal shoal water is taken to produce 125,000 pounds of algae, wet weight. Also, 1 acre of muddy and sandy bottom is taken to produce 125,000 pounds of miscellaneous foods (assumed to be plant type).

B.3 *Cod Production*

The data on cod production presented in Section 3.6.3 of the text are taken primarily from Petersen ([37], plate facing p. 22) with the further assumptions that the herring eat ten times their weight in plankton and that 80 grams of herbivorous invertebrates are available per square meter of intertidal and shoal subtidal area per year. If it is further assumed that the cod food (namely, the small fish and carnivorous invertebrates) is indifferent to type of herbivorous food (e.g., annelida, mollusca, and crustacea), then 1,420 acres of intertidal and shoal subtidal areas are required per million pounds of cod food, and roughly 14,200 acres per million pounds of cod. If, however, the cod food (small fish and carnivores) do have preferences for annelida, as do the winter flounder, then a larger area would be required, as is the case with the winter flounder.

Table B.1 Requirements for Production of Cod Food

Output	
Herbivorous Invertebrates	1,000,000 lb.
Inputs	
1. Plant-type food	10,000,000 lb.
2. Intertidal and shoal subtidal area	1,420 acres

B.4 *Shellfish Production*

The study of shellfish is of interest for several reasons. First, shellfish are a

[16] Lux [28], p. 4, in his stomach content analysis, could not identify a portion of the winter flounder diet; thus he defined this portion as "other." For the purpose of classifying "other" into usable form, the authors redefined this input as a "plant type food with the same production characteristics as algae."

Odum's [33], p. 13, productivity estimate of approximately 20,000 lbs. of dry organic weight content per acre of estuary (Georgia) is taken to be valid for Massachusetts waters. Since Odum does not break down "dry organic matter" into identifiable parts, we assumed that "dry organic matter" consisted primarily of algae and/or eel grass. Since there is apparently no data available on the actual composition of organic matter in quantitative terms, and because plant-type food is generally held to be the basic component of all food chains, we felt justified in making this assumption. In actuality, however, organic matter is composed of many forms of decayed material other than plants.

relatively stationary species and thus present fewer problems for study than mobile species such as winter flounder and cod. Second, the food chain of shellfish is shorter and simpler than that of finfish and consists of a direct link of the shellfish feeding upon detritus and plankton, with detritus forming a major portion of the shellfish diet.[17]

Third, shellfish are good indicators of an estuarine area's biotic health.[18] Fundamental problems, however, arise in their study. For example, molluscs are extremely erratic in their propagation and variable in their growth and survival. Isolated localities may be phenomenally productive at one time and completely barren for long periods.[19]

Shellfish are valuable on several accounts. First, as indicated in Section 3.6.8 of the text, shellfish, such as mussels, play a major role in the cycling and retention of valuable phosphorus in an estuarine system, even though these species are but a small component of the community in terms of biomass and energy flow. Second, certain shellfish have food value to man. Shellfish such as the soft-shelled clam have a potential of becoming important both on a recreational and commercial basis. Extensive acreage of mudflats in Massachusetts, especially in Plymouth Bay, could become productive for clam farming. Other shellfish, such as the blue mussel, are very abundant in New England but are in little demand, primarily because of the food consumption habits of the U.S. population.[20]

In the estimation of the production requirements of soft-shelled clam, as listed in Table 3.6e of the text, the prey-predator ratio of 10 to 1, used in the estimate of winter flounder production requirements, is employed here.[21] We estimate that 1,000,000 pounds of shellfish requires 33 acres of muddy and sandy bottom.[22] We

[17] Petersen's [37], pp. 8–9, statement on the importance of detritus as a primary food for molluscs is confirmed by Coe [8], p. 591, who states that detritus forms a significant portion of the food of at least certain filter-feeding bivalves.

Clarke [7], p. 503, maintains that very high yields of shellfish in the littoral zone can be harvested. This is partly due to the fact that these animals act as food concentrators. They feed on detritus and plankton brought to them by currents from regions far beyond the area in which they are harvested.

[18] In general, they are equipped not only to bring in oxygenated water but also to close themselves off from their environment during periods of unfavorable conditions. Since shellfish molluscs, especially bivalves, are relatively immobile, they serve, according to Hedgpeth, as "biological integrators of the fluctuating processes of nutrient supply and regeneration in their environment and the abundance of bivalves is doubtless a direct indication of the magnitude of the nutrient and detritus cycles of the estuary." See Hedgpeth [20], p. 708.

[19] Turner [43], p. 42. This fact is especially apparent from Annual Shellfish Reports of towns bordering Plymouth Bay. At one time Plymouth Bay was highly productive (with an annual yield of 77,975 bushels of soft-shelled clams in 1936); today it is highly unproductive (yield of 100–200 bushels in 1966). Possible reasons for this change may be past indiscriminate digging and shifting substratum.

[20] Fiske *et al.* [14], p. 38, states that while the blue mussel is the most abundant edible shellfish in New England, it is also the most neglected as a seafood item. In Britain, on the other hand, mussels are considered a delicacy and soft-shelled clams are relatively neglected for human consumption.

Field [12], p. 125, maintains that as food, the blue mussel is superior to many items which are commonly consumed. Relative to the oyster, it is considered to be equal in flavor, if not superior. It is easily digested and has high nutritive value.

Russell and Yonge [39], p. 302, cite a report which indicates that an acre of mussel ground can produce 40,000 lb. of mussels annually, which is equivalent to 10,000 lb. of mussel meat. For people living on the coast the mussel is an especially cheap food. Field [12], p. 110, states that for equal weights of shellfish, the caloric value of the mussel is about equal to that of the soft-shelled clam, three times that of the oyster, and one-third that of lean beef. This superiority over the oyster is due to the thin, light shell of the mussel in contrast to the thick heavy shell of the oyster. According to Field [12], p. 125, the blue mussel also breeds at a prolific rate, develops rapidly, requires fewer special conditions for growth than the oyster, and may therefore be more easily cultivated.

[21] This ratio also approximates Hedgpeth's ([18], p. 39) figures of 9 to 1 for bivalves such as the soft-shelled clam.

[22] Using Petersen's and Blegvard's figures of 50 gm. of shellfish produced per square meter, or 200 kg (440 lb.) per acre, 1,000,000 lb. of shellfish requires 2,300 acres. In relation to production figures for Massachusetts this figure, 440 lb. or 7 bushels/acre, is low when compared to 500 bushels/acre, according to Thomas V. Binmore, Shellfish Technician, Boston, and to 1,000 bushels/acre taken to be a high yield per acre in Massachusetts. Thus, 1,000,000 lb. of soft-shelled clam production is taken to require an area of *33 acres*.

suggest the following environmental conditions as necessary for soft-shelled clam production:

1. Current[23]	(max. 0.7 ft./sec.)
2. Substratum[24]	$\frac{1}{3}$ mud–$\frac{2}{3}$ sand
3. Water salinity[25]	6‰–25‰
4. Water temperature[26]	17°C–20°C

The most favorable location for production is at or immediately below the low-water mark.[27]

In the estimation of the production requirements of blue mussel, as listed in Table 3.6e in the text, a prey-predator ratio of 10 to 1 is again used.[28] We estimate that 1,000,000 pounds of blue mussel require 42 acres of bottom which is firm or of solid material.[29] We suggest the following environmental conditions as necessary for blue mussel production.

1. Current[30]	(max. 7.3 ft./sec.)
2. Substratum[31]	Solid material

[23] Belding [1], p. 20, maintains that a good current, not necessarily exceedingly swift but having a fair circulation of water, is the most important factor in clam growth. In general, current plays a vital role as a food carrier, oxygen bearer, lime furnisher for shell construction, and sanitary agent for carrying away products of decomposition and contamination. However, excessive current action can shift flats, destroy clams, and prevent clam set. The estimate of maximum current of 0.7 ft./sec. was based on Moore's ([29], p. 63) citation of Johnson [24], who states the following:

A current of 0.4 knots (0.7 ft./sec.) will shift ordinary sand along the bottom; 1 knot (1.6 ft./sec.) will shift fine gravel; 2.15 knots (3.4 ft./sec.) will move shingle 2.5 cm. in diameter; and 3.5 knots (5.6 ft./sec.) will move angular stones 3.8 cm. in diameter.

[24] Belding [1], p. 36, suggests that a good flat has a tenacious and compact soil which nevertheless affords comparatively easy digging, and that the best consistency is a mixture of fine sand and mud in a ratio of $\frac{1}{3}$ mud to $\frac{2}{3}$ sand.

Turner [43], p. 56, states that the soft-shelled clam seems to grow fast and to lay down a thin shell in clean sandy soil while in muddy or gravelly soils the growth is slow and the shell is thick.

[25] Data from Belding [1], p. 21, suggest that clams will grow in practically all degrees of salinity but grow best in the range from 6‰–25‰. According to Turner [43], pp. 55–56, salt concentrations above or below the optimal level may cause the organisms to expend energy in maintaining their water balance that might otherwise be expended on growth. In addition, changes in the salinity of the medium beyond the characteristic tolerance of a species may interfere with a number of fundamental processes. This condition may cause the organism to close its shell (and thus be unable to feed), or it may interfere with a number of physiological mechanisms by disturbing the salt balance of the body fluids.

[26] Coe [8], p. 597, maintains that clams grow most rapidly when the temperature of the water is from 17°C–20°C. Feeding and growth continue, but at a much lower rate, at temperatures of 14°C or less.

Gunter [16], p. 164, states that a low temperature near 0°C where metabolic activity slows to practically a stop is not nearly so lethal as heat. Many organisms will recover from cold that has caused near cessation of their activities, provided the cold is not protracted.

[27] Belding [1], p. 35, maintains that clams grow best near the low-water mark within the area above low tide. When the flat is exposed, the clam cannot feed and consequently the longer the exposure the less the growth, since growth depends largely on the food intake. Clams that are constantly submerged in moving water show the best growth. For recreational clam digging, a reasonable time between tides for digging is estimated to be 4 hours. For commercial operations this time length is not a relevant factor since mechanical equipment can obtain clams which are continually submerged.

Turner [43], p. 57, states that the soft-shelled clam is seldom taken far beyond the low tide mark. However, south of Cape Cod, where the amplitude of the tide is relatively small, it may be commercially exploited in depths as great as 6 feet at low tide. It is generally agreed that the soft-shelled clam grows more slowly between the tide lines as the upper limits are approached; and it is generally concluded that this phenomenon is attributable to the short feeding time.

[28] White [44], p. 8, supports Petersen's statement on the importance of detritus as the principal food of the blue mussel.

[29] According to Fiske *et al.* [14], p. 38, the yield per acre in the North River, Massachusetts, was estimated at 428 bushels. As a reasonable figure for potential yield in Massachusetts, we have selected 400 bushels/acre or 24,000 pounds/acre. Thus, 1,000,000 pounds of blue mussel production requires an area of roughly 42 acres.

[30] Moore [29], p. 64, cites Dodgson [10] as giving an upper current limit of 5 miles per hour (7.3 feet per second) for the mussel *Mytilus edulis*.

[31] White [44], p. 5, states that adult mussels are always attached by the byssus, or "beard" (a thread-like material which the mussel uses to attach itself to a structure), and are therefore not found on sandy shores unless there is some adequate supporting structure present. Where there are

3. Water salinity[32]	9‰–35‰
4. Water temperature[33]	10°C–20°C

The most favorable location for the production of blue mussel is the mean low-water level.[34]

Bibliography

1. Belding, David L., "The Soft-Shelled Clam Fishery of Massachusetts," *Marine Fisheries Series–No. 1*, Commonwealth of Massachusetts, 1930 (Reprinted 1964).
2. Blegvad, H., "Food and Conditions of Nourishment among the Communities of Invertebrate Animals Found on or in Danish Waters," *Report of the Danish Biological Station*, XXI, Copenhagen, 1914.
3. ———, "Continued Studies on the Quantity of Fish Food in the Sea Bottom," *Report of the Danish Biological Station*, XXXI, Copenhagen, 1925.
4. Bigelow, Henry B., and William C. Schroeder, *Fishes of the Gulf of Maine*, United States Department of the Interior, Fish & Wildlife Service, Fishery Bulletin 74, 1953.
5. Breder, Charles M., *Field Book of Marine Fishes of the Atlantic Coast from Labrador to Texas*, New York, G. P. Putnam & Sons, 1948.
6. Carr, Arnold, *Resumé of Main Facts in the Natural History of the Following Shellfish: 1. Blue Mussel, 2. Soft Shell Clam, 3. Bay Scallop, 4. Quahog, 5. Oyster, 6. Surf Clam.* Massachusetts Division of Marine Fisheries, Department of Natural Resources, Boston, 1965 (mimeographed).
7. Clarke, George L., *Elements of Ecology*, 1st ed., revised, John Wiley, & Sons, Inc., New York, 1967.
8. Coe, Wesley R., "Nutrition, Environmental Conditions and Growth of Marine Bivalve Mollusks", *Journal of Marine Research*, VII: 8 (1948), 586–601.
9. Coulthard, H. S., "Growth of the Sea Mussel," *Contributions to Canadian Biology*, IV: 10 (1929), 121–136.
10. Dodgson, R.W., *Report on Mussel Purification*, British Ministry of Agriculture and Fishery, Invest., Ser. 11, Vol. X, 1928.
11. Eisler, Ronald, "Some Effects of a Synthetic Detergent on Estuarine Fishes," *Transactions of the American Fisheries Society*, 94 (January, 1965).
12. Field, Irving A., "The Food Value of Sea Mussels," *Bulletin of the Bureau of Fisheries*, U.S. Department of Commerce and Labor, Vol. XXIX, 1909, pp. 85–128.
13. ———, "Biology and Economic Value of the Sea Mussel, *Mytilus Edulis*," *Bulletin of the Bureau of Fisheries*, U.S. Department of Commerce and Labor, Vol. XXXVIII, 1921–22, pp. 127–259.
14. Fiske, John D., Clinton E. Watson, and Philip G. Coates, *A Study of the Marine Resources of the North River*, Monograph Series Number 3, Division of Marine

rocks, piles, or piers anywhere around the shores (Britain), the blue mussel is usually plentiful. Estuaries and harbors are common habitats.

Hedgpeth [18], p. 723, cites Kuenen [25] as stating that *Mytilus edulis* tends to form elongate reefs on suitable substrates along the margins of deeper channels in tidal flats near the low-tide level where the currents are of intermediate strength. Lack of food, stronger currents, and predominantly sandy substrate prevent *Mytilus edulis* from establishing beds on the higher parts of the tidal flat. At lower levels, where currents are weaker, the food supply is also smaller.

[32] Carr [6], p. 2, states that the salinity tolerance is 9‰–35‰. White [44], p. 7, states that the blue mussel is tolerant of great variation in salinity and occurs in salt, brackish, and nearly fresh water.

[33] White [44], p. 7, cites Coulthard [9] as stating that the optimal temperature range is 10°C–20°C. She also cites Dodgson [10] as saying that mussels have functioned with ordinary activity at temperatures between 0°C–26°C.

Coe [8], p. 598, quotes Loosanoff [26] as stating that on the coast of southern New England *Mytilus edulis* may remain open and active at temperatures ranging from −1.0°C to 24.9°C. It continues to feed at or near 0°C. There is a rather close correlation between growth rate and temperature.

[34] Turner [43], p. 57, cites Loosanoff and Engle [27] as stating that the blue mussel grows best at the mean low-water level. Growth is slower when they are in a position either below or above this point.

Scattergood [40], p. 12, states that Mossop [30], Coulthard [9], and others have demonstrated that the rate of growth varies inversely with duration of exposure between tides.

Fisheries, Department of Natural Resources, The Commonwealth of Massachusetts, May 1966.

15. Fitzpatrick, William, and Sargent Russell, *Massachusetts Marine Sport Fisheries Inventory*, Massachusetts Division of Fisheries and Game, Fisheries Bulletin No. 36, 1961.
16. Gunter, Gordon, "Temperature," Chapter 8 in Joel W. Hedgpeth (ed.), *Treatise on Marine Ecology and Paleoecology*, Vol. I—Ecology, New York, Geological Society of America, 1957.
17. Hay, John, and Peter Farb, *The Atlantic Shore*, New York, Harper & Row, 1966.
18. Hedgpeth, Joel W., "Estuaries and Lagoons, II Biological Characteristics", in Joel W. Hedgpeth (ed.), *Treatise on Marine Ecology and Paleoecology*, Vol. I—Ecology, New York, Geological Society of America, 1957.
19. ———, "Concepts of Marine Ecology," Chapter 3 in Joel W. Hedgpeth (ed.), *Treatise on Marine Ecology and Paleoecology*, Vol. I—Ecology, New York, Geological Society of America, 1957.
20. ———, "The Sense of the Meeting," in George M. Lauff (ed.), *Estuaries*, Publication No. 83, American Association for the Advancement of Science, Washington, D.C., 1967.
21. Jensen, P. Boysen, "Studies Concerning the Organic Matter of the Sea Bottom," *Report of the Danish Biological Station*, XXII, Copenhagen, 1914, pp. 1–39.
22. Jerome, William C., Arthur P. Chesmore, and Charles O. Anderson, *A Study of the Marine Resources of Quincy Bay*, Monograph Series No. 2, Division of Marine Fisheries, Department of Natural Resources, Commonwealth of Massachusetts, March 1966.
23. ———, Arthur P. Chesmore, Charles O. Anderson, Jr., and Frank Grice, *A Study of Marine Resources of the Merrimack River Estuary*, Division of Marine Fisheries, Department of Natural Resources, The Commonwealth of Massachusetts, June 1965.
24. Johnson, Douglas W., *Shore Processes and Shoreline Development*, New York, John Wiley & Sons, 1919.
25. Kuenen, D. L., On the Distribution of Mussels on the Intertidal Sand Flats Near Den Helder, *Archives Néerlandaises de Zoologie*, VI (May, 1942), Leiden.
26. Loosanoff, V.L., "Shell Movements of the Edible Mussel, *Mytilus edulis* (L.) in Relation to Temperature," *Ecology*, 23, 231–234.
27. ———, and J. B. Engle, "Growth Increase in Weight and Mortality of Mussels, (M. edulis, Linn.) Living at Different Depth Levels," *Anatomic Record*: 87, 4, 1943.
28. Lux, Fred, "Food Habits of the Winter Flounder in the Woods Hole Area", unpublished paper, Bureau of Commonwealth Fisheries, 1961–62.
29. Moore, Hillary, *Marine Ecology*, New York, John Wiley & Sons, 1958.
30. Mossop, B.K.E., *A Study of the Sea Mussel* (*Mytilus edulis* Linn.), Contributions to Canadian Biology, No. 2, 1921, pp. 17–48.
31. ———, *The Rate of Growth of the Sea Mussel* (*Mytilus edulis* L.), Transactions of the Royal Canadian Institute, Vol. 14, Part 1, May 1922, Toronto, pp. 3–22.
32. Odum, Eugene P., *Fundamentals of Ecology*, 2nd ed., Philadelphia, W.B. Saunders Company, 1959.
33. ———, "The Role of Tidal Marshes in Estuarine Production," *Conservationist*, The State of New York Conservation Department, Vol. 15 (June–July 1961), pp. 12–15.
34. Outdoor Recreation Resources Review Commission, "Water for Recreation—Values and Opportunities," ORRRC Study Report 10, Washington, D.C., 1962.
35. Pearcy, William G., "Ecology of an Estuarine Population of Winter Flounder *Pseudopleuronectes Americanus*," Parts I-IV, The Bulletin of the Bingham Oceanographic Collection, Vol. 18, Yale University, New Haven, Connecticut, August 1962.
36. Perlmutter, Alfred, "The Distribution of the Winter Flounder (*Pseudopleuronectes Americanus*), and its Bearing on Management Possibilities," *Transactions of the Eleventh North American Wildlife Conference 1946*, American Wildlife Institute, pp. 239–250.
37. Petersen, C. G. Joh., "The Sea Bottom and Its Production of Fish Food," *Report of the Danish Biological Station*, XXV, Copenhagen, 1918.
38. Raymont, John E. G., *Plankton and Productivity in the Oceans*, New York, Pergamon Press, 1963.

39. Russell, F.S. and C.M. Yonge, *The Seas—Our Knowledge of Life in the Sea and How It Is Gained* (New and Revised 2nd edition), London, Frederick Warne and Company Ltd, 1963.
40. Scattergood, Leslie W. and Clyde C. Taylor, *The Mussel Resources of the North Atlantic Region*, U.S. Department of Interior Fish and Wildlife Service, Fishery Leaflet 364, January, 1950.
41. Sverdrup, H.U., Martin W. Johnson, and Richard H. Fleming, *The Oceans*, Englewood Cliffs, N.J., Prentice Hall, 1942.
42. Thorson, Gunnar, "Bottom Communities," Chapter 17 in Joel W. Hedgpeth (ed.), *Treatise on Marine Ecology and Paleoecology*, Vol. I—Ecology, The Geological Society of America, 1957
43. Turner, Harry J. Jr., "A Review of the Biology of Some Commercial Molluscs of the East Coast of North America," in the *Sixth Report on Investigations of the Shellfisheries of Massachusetts*, Prepared by the Woods Hole Oceanographic Institute for the Department of Marine Resources for The Commonwealth of Massachusetts, 1953, pp. 39–74.
44. White, Kathleen M., *Mytilus*, Liverpool Marine Biology Committee (LMBC) Memoirs on Typical British Marine Plants and Animals, Vol. XXXI, Department of Oceanography, University of Liverpool, 1937.

Subject Index

Index

Author Index

Author Index

Lewis and Clark College - Watzek Library
HT391 .I82 wmain
Isard, Walter/Ecologic-economic analysis
3 5209 00420 6559